ENTERPRISE

ENTERPRISE

by
JERRY GREY, Ph.D.

WILLIAM MORROW AND COMPANY, INC.
NEW YORK   1979

Library of Congress Cataloging in Publication Data

Grey, Jerry.
    Enterprise.

    1. Enterprise (Space shuttle) I. Title.
TL795.5.G73   629.44   79-10544
ISBN 0-688-03462-4

BOOK DESIGN   CARL WEISS

Printed in the United States of America.

First Edition

1 2 3 4 5 6 7 8 9 10

To Florence, who is my strength, and to our daughters, Leslie and Tina, who will inherit the future we create.

COMING OF AGE

A FOREWORD

TO *ENTERPRISE*

by ISAAC ASIMOV

IT ISN'T EASY TO DECIDE THE MOMENT OF BIRTH OF GREAT EPOCHS in human history. Why should it be? It isn't even easy to determine when a human being is born.

You might have been born on a certain day of a certain year. You may even have a record of the exact hour, minute, and second in which you drew your first breath, but is that the moment you came into existence?

It is only the moment you emerged from the womb. You existed as a genetically distinct individual from the moment of conception some nine months before. And you did not become an independently functioning member of society (a functional kind of birth) until you "came of age" some years after you emerged from the womb.

It is the same for space flight. It had a birth, but before that it had a conception, and after birth there is a coming of age.

To begin with, when was space flight born?

The conventional wisdom is that space flight was born on October 4, 1957, when Sputnik 1 was sent beeping its way around the earth. That was widely heralded, both at the time and since, as the birth of the "space age." That's reasonable enough. With Sputnik 1, humanity had come out of its planetary womb, and for a short period of time a man-made object was an independent member of the solar system.

And, of course, there was conception before birth. It may have been with Goddard in 1926 or with Tsiolkovsky in 1903, or with some Chinese technician who manufactured the first rocket in the 1200s or with some ancient who first looked at the moon with longing.

No matter. The question of conception may be a purely academic point.

Let us move, instead, forward from birth and ask when space flight came of age. Was it when the first human being went into orbit on April 12, 1961? Was it when the first human being landed on the moon on July 21, 1969?

It can easily be argued that it was neither event, for both were, to a certain extent, stunts—highly expensive adventures designed to gain political advantage in the Soviet-American "race" into space. Both were episodes of the childhood of space flight, rather like children being groomed to perform in public. The children might do so with impressive skill, but it would still be only a stunt, and the performers would still be only children.

The proof of this is that once Americans reached the moon and "won" the race with the Soviet Union, the American public quickly lost interest in space spectaculars. The game was over and it was time to pick up the ball and go home.

But to do this means abandoning space flight while it is still in its childhood; before it has come of age and has become a living and inseparable part of human history.

When, then, will space flight come of age?

When it becomes cheap enough to do something more than stunts. When it can make homes for human beings in space. When it can be used to draw on resources of energy and material from space for the good of humanity. When it can be used to extend human knowledge of the universe and human ability to manipulate and make use of the universe.

How can that be done?

Well, the great expense of space flight is that the spaceships have till now been one-shots. They are used—once!—then discarded. It is rather like taking the *Queen Elizabeth 2* for one round-trip across the Atlantic and then scuttling it.

But now that is no longer necessarily the case. We have the space shuttle.

The shuttle is a spacecraft that can, in principle, be reused; that can venture out into space and return in condition to make another venture, and another, and another. That represents the first major drop in expense.

It heralds the coming of age of space flight.

As the concept and design of the reusable spaceship is steadily improved, space flight will become cheaper still. As such spaceships are used to build structures in space—solar-power stations, lunar mining stations—there will cease to be any expense at all.

Space will begin to return a profit, first a small one and then an enormous one.

It will no longer be political advantage and publicity-stunting that will drive space technology forward; it will be straight economics and the desire for a better life.

To take full advantage of space, settlements will be built out there and the human habitat will be vastly expanded—for the first time enlarging the human living space beyond earth. New pioneering horizons will be stretching out as far as the eye can see or the mind conceive.

Before another century is done it will be hard for people to imagine a time when humanity was confined to one world, and it will seem to them incredible that there was ever anybody who doubted the value of space and wanted to turn his or her back on the universe in order to burrow more deeply into the planetary prison.

The real beginning of the space age, then, is *right now*.

This book is the story of that beginning, how it came about, and what it will lead to. It is the story of real people who made dreams come true and are utterly revolutionizing space flight—and humanity in doing so.

And it is told by someone who's *lived* the story.

PREFACE

THIS BOOK IS ABOUT MANKIND'S GREATEST ENTERPRISE—THE CON-
quest of space.

But it doesn't describe a mere "grand dream." These pages are
laden with realities—the realities of the past and the present, of
course; but more important, the realities of what we can expect in
the future. And because the story of any real enterprise must necessarily be the story of the people who formed it, this *Enterprise* is built
around the real people of the United States space program.

Media spotlights on the space extravaganzas of the past have dwelt
only on the "front" men of space—the Neil Armstrongs, the Jim
Webbs, the Wernher von Brauns. These leaders were unquestionably
men of key importance in the development of space, but the heroes
of my story played very different roles in the shaping of the space
enterprise. Some of them, in fact, had little apparent impact on the
course of our national space program. But all of the people in these
pages—Arthur Clarke, Bob Truax, Pres Layton, Del Tischler, Glen
Wilson, Klaus Heiss, Gil Moore, Philomena Grodzka, Burt Edelson,
Mike Malkin, Bob Bussard, Marcia Smith—have one very important
characteristic in common: they are totally committed to the premise
that space is an essential element in mankind's future. The thread of
that dedication is the thread of the story, *Enterprise*.

These people of the space program are an odd lot. Talk of a "dull
gray exterior"—science-fiction and *Star Wars* aficionados would have
a tough time picking the people of *Enterprise* out of a police lineup
of bookkeepers, bankers, college professors, and briefcase-toting busi-
nessmen commuters. But behind those clean-shaven jowls, horn-
rimmed glasses, rumpled suits, narrow neckties (*always* worn!), and

short haircuts there rage flaming imaginations. The fiction writers, the film and TV producers like Stanley Kubrick, George Lucas, and Steven Spielberg, depend ultimately on the imaginations of space scientists and engineers for all their brilliant creations. But the engineers who want to realize their dreams have to develop their theories into designs that make sound physical sense and then into tangible hardware that works—a far more creative, difficult, and demanding task. I thank them for their creativity, for their dedication, and, in the case of those few I've identified by name, for their time and effort in reviewing and correcting what I've written about them and their work.

It is no coincidence, incidentally, that *Enterprise* is the name of Captain Kirk and Mr. Spock's *Star Trek* spaceship and of the first *real* U.S. spaceship, Shuttle Orbiter No. 101; it is also the word John F. Kennedy used to characterize space in his historic 1961 message announcing that the United States would put a man on the moon. This book goes a step further—beyond the adventurous but fictional exploration of Captain Kirk's *Enterprise*, beyond the real politics of John Kennedy's enterprise, and even beyond the first faltering steps of the U.S. space shuttle *Enterprise*. The enterprise of space *is* the future of the human race, and that future is in the process of becoming the present—*right now*. Most of the readers of this book will be lucky enough to see the most important transition mankind has undertaken since an ocean-dwelling creature first crawled up on land and gulped a lungful of air.

J. G.

Bridgehampton, N.Y.
September 1978

CONTENTS

CHAPTER

1

THE RATIONALE

"We have examined where we are strong and where we are not, where we may succeed, and where we may not. . . . Now is the time to take longer strides—time for a great new American *enterprise*—time for this nation to take a clearly leading role in space achievement, which in many ways may hold the key to our future on Earth. . . . I believe that this nation should commit itself to achieving the goal, before this decade is out, of landing [a man] on the Moon and returning him safely to Earth."

—John F. Kennedy
May 25, 1961

I SAT FIDGETING IN THE MAKESHIFT BLEACHERS. IT WAS ONLY NINE A.M., but I was already sweating profusely in the blazing Florida sunshine. It was July 16, 1969.

Along with the Vice-President of the United States and a thousand or so other invited guests, I stared at the tall Saturn V rocket shimmering in the sun three miles away. It looked like the Empire State Building; it was, in fact, just about a third as tall. But there was one big difference: *this* behemoth was about to blast itself off the earth.

"T minus twenty minutes and counting," droned Shorty Powers' amplified voice from the blockhouse. Florence and I had been there the day before, watching the launch crew prepare for the flight. We had stood less than a hundred feet from the Saturn V on its pad at launch complex 39, craning our necks upward and marveling at our temerity in believing that such a skyscraper would actually fly.

The day of the launch we had staggered out of bed at 3:30 A.M., proceeded bleary-eyed to the Holiday Inn North in Daytona, where we had been fed a breakfast of hominy grits, and at 4:30 boarded a bus for the launch viewing site at what was then Cape Kennedy. Unfortunately, a million other people were also converging on the Cape. The stop-and-go traffic, the leaden grits weighing in our stomachs, and finally the hour-long wait in the blistering sun had taken their toll.

"Fifteen minutes and counting." Florence looked at me accusingly. "What's a nice New York fashion artist doing in a place like this?" she demanded.

I shrugged. Space was my business, and I could no more have missed this flight than I could have cut off my arm. "Let's go for a walk," I suggested.

Our brief stroll helped. We identified all the show-business celebrities clustered near the Vice-President, and nodded frequent greetings to my space-program friends and colleagues. Back in our bleacher seats (no cooler, but a little more bearable), we felt the tension begin to mount.

I'd been present at launches before, occasionally in the blockhouse itself. My first launch at Cape Kennedy (then still Cape Canaveral) was of the ill-fated first Vanguard rocket, hailed as the United States' answer to Sputnik 1—until it collapsed and blew up on the pad. But somehow *this* launch was different. It wasn't just the size of the rocket —the three-mile perspective tended to dwarf its real enormity—but the fact that there were three people up there in that tiny capsule. "Those three guys are actually going to the moon!" Florence said.

"Three minutes and counting!" Things began to happen. Announcements came faster. Even Shorty's bland, professional announcer's voice began to increase in pitch. "Ignition—we have ignition—three, two, one, zero!"

Great gouts of orange flame shot out on both sides of the rocket. Ever so slowly—just like the slow-motion television shots of previous launches—the Saturn rose off its pad. It gathered speed, passed the top of the gantry—and suddenly it hit me. Absolute silence! The hushed crowd, not even a sea gull squawking, and no thunderous rocket-engine roar! Then I remembered that we were three miles away. It takes fifteen seconds for sound to travel three miles. At that instant unbelievable sound engulfed us. It came in waves, reverberating against our ears—a deep, massive, *basic* sound, not unpleasant, but all-encompassing. Slowly it faded, as the blinding tongue of yellow flame behind the now-leaping rocket shrank to a brilliant point in the eastern sky.

Inexplicably, I was crying. Wiping the tears from my eyes, I looked around me at the people I'd worked with over the past decades. Not a dry eye in sight. Even Florence, whose total association with the space program was less than a year old.

For most of us, *Apollo 11*, the landing of three men on the moon, represented the end of an era—*our* era. I had helped Rocketdyne solve rocket-engine combustion problems on the old Redstone missile that had launched our first American, Alan B. Shepard, Jr., on his brief flight into space back in May 1961. At Princeton University in the early 1950s, I had directed the experimental rocket research that proved out the elusive theories on combustion instability developed by the brilliant aerodynamicist Luigi Crocco. All my formal education, from Brooklyn Technical High School through degrees in engineering, physics, and aeronautics at Cornell and Cal Tech, had been aimed at space. I even remember myself as a frustrated five-year-old, sitting on the hardwood floor of my family's home in Brooklyn's Brownsville section, trying unsuccessfully with my unskilled child's fingers to assemble a balsa-and-tissue flying model of a World War I Fokker triplane.

So *Apollo 11* in July 1969 was for me—and for the people around me in the bleachers—the end of our era as dominant factors in space. We were, almost all of us, well over forty, and isn't it a fact that a scientist's best and most productive years are his twenties? So part

The pinnacle of U.S. space success: the Saturn V rocket carrying *Apollo 11* blasts off for the moon on July 16, 1969.

Ex-President Lyndon B. Johnson (left) and Vice-President Spiro Agnew watch *Apollo 11* take off in the blazing Florida sunshine.

of the reason for our tears as we watched Neil Armstrong, Edwin "Buzz" Aldrin, Jr., and Michael Collins on their way to the moon was the implicit feeling that our days of excitement and involvement were over.

We were so wrong!

Apollo 11 did mark the beginning of the end of one era—the era of space as a "gee-whiz" arena for stunts and extravaganzas. With a few exceptions in the 1970s, the six moon landings of the Apollo program marked the final phase of what I now call the demonstration of our ability to enter and work in space, and therefore to *use* "this new ocean" to the maximum extent possible.

We have already entered a second epoch—the real "space age." A multitude of operational satellites perform everyday tasks that we now couldn't readily do without—global and domestic communications, navigation, weather forecasting, environmental monitoring, prospecting for mineral resources (including oil), pest control, monitoring military treaties and agreements. The list grows almost daily.

But one important vestige of the Apollo "stunt" era still remains very much with us: the high cost of space operations. All our satellites and spacecraft are still launched from the earth's surface by "expendable" rockets—large, expensive handcrafted devices that we literally throw away after using them only once. Moreover, to keep the launch costs as low as possible, the satellites and spacecraft that these expendable rockets carry into orbit have to be so small, light, and ultrareliable (to last a long time without needing repair) that *their* cost becomes truly astronomical.

The operational Saturn V rocket, for example, cost about twice as much as our most expensive operational airplane, the giant C-5A military transport. Nobody in his right mind would think of throwing away a whole C-5A airplane after only one overseas trip, and yet that's exactly what we did with every Saturn V we launched! So until we can launch our "payloads" (the useful satellites and spacecraft) into space as routinely as we now fly freight from, say, New York to Tokyo, we must still drag along with us the millstone of high space-operations costs.

The obvious answer to this problem is to make our spacecraft launchers reusable—a concept recognized by space planners as far back as 1953. The technical problems are formidable enough now, but in 1953 they were totally inconceivable. Getting a high-performance rocket to last as much as a minute without burning up or exploding was considered a reasonably good achievement.

Eventually, of course, the performance and reliability of rocket launchers were improved to such a point that the very lives of astronauts and cosmonauts could be trusted to them. We have grown rather complacent, for example, in expecting our space launchers to work just right every time. The levels of reliability required to achieve that kind of performance are truly staggering. The definitive cliché on this subject comes from the Saturn V test engineer who, when asked if he didn't yearn to be an Apollo astronaut and reap all that glory, is said to have snorted, "Nah! You'd never catch *me* trusting my life to a gadget with five million parts, every one built by the lowest bidder!"

By the early 1960s, however, rapidly developing technology began to make the concept of reusable spacecraft launchers look a lot more practical. By then, though, the nation was embarked full tilt on President Kennedy's goal of landing an American on the moon, a goal motivated by political rather than economic considerations. The development of a reusable airplanelike space launcher had to wait, and with it waited the era of real space enterprise. So it was fully ten years after Neil Armstrong took his "giant step for mankind" before we were ready.

That era has finally arrived. The decade of the 1980s marks the beginning of maturity for the true space age. The first reusable launch vehicle, the space-shuttle orbiter *Enterprise* (named by popular request of over one hundred thousand *Star Trek* fans), was rolled out of its California hangar in 1976, test-flown in the atmosphere in 1977, and its sister ships—*Columbia, Challenger, Discovery,* and *Atlantis*—are now our nation's space "trucks," available for routine duty in the 1980s.

The world will never be the same again.

CHAPTER

2

THE PRECURSORS

"There can be no thought of finishing, for aiming at the stars, both literally and figuratively, is the work of generations, but no matter how much progress one makes there is always the thrill of just beginning." —*Robert Hutchings Goddard* *(Letter to H. G. Wells)* *April 20, 1932*

THE TRUE BEGINNING OF ANYTHING IS RARELY EASY TO IDENTIFY. But ask a hundred people what started the space age and at least ninety will answer "Sputnik." For anyone who doesn't remember, that's 1957 Alpha-2, as it was formally designated, the first artificial satellite to be placed in orbit around the earth. Launched by the Soviet Union on October 4, 1957, Sputnik 1 marked a truly unique milestone in what was even then a long and active history of interest in space. Goddard himself, "the father of modern rocketry," was antedated by a host of space philosophers, storytellers, and scientists. But if one looks for a single specific happening, a springboard that launched the string of events we now think of as a global space program, it was undoubtedly the orbiting of Sputnik 1.

Most Americans were shocked and stunned by the realization that the first giant step off our planet was accomplished by the Soviets. Several years earlier, in 1955, President Dwight D. Eisenhower had announced—with much fanfare—an American plan to develop and launch a series of small artificial satellites as part of a major global scientific undertaking—the International Geophysical Year (IGY).

The purpose of the U.S. Vanguard program, in keeping with the goals of the IGY, was to garner scientific data about the earth which could be obtained only with orbiting satellite instruments.

The U.S.S.R. was also a participant in the IGY. Yet few paid much attention to the Soviet announcement, over three months *before* the 1955 U.S. declaration, that a special commission had been set up to develop artificial satellites. And when they repeated their announcement after the Americans did, those few who noticed it responded with amused skepticism.

This false view of the Soviet technologists as bumbling newcomers to the advanced-technology arena, where the United States had been the acknowledged world leader since World War II, had little if any real basis. Exactly six years before Sputnik, on October 4, 1951, a Soviet rocket expert named Tikhonravov said that their technology was at least comparable with that of the United States, and that the Soviets planned to launch an artificial satellite. At the World Peace Council in 1953, Soviet academician Nesmeyanov announced that "the creation of an artificial satellite of the earth is a real possibility." And especially after the United States and U.S.S.R. had publicized their satellite programs in 1955, the Soviets were not at all reticent about their intentions:

• August 1955. At the Sixth International Astronautical Congress in Copenhagen, Leonid Sedov (chairman of the new Soviet commission) said, "It will be possible to launch an artificial satellite of the earth within the next two years." He even said that the Soviet satellites could be much larger than those of the United States.

• June 11, 1957. Nesmeyanov announced that both the carrier and the instrumentation for the first Soviet satellite were ready, and that the launching would occur within a few months.

• August 1957. Academician Federov said that a launch would occur within a few months. He gave specific data: orbital altitude, 200 to 500 kilometers; orbital speed, 29,000 kilometers per hour. It is interesting to note that academician Kotelnikov, an electronics expert, expressed doubt that the U.S.S.R. had the hardware to put a sphere in orbit. Perhaps it was a deliberate psychological "red" herring.

• September 18, 1957. Moscow radio announced that the launch would be soon.

• October 1, 1957. The U.S.S.R. issued a public announcement of the transmission frequencies for their first satellite.

So it really shouldn't have surprised the world when 184-pound Sputnik 1 was launched on October fourth. The launch stimulated a literal media orgy, which included disparaging United States (White House) statements comparing the Sputnik to "a hunk of iron" and expressing disinterest in "the basketball game in outer space" (the first projected U.S. Vanguard satellite was to weigh just twenty-one and a half pounds). But the Soviets weren't kidding; they followed their stunning "first" with an incredible second and third: a living dog sent into orbit on November 3 (Sputnik 2, weighing 1,120 pounds) and on May 15, 1958, Sputnik 3—a full-fledged flying laboratory weighing 2,925 pounds.

The U.S. response to the unaccustomed and uncomfortable position of being second in a two-horse race was confused but massive —a reassessment and adjustment, not only in space efforts but in such far-reaching areas as politics, national defense, and even national educational goals and methods. Two decades of hindsight, though, now suggest that the shock of Sputnik 1 to the United States was probably one of its most valuable national experiences.

Although Sputnik 1 was the first visible sign of the Russian entry into space, it was a Russian scientist, Konstantin Tsiolkovsky, who is generally recognized as the founder of modern space technology. But long before Tsiolkovsky people had looked at the heavens and dreamed.

Most of the early dreams focused on the moon. It wasn't until Galileo invented his telescope that the planets were recognized as worlds, but even in antiquity people could see with their own eyes the mountains and valleys of the moon. The first recorded "science-fiction" author, Lucian of Samosata, lived in the second century A.D. His *True History* (which Lucian took great pains to make clear included "not a word of truth throughout") describes a trip to the moon via a waterspout encountered by the protagonist while sailing between the Pillars of Hercules. Lucian also wrote a second space-fiction story, *Icaro-Menippus*, in which Menippus used birds' wings (a la Icarus) to fly up to the moon.

Aside from an epic poem by the Persian Firdausi in 1010, there was a hiatus in known writings about space until the sixteenth century. Many of the Renaissance scientists dallied in "science" fiction, notably the famous astronomer Johannes Kepler (*Somnium*, or *Dream*, published in 1634). Other early writings included Francis Godwin's *The Man in the Moon: or a Discourse of a Voyage Thither*, published in 1638 under the pseudonym Domingo Gonsales; and Cyrano de Bergerac's *Voyage to the Moon* (1649) and *History of the States and Empires of the Sun* (1652). Cyrano was the first to introduce the use of a rocket for space travel; in fact, he suggested a very modern jet-propulsion-engine concept known as the ramjet.

Subsequent space stories by such well-known authors as Voltaire (*Micromegas*, 1752), Edgar Allan Poe (*Hans Pfall—A Tale*, 1835), and others culminated in the classics of Jules Verne, who probably influenced our modern space pioneers more than any single person (both Goddard and Tsiolkovsky, as well as the German rocket designer Hermann Oberth, credit Verne for their initial interest in space flight). His *From the Earth to the Moon* and *Around the Moon* were as accurate as the science of 1865 permitted. The Verne period saw a veritable cascade of science fiction; one of the most prophetic was Edward Everett Hale's *Brick Moon*, published in *The Atlantic Monthly* in 1869, describing the first earth-orbiting space station.

The final chapter in wholly imaginative space voyages was written by H. G. Wells. *First Men in the Moon*, which appeared around 1900, was the last significant story based on implausible invention—the rocket engine had finally been identified (by Tsiolkovsky) as the key to *real* space travel. Tsiolkovsky's diary entry for March 28, 1883, revealed his understanding of the rocket's reaction principle; he completed his formal rocket-propulsion theory on August 25, 1898. His *The Exploration of Space with Reactive Devices*, published in 1903, marked the dawn of practical space technology—and appeared the same year that the Wright brothers demonstrated their conquest of the air.

Konstantin Tsiolkovsky's achievements were truly remarkable. Not only did he develop his rocket-propulsion theories without the aid of experimental observations (in direct contrast to Goddard), but he conceived such modern ideas as the multistage rocket (the only practical method capable, even today, of launching spacecraft) and the liquid-oxygen, liquid-hydrogen rocket propellant combination (used in the upper stages of Apollo's Saturn V rocket and in the present space shuttle's main engines). Tsiolkovsky was also the first to suggest manned settlement in space, a concept developed extensively by Gerard O'Neill in the late 1970s. It is almost certainly not a coincidence that Sputnik 1 was launched by the Soviet Union within a few weeks of the centennial of Tsiolkovsky's birth (September 17, 1857); in fact, knowledgeable U.S. space experts think the Soviets' intended launch date slipped for the usual technical reasons.

Important as Tsiolkovsky's theories were, the practical development of rocketry is credited to an American physics professor, Robert Hutchings Goddard. Like Tsiolkovsky, he was a "loner," but more of an experimentalist than a theoretician. Sparked by Jules Verne's and H. G. Wells' stories, at the age of twenty (in 1902) he submitted an article titled "The Navigation of Space" to *Popular Science News*; it was rejected. Without learning of Tsiolkovsky's work, he developed independently the same basic theories and concepts, including the liquid oxygen/hydrogen propellant combination and multistaged rockets. He clearly (and correctly) identified multistaging as the only practical method for reaching high altitudes. The principle is simple and almost obvious (today): Use one rocket to launch another, so that the "second stage" (the upper rocket) *starts out* with the maximum speed of the "first stage." In theory, any number of stages could be used; in practice five seem to be a practical limit. Sputnik 1 used three; the first American satellite (Explorer 1) used four.

Goddard went much further than Tsiolkovsky in his rocketry: he built and tested models and—a truly practical man—he filed over two hundred patents on the rocket designs and components he invented and tested. After his death the United States government awarded his widow, Esther Goddard, an unprecedented one million dollars for the use of his patented ideas in military rockets.

Goddard's classic publication (in December 1919), a Smithsonian paper titled *A Method of Reaching Extreme Altitudes*, served as the basic text for a generation of rocket engineers. Its most noteworthy section was "Calculation of Minimum Mass Required to Raise One Pound to an 'Infinite' Altitude." Goddard translated this calculation into a relatively practical (thanks to hindsight) suggestion for placing a recognizable payload (flash powder) on the moon. However, it brought down on him a flood of sensationalist news stories about the "moon man." Such publicity further strengthened his already well-developed resolve to work alone.

On March 16, 1926, he launched the world's first liquid-propellant

Dr. Robert H. Goddard, the "father of modern rocketry," stands beside the world's first liquid-propellant rocket ever to fly (Auburn, Massachusetts, March 16, 1926).

Goddard (center) with two of his principal supporters, Harry Guggenheim (left) and Charles A. Lindbergh, in front of his Roswell, New Mexico, rocket launch tower (September 23, 1935).

rocket in a Massachusetts meadow: it flew for two seconds to an altitude of forty feet, and reached a speed of sixty miles per hour. It was the basic tool for all current space efforts.

Supported by small research grants, initially from the Smithsonian and later from the Guggenheims, Goddard almost single-handedly formulated much of the technology on which modern rocketry was built. He left his home territory of Worcester, Massachusetts (where he was a professor at Clark University), because the noise of his rocket tests disturbed the local residents. A respiratory condition caused him to look toward New Mexico. With Guggenheim Foundation support instigated by Charles Lindbergh, who believed implicitly (and correctly) that Goddard held the key to the future of space flight, he set up shop with his wife and four assistants near Roswell, New Mexico, where the bulk of his work was done.

While at Roswell Goddard received several letters from a young Navy midshipman, Robert C. Truax, who bombarded the rocket expert with a barrage of technical questions. Truax built and tested his own rocket design while still at Annapolis. He graduated in 1939 and went off for two years of sea duty. In 1942, when the Navy moved Goddard's lab to Annapolis to work on rockets designed to assist Navy planes in quick takeoffs (jet-assisted takeoff, or JATO), Ensign Truax was officer in charge of jet propulsion for the Ship's Installation Division of the Navy's Bureau of Aeronautics (BuAer).

During World War II Truax rose quickly to the rank of commander and went on to dominate early rocket development in the United States, just as he'd predicted in 1936 when, as a brash midshipman, he'd written to Goddard, "Who knows? The day may come when I shall be as active in the development of the rocket as you yourself." Truax was later responsible for developing the Navy's significant rocket capability; indeed, in 1955 it was an arm of the Navy, the Naval Research Laboratory, that was selected to manage the nation's first artificial satellite launcher. Ray Stiff and Robertson Youngquist, two of Truax's cohorts, went on to become technical sparkplugs for the United States' first two rocket companies, Aerojet Engineering Corporation and Reaction Motors. Bob Freitag, another Truax associate, was instrumental in bringing satellite communications to the Navy; he went on to plan advanced space programs for the nation.

Truax was president of the American Rocket Society when Sputnik flew in 1957, and was instrumental in generating the society's detailed recommendation to President Eisenhower for a strong, long-term, *nonmilitary* commitment to a national space program. Although Truax himself was not in favor of the course the nation finally took (he felt that space and aeronautics should *not* be combined into a single organization), he and the society were undoubtedly a strong factor in the ultimate establishment of NASA, the present National Aeronautics and Space Administration.

Bob Truax slid out of the mainstream of rocket development around 1960. He retired as a Navy captain and became director of advanced development for Aerojet. In the early 1960s, when rocket development efforts were continually multiplying the complexities of larger and larger turbopump-pressurized rockets, Truax pushed for the "big dumb booster" concept—an enormous, cheap launch rocket whose propellants were fed to it by the pressure generated through its own acceleration. In true Navy fashion, he solved the problem of launching his rocket by simply having it float vertically in the ocean, from whence it could take off without the need for complex, massive, and expensive launch facilities. More important, Sea Dragon, as he called his project, could be recovered at sea and reused. The present space-shuttle booster rockets are recovered in very much the same way Truax first suggested in 1963.

Sea Dragon never got off the ground (or the ocean), but its basic principles—simplification and recoverability to reduce costs—kept cropping up as long as expendable rocket boosters were used. A large pressure-fed liquid-propellant rocket just barely missed being used as the space-shuttle booster.

Despite the cool reception Truax received from the space "establishment," he continued to pop up with new ideas. In 1974 he convinced Evel Knievel that he could make it across the Snake River in a rocket-propelled Sky-Cycle, and hauled out one of his earliest and most reliable steam-rocket designs to do the job. Today Bob Truax has a standing offer to the general public (Project Private Enterprise) to launch *anybody* fifty miles up into space in a Truax-designed "Volks-rocket" (as he calls it)—at a bargain price of only a million dollars. It's designed to land in the water, of course!

As late as 1979 a German company called OTRAG offered to launch commercial satellites from Zaire using launch rockets based on Truax's "big dumb booster" philosophy.

Another young Navy lieutenant who worked with Truax at Goddard's Annapolis laboratory was J. Preston Layton. (The *J.* was for James, but he and all five of his children never used any but their middle names. Layton has been "Pres" to everyone all his adult life.) He too was inspired by Goddard to devote his life to rocketry, and although he went on to gain a sound technical education and a respected reputation as a first-class astronautical engineer, he, like Truax, continued to probe into and pursue novel and advanced concepts with an almost quixotic doggedness. His principal impact on early rocketry was as "Mr. JATO" for the Navy in World War II.

One of the Navy's chief problems with early underpowered sea-going aircraft such as the PBY and PBM flying boats was their reluctance to take off in choppy seas, especially when heavily loaded. This was the reason the Navy brought Goddard to Annapolis—to help develop lightweight ultra-reliable rockets to boost the clumsy "109'ers" (their top speed was 109 miles per hour) off the water. Actually, it was the solid-propellant rockets developed by Theodore von Karman's Cal Tech engineers and produced by Aerojet that became the Navy's JATO mainstay rather than Goddard's more complex liquid-propellant devices. But it was Pres Layton's job to cart these JATOs around the Navy's Pacific Theater and instruct Navy pilots in their use. Because of the uniqueness of his job (and the almost total lack of rocket-technology knowledge on the part of virtually everyone in the Navy outside BuAer's rocket branch), Layton was looked upon as a "rocket missionary." Further, he carried with him the chief of the Bureau of Supplies and Accounts' carte blanche: "This officer may sign for *anything*." So Layton and test

Two of the first operational JATO units help a sluggish Grumman J2F seaplane take off like a jackrabbit (Hawaii, 1943).

Photograph from collection of J. P. Layton.

pilot Bill Gore (the Marine gunner who operated Goddard's first test rockets on "109'er" flight tests in Chesapeake Bay and is presently the senior vice-president of Aerojet) cruised the Pacific with their bomb-like JATO units. They occasionally sank a flying boat when the still-not-quite-totally-reliable rockets malfunctioned, but they were always able to requisition another, along with necessary supplies and enough "scarce amenities" to keep them both glowing with enthusiasm throughout their tour of duty. No wonder the "rocket crazies" developed the reputation they did: who else would leave the remnants of a PBM sinking slowly into wind-driven whitecaps off Kwajalein, with all their possessions on board, and casually drop by the local Navy storekeeper's office for a full resupply—including the airplane?

During the war there was little talk of space flight; the primary emphasis was on rocket development for military uses, principally

The U.S. Navy was the first "customer" for Goddard-developed rockets. Here Goddard poses with his crew at Annapolis in 1942. J. Preston Layton stands third from the right; just behind him, fourth from right, is Marine test pilot Bill Gore, who flew the first seaplane takeoffs using JATO rockets. Photograph from collection of J. P. Layton.

the bazooka (an Army infantry weapon used against tanks), other ordnance applications, and JATO. Solid-propellant rockets received far greater attention; the liquid-propellant efforts, such as Goddard's at Annapolis, some work at Cal Tech's Jet Propulsion Laboratory (JPL), and later by two fledgling companies, Reaction Motors, Inc., of Pompton Plains, New Jersey, and Aerojet Engineering Corporation of Azusa, California, found far fewer applications. The transition to the much higher energy liquid-propellant systems needed for space flight was unquestionably driven by the German Peenemunde rocket team led by Wernher von Braun, when they and much of their V-2 rocket-bomb hardware were spirited to the United States from under the noses of the Soviets in 1945 at the end of World War II.

Von Braun had grown up under the tutelage of the Hungarian (actually Transylvanian) Hermann Oberth, who with Tsiolkovsky and Goddard rounded out the trio of early rocket pioneers. A theoretician like Tsiolkovsky rather than an experimental engineer like Goddard, Oberth was the only one of the three who recognized the importance of having the public on his side, and worked actively to promote it. One of his early, abortive rockets was funded by the German motion-picture company Ufa as part of a Fritz Lang movie, also abortive, called *Girl in the Moon*. His earliest book, *The Rocket into Interplanetary Space* (1923), discussed virtually every aspect of rocket-propelled flight and paralleled much of Goddard's and Tsiolkovsky's early publications. He was, in fact, quite sensitive to the fact that his book had followed Goddard's 1919 milestone paper, which he had written to Goddard for in 1922, and as late as 1959 reiterated the independence of his own and Goddard's work.

The principal impact of his work was its effect on a phalanx of young, bright engineers in Germany. Among them were Max Valier, who convinced auto tycoon Fritz von Opel to build the first successful rocket-powered car (1928); Friedrich Sander, who built the highly successful line of solid-propellant rockets used by most early experimenters; Walter Hohmann, who developed the fundamental theories of space-flight mechanics (now called astrodynamics); and, of course, von Braun, who probably had more influence on our current space activities than any other single person since Goddard.

The bulk of the efforts of the early groups—in Russia, the United States, Germany, and elsewhere in the world—were devoted to rocket-engine research and development, for without a practical and

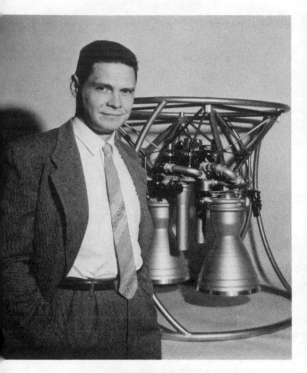

Navy Captain Robert C. Truax was an early Goddard admirer who sparked the Navy into the forefront of U.S. rocket technology. Designer of Evel Knievel's "Sky-Cycle" power plant, Truax still offers to launch private citizens into space. Photograph courtesy of *Astronautics and Aeronautics*.

German rocket pioneer Hermann Oberth (foreground) visiting one of his famous followers, Wernher von Braun (sitting on table), at the U.S. Army Ballistic Missile Agency, Huntsville, Alabama, in 1956. Von Braun's use of ideas and technology developed by Oberth and Goddard put the United States in the forefront of space exploration in the 1960s.

reliable rocket engine, there could be no space flight. This single device continues to dominate virtually all space endeavors.

The rocket, like every method ever used for propulsion, including walking, relies on Isaac Newton's principle that every action produces an equal and opposite reaction. The basic difference between the rocket and all other reaction devices is that it carries on board all the elements it needs to propel itself—unlike a walking person, who requires the presence of the ground to react against, or an aircraft jet engine, which requires air to develop its thrust.

The rocket's principle is simple: its thrust (force in the desired direction) is produced in exactly the same way the recoil of a gun is produced when it fires a bullet. That is, a rocket engine is simply a chamber with a hole in it. When the pressure inside the chamber is raised above the outside pressure (the atmosphere or space), that pressure pushes on the entire inside of the chamber—*except the hole*. All pressure forces on the inside wall of the chamber balance each other out, except for the hole and a spot of equivalent area exactly opposite it on the inside of the chamber. Since there is pressure on that spot, but none on the hole (simply because there isn't any wall there for the pressure to push on), the net result is a force in the direction opposite the hole—the rocket's thrust. The simplest demonstration that it works is to blow up a balloon and then let go of the neck; the balloon skitters off in the *opposite* direction from the neck. Moreover, a few seconds' thought will show that the same thing will happen whether the balloon is in the atmosphere or in the vacuum of space; in fact, the thrust force for a given chamber pressure will be greater in space than in the atmosphere, because of the greater *difference* in pressures between the hole and the spot on the chamber wall opposite the hole.

But in order to make a rocket work, it is necessary to generate pressure in the chamber. This is most generally done by burning a fuel-oxidizer mixture. The resulting combustion generates a large volume of hot gases, which build up the pressure to the desired level. But since the chamber must have a hole in it to develop thrust, the gases escape through the hole. So one by-product of producing thrust is the visible flame of the rocket's exhaust jet. Remember, though, that it isn't the jet itself that produces the thrust.

The rocket's thrust can be increased by replacing the simple hole with a scientifically shaped passage called a nozzle, but the basic principle is still the same: the rocket works because its hot propellant gases push on the rocket engine itself, not on anything outside the rocket.

To maintain its thrust, the rocket's propellants (the fuel and the oxidizer) have to burn at a rate exactly equal to that at which the combustion gases flow out the nozzle. If the two rates don't exactly match, pressure in the chamber will go either up or down; too much of a change will either blow up the rocket or shut it down altogether. Now, because the generation of large amounts of thrust requires a large nozzle and high pressure, a rocket demands both high propellant-flow rates and very high combustion temperatures (to develop the maximum volume of gases for each pound of propellants burned).

Learning how to control such large quantities of highly combustible materials burning at very high pressures required a great deal of ingenuity and experience. This was the purpose of the extensive worldwide research efforts: to continue to increase the size, temperature, and pressure of the rocket, while at the same time to decrease its weight (more properly called mass), as well as the mass of propellants, tanks, pumps, etc., needed to produce high thrust. The key problem was reliability: making the rocket *always* work under these difficult conditions for whatever time was required by its mission.

The *concept* of the rocket, like space flight itself, extends back to antiquity. In 360 B.C. Gellius described a "pigeon" made to move by ejecting steam from small exhaust ports. Hero's famous first-century "aeolopile" was an actual steam turbine, using the same principle. The genealogy of the rocket itself is somewhat hazy, but it is well known that the Chinese were regularly using rockets as weapons in the thirteenth century A.D. These early devices, like the familiar Fourth-of-July skyrocket fireworks, used *solid* propellants; that is, in these rockets the fuel and oxidizer were mixed together and formed into a solid cake (called a *grain*) inside the rocket chamber. The mixture and shape of the grain were designed such that, when ignited, the grain burned at the rate needed to sustain the desired chamber pressure. The Chinese used black gunpowder, which they had invented around the tenth century. Modern solid-propellant rockets (still used for ordnance almost exclusively and also for many other purposes, such as boosting the new U.S. space shuttle) employ much more energetic chemicals, most of which have many times the power of TNT.

Solid-propellant rockets were used in all early experiments mainly because they were simple to build and operate, and therefore relatively reliable. However, *because* their propellant had to be in solid form, they couldn't use the most efficient chemicals—those with the lightest combustion gases (which would provide maximum combustion-gas volume per pound of propellants burned). Further, once ignited, there is no way to change the thrust program of a solid-propellant rocket, or to restart it after stopping it. And, efficient methods for *steering* it (by changing the direction of the exhaust jet) were not developed until the 1960s.

By the early 1940s, however, Goddard had developed *both* controllable thrust and steering mechanisms (swiveling rocket nozzles) using *liquid* propellants. It had been recognized very early in the rocket game by all three rocket pioneers that the most efficient propellants would be liquids—namely, liquid oxygen and liquid hydrogen. So all space-flight enthusiasts, notably the nongovernment societies such as the American Rocket Society, the British Interplanetary Society, and the German Society for Space Travel, devoted the bulk of their efforts to the far more difficult but more promising liquid propellants.

Much of the difficulty with liquid-propellant rockets arises in maintaining constant flow and rapid, efficient mixing of the propellants. Early rockets used high-pressure gas to force the two propellants into the chamber, but the need for tanks heavy enough to withstand the pressure dictated the use of pumps instead. One of the basic problems common to both designs was that a slight change in chamber pressure (due to a small variation in either flow, mixing, or burning) caused a change in propellant flow rate. This coupling, which generally resulted in amplification of *any* disturbance, led to a whole family of different kinds of rocket "combustion instability"—most of which resulted in the destruction of the rocket chamber or its parts. Besides this problem (which is solved, even in today's ultra-reliable rockets, mainly by trial and error for each new design), there were the "routine" difficulties: pumps the size and weight of a washing-machine motor which had to have the power of a diesel locomotive; chamber walls less than a sixteenth of an inch thick that withstood pressures of one hundred atmospheres and temperatures of 6,000° F, and so on. So the construction of a reliable rocket engine became the principal focus of attention.

Even in our research on rocket combustion instability at Princeton back in 1953, we had to incorporate into our tiny little test rockets such rude safety features as "necked-down" bolts to fasten the nozzle to the chamber, so that our frequent explosions would blow the nozzle off instead of damaging our expensive propellant injectors and instruments. We blasted a lot of rocket nozzles across the Princeton meadows, but we saved a lot of valuable instruments.

The early literature of rocket research is replete with funny-sad stories. John Sloop, director of the first NASA rocket combustion group (then part of NACA, the National Advisory Committee for

Aeronautics, NASA's predecessor) tells of his first experiences with the high-energy fuel diborane, which was so reactive it would ignite instantly when exposed to air: "The engineer [from Buffalo Electro-Chemical Company] delivered it in his own car, complete with a safety device: a whisk broom. Whenever a small amount of diborane leaked out of the valve and ignited, the engineer neatly whisked the flame away." And by now almost everyone has seen the spectacular films of early rocket-launch debacles—the early V-2 explosions, the U.S. Viking rocket that tore loose from its moorings on a "static" (nonflight) test, and, of course, the dashing of U.S. spaceflight hopes after Sputnik 1, when our first Vanguard crumpled into a fiery grave on its launch pad. These were the "growin' pains" of high-performance rocket development from the end of World War II to the launch of Sputnik 1 and the space age.

The defeat of Germany in World War II had left only the United

Early rocket development was fraught with problems. Here a Juno II launcher undergoes a spectacular demise (1953).

States and the U.S.S.R. with any appreciable rocket capability. The United States had captured most of von Braun's Peenemunde engineers, virtually all their documents, and most of the V-2 hardware in the field. The Soviets got the lower-echelon people, plus a few engineers and the V-2 production facilities in Nordhausen, Germany. Although German technology got the Soviets off to a flying start, it apparently had little long-term impact on the Soviet space program, whereas von Braun's team dominated much of the U.S. efforts for almost two decades. So where did the amazingly advanced 1957 Soviet space technology come from?

The relative capabilities of the United States and the U.S.S.R. at the time of Sputnik were predetermined over ten years earlier by the different military emphases of the two nations. At the end of World War II, the United States had a large, powerful fleet of B-29 aircraft that could carrry the great weight of the new nuclear bombs that had brought an end to World War II. Two other methods had been proposed for carrying such bombs: pilotless guided missiles, which were simply unmanned, single-purpose, expendable airplanes, and ballistic missiles, essentially upgraded versions of the V-2, which were launched into space and traveled a coasting, unpowered path dictated solely by the external ("ballistic") forces of gravity and, upon reentering the atmosphere, aerodynamics. The pilotless aircraft used existing jet-propulsion technology, could travel the 5,000 to 7,000 miles necessary for intercontinental missions, could carry the heavy, five-thousand-pound nuclear bombs, and could be remotely controlled and guided to their targets. Ballistic missiles needed advanced (and still unreliable) rocket propulsion, had to be aimed exactly by their rocket-launch systems, and, most important, required enormous rocket launchers to carry the required five-thousand-pound payloads over intercontinental ranges.

The United States military therefore decided shortly after World War II not to pursue actively the development of intercontinental ballistic missiles (ICBMs) and to concentrate instead on the existing manned-aircraft fleet capability and to some extent on pilotless aircraft. Even when the cold war with the Soviet Union began to heat up, the United States remained complacent, resting on its overwhelming dominance in manned bombers and advanced nuclear-bomb technology.

The Soviets, on the other hand, came out of World War II with essentially no air power, and far behind the United States in nuclear-warhead technology. Rather than attempt to play catch-up with the United States' advanced bomber fleet, they elected to develop the enormous rocket boosters needed to carry their primitive, heavy nuclear bombs over intercontinental ranges. In 1953, when their test of August 12 announced to a shocked world their mastering of the hydrogen bomb, they were well ahead of the United States in the development of long-range missiles capable of carrying those nuclear warheads.

A frantic scurry of activity ensued in the United States, with all three armed services vying for the lead in the ICBM race. The Army was well ahead because they had inherited the von Braun team. By August 1953 they had already fired the Redstone, the first U.S. liquid-propellant long-range (200 miles) military missile capable of carrying a nuclear warhead. The Air Force, which had continued to reject ballistic missiles all these years, began intensive development of the Atlas, setting up an elaborate command structure to accelerate its efforts. The Navy first joined with the Army in developing an advanced Redstone called Jupiter. But the hazards of launching large liquid-propellant rockets from ships at sea deterred the Navy from pursuing this course. And, when the U.S. Atomic Energy Commission (AEC) announced in 1956 a breakthrough in hydrogen-bomb technology, which made small, high-yield warheads practical, the Navy immediately turned to the less efficient but much more reliable and easy-to-handle solid-propellant rockets. They went on, eventually, to develop the submarine-launched missile system, probably the most effective long-range weapon delivery system in the world today.

The Army Ballistic Missile Agency (ABMA) continued to work on Jupiter and, by September 1956, had succeeded in lofting a test nose cone 3,400 miles downrange from Cape Canaveral. Two months later, however, the Army finally lost the interservice missile battle when responsibility for all ground-to-ground missiles with range greater than two hundred miles was given to the Air Force by Defense Secretary Charles Wilson.

Meanwhile, a relatively low-level program to use rocket-launched payloads for scientific purposes had been proceeding strongly and steadily in the United States. The Naval Research Laboratory had set up an upper-atmosphere research program using rocket-sondes, or "sounding rockets," back in December 1945. The German V-2's were used first, but were really not suitable for scientific measurements. The Navy went on to develop both small Aerobee sounding rockets based on the Jet Propulsion Laboratory's (JPL's) first liquid-propellant sounding rocket, the WAC Corporal, and later a larger rocket called Viking (no relation to the 1975 Viking mission that landed on Mars).

Viking was in its time (1946) the most advanced U.S. liquid-propellant rocket. Its engine, built by the first United States rocket company, Reaction Motors of Pompton Plains, New Jersey, had a gimbaled (swiveled) thrust chamber burning alcohol and liquid oxygen, patterned closely after Goddard's ideas and designs of the American Rocket Society. The Martin Company of Baltimore, Maryland, was the Navy's prime contractor, and Pres Layton, the Navy's JATO man during World War II, was Viking's chief test engineer. He had left the Navy after the war, taken his Master's degree at Purdue University under jet-propulsion pioneer Maurice J. Zucrow, and aimed himself for a career in rocket development at Martin.

The Viking claimed many firsts, including the first photos of earth from space (in 1950). It was the largest sounding rocket the United States ever built: it reached a peak altitude of 158 miles carrying the then-massive instrument payload of 825 pounds. But its main impact on the U.S. space program was on the Vanguard satellite launching effort. That effort was part of a much broader story—the International Geophysical Year.

The IGY was established by an international organization of scientists as a period for intensive study of the earth and its environment. The designated period was July 1, 1957, through December 31, 1958. A large number of sounding-rocket flights were scheduled and flown: 210 by the United States and 125 by the Soviet Union. (Another preview of Soviet capability occurred in May 1957 when one of their sounding rockets lofted to 132 miles altitude the unprecedented payload of 4,850 pounds, including two dogs who were parachuted safely back to earth.) One of the experiments included in the broad spectrum of IGY activities was to be the launching of artificial satellites, announced by both the U.S.S.R. and the United States in 1955.

The idea of artificial satellites came long before the IGY. In 1953 the American Rocket Society had formally proposed such a project, based in part on Fred Singer's earlier (1952) proposal presented to the International Astronautical Congress and appropriately designated MOUSE—Minimum Orbital Unmanned Satellite of Earth. United States Navy studies of artificial satellites had been made as far back as 1945, and an extensive report by the Army Air Corps' Project RAND, entitled "Preliminary Design on an Experimental World-Circling Spaceship," was issued on May 12, 1946.

But again, twenty-twenty hindsight reveals several obvious errors made in carrying out the satellite-launching program. The most important of these was in not recognizing the potential importance of the Soviet rocket-launcher capability, which had been clearly in evidence for years. Thus, although the Soviets made no distinction between military and civil (IGY) launch systems, the United States set up a wholly nonmilitary satellite program that was, in fact, specifically directed *not* to interfere with the intensive military ICBM development activities. The choices for satellite launchers in 1955 were: using the as-yet-unproved Atlas ICBM; adding an upper stage to the already-proven Jupiter-C (which had, remember, demonstrated a 3,400-mile range in 1956); or an entirely new launch vehicle based on U.S. sounding-rocket technology: a Viking-derived first stage, an improved Aerobee second stage, and a new solid-propellant third stage.

The decision went to the new, nonmilitary system, partly because the satellite carrier would be designed specifically for the job of launching a satellite and hence would be more efficient, but mainly because its development would not detract from or interfere with the military ballistic-missile program, which was by then in a desperate catch-up race with the Soviets' big-missile capability (the well-publicized "missile gap" of the Eisenhower administration). It was also recognized that Atlas might not be ready in time, and that the Jupiter-C Army team would evoke a "military image" rather than the more desirable civilian character appropriate to the IGY effort.

The new project was designated Vanguard. Scientific jurisdiction was under the National Academy of Science, with funding by the National Science Foundation. The carrier rocket was assigned to the Naval Research Laboratory, which formed a team from its almost-completed Viking program; the Martin Company was again the prime contractor. The Vanguard carrier's basic problem, according to project director John Hagen, was the "ground rule" that he was to receive no assistance from military programs, which deprived him of existing flight-proven components and technical experience. Despite

The most catastrophic failure in U.S. space history: America's first "all-up" satellite launcher, Vanguard test vehicle 3, crumbles on its launch pad at Cape Canaveral on December 6, 1957—two months after Sputnik's flamboyant success.

Despite its "opening night" debacle, the Vanguard program finally came through. This is Vanguard I, launched by the U.S. Navy March 17, 1958, and today the oldest orbiting artificial satellite. It will stay in orbit another 400 years, and is still used to track other spacecraft and to garner data on the effects of the sun, moon, and atmosphere on satellite orbits. Photograph courtesy of Naval Research Laboratory.

the enormous enthusiasm engendered by the Vanguard, and the not inconsiderable heritage of technology it bestowed on its many descendants in the subsequent U.S. launch-vehicle stable, Vanguard was pretty much of a failure in achieving its primary mission. Its celebrated first all-up launch on December 6, 1957, collapsed on the pad in full view of the U.S. television audience, and it wasn't until March 1958 that its first full-scale satellite was orbited.

Vanguard was the first instance of a theme that continues to pervade almost all the United States endeavors in space: the need to operate ultra-advanced-technology programs on a minimal "shoe-string" basis. It took the enormous negative psychological impetus of Sputniks 1 and 2 to shake loose a U.S. decision to authorize on November 8, 1957 (five days after Sputnik 2), a satellite launch using the existing Jupiter-C military rocket, plus an existing solid-propellant fourth stage which gave the carrier the new name Juno. In *less than three months*, on January 31, 1958, the United States' first artificial satellite, eighteen-pound Explorer 1, was in orbit.

The value of the first rudimentary earth satellites in fulfilling their primary mission was almost lost in the political hullabaloo that resulted from the Soviet triumph. It was Explorer 1 that discovered the enormous radiation belts that surround the earth. They were named after the Iowa professor who designed Explorer's payload, James Van Allen. Discovery of the Van Allen belts was undoubtedly the most important single scientific achievement of the entire IGY. But meanwhile the massive wheels of American politics were grinding their slow path in setting up a U.S. space program.

After the Sputnik 1 and 2 humiliation, Senate Majority Leader Lyndon B. Johnson launched his Military Preparedness Subcommittee (of the Armed Services Committee) on an intensive investigation of the nation's missile and satellite activities. One of his staff members was a young Texan named Glen Wilson, who had left an early career as an aeronautical engineer to take a Ph.D. in psychology and, through a mutual Texas friend, had landed a job with Johnson.

The testimony before Johnson's committee lasted for three months and filled 2,300 pages of the committee hearings record. It prompted two important results: first, the establishment of a clear distinction between the military significance of ballistic missiles and the scientific significance of earth satellites, and second, the formation (on February 6, 1958) of a blue-ribbon Special Committee on Space and Astronautics in the Senate, chaired by Johnson and composed exclusively of the chairmen and ranking minority members of all pertinent Senate committees. The eventual consequence of the first result was the eventual formation of a new *civilian* space agency rather than one in the military services; the consequence of the second was the emergence of Lyndon Johnson as the chief national spokesman on space matters, and, perhaps even more important, the concurrent emergence of Congress as a significant factor in the development of a national space program. In effect, Congress forced the hand of the foot-dragging

The United States finally makes it into space. William Pickering, James Van Allen, and Wernher von Braun joyously lift a model of the first American satellite, Explorer I, and its final rocket stage (January 31, 1958).

Eisenhower administration, which eventually (February 4, 1958) assigned presidential science adviser James R. Killian (appointed to his newly created post only two days after Sputnik 2) the job of setting up the mechanism for managing a national space program. With Congress's quick approval, President Eisenhower signed the National Aeronautics and Space Act of 1958 into law on July 29, 1958. The U.S. space baby was thus born, most appropriately for a civilian effort, about nine months after the conception of the space age by the Russian Sputnik.

Congress played a rare role in setting up the United States space program. In most cases new agencies or federal activities are proposed by the administration and then reviewed and acted upon by Congress. This was, of course, the formal procedure that was followed once the

President drew up the proposed National Space Act, but in this case it was Congress that had forced Eisenhower's hand in drawing it up. Lyndon Johnson, always a consummate politician, had recognized in Sputnik an opportunity to gain considerable power, and he had acted fast. "In early 1958," Glen Wilson told me, "when Congress reconvened [after Sputniks 1 and 2], everybody and his kid brother put in a bill about the space program. But Johnson very quickly moved to cut off what could have been a chaotic situation. In typical Johnson fashion, he introduced a resolution on February fifth to create the Special Committee on Space and Astronautics; it was passed on February sixth!"

Glen Wilson was the first staff appointee to the new committee: as coordinator of technical information. He was, incidentally, the only staff member who served the Senate Space Committee through its entire life, until it was finally terminated (as the Aeronautical and Space Sciences Committee) by the Senate reorganization in 1977. Now, staff members certainly do not make decisions for senators or congressmen, but "to a significant extent, the laws of the country are not written by elected representatives, they are written by staff members. . . ." That is, "The staff tends to frame the options, and if you frame the options you can often frame the outcome." * So Glen Wilson, a graduate but nonpracticing aeronautical engineer when he came to the original Special Committee on Space and Astronautics, soon became a staunch advocate of an active national space program, and used whatever advantages his position gave him to further that program in Congress. The key battles in which the staff played a significant role came later, after the "bloom" had worn off the space program; the early days, when the entire nation wanted to catch up with the Soviets, were relatively clear sailing.

But it was during this early formative period, when both the Senate and the House were feeling their ways through the unfamiliar corridors of space activities, that Wilson believed LBJ made a fundamental error in judgment. The Senate Special Committee was set up only to bridge the period during which the National Space Act was being prepared. Once enacted and NASA created, a standing committee of each house of Congress had to be assigned budgetary cognizance of the new agency. The House of Representatives promptly created the Com-

* Steven V. Roberts, "The Making of a Congressional Bill: Aides Taking Larger Role in Legislative Process," *The New York Times,* May 17, 1978, p. A9.

mittee on *Science* and Astronautics and gave the new committee a relatively broad scope of responsibilities (including the National Science Foundation and the fledgling NASA). But when Johnson recommended the formation of a standing Senate committee, he was a behind-the-scenes presidential candidate, and he was acutely aware of his well-known reputation for trying to grab every bit of power in sight. So when he created the new standing committee (of which he would be chairman), he was very careful to draw up its jurisdictional responsibilities as narrowly as he could, so that they didn't interfere with or step on the toes of anybody else. The new Senate Committee on the Aeronautical and Space Sciences, therefore, had as its only responsibility overseeing the NASA budget.

Glen Wilson was deeply concerned about this narrow authority. "From that day until the day we went out of existence," he worried, "one of my main goals was to try to expand the jurisdiction of the committee, because I knew that sooner or later that narrow scope was going to get us." Wilson's dire prophecy was ultimately borne out: when the Congress reorganized its committee structure in 1976-77, the House committee, which had continued to expand its scope each year, became the all-powerful Committee on Science and Technology, but the Senate space committee was eliminated altogether and its NASA cognizance transferred to a subcommittee of the old Commerce Committee.

Although the National Space Act of 1958 did not formally become law until July, and NASA did not actually come into existence (in keeping with that law) until October 1, the real decision to convert NACA into NASA had been made in March 1958. A formal plan for space technology had been formulated by the old NACA in January, and Abe Silverstein, associate director of NACA's Lewis Propulsion Laboratory in Cleveland, had been picked to come to Washington and organize the space-flight development program. Silverstein brought with him from Lewis a rocket research engineer named Adelbert O. Tischler to set up the NASA rocket research and development program.

Del Tischler had "backed into" rocket research as a result of the chronic illness of Don Bellman's oldest son. Bellman had been working at NACA's Lewis Laboratory in what was then called the High-Pressure Combustion Laboratory (a rocket laboratory in disguise, since NASA's leadership didn't really want to recognize that such a "way-out" activity existed there). In 1953, when Bellman had to move to a better climate because of his son's respiratory ailment, Tischler was asked to leave his work on jet engines and take Bellman's place in the rocket lab. He took the job. He reasoned that if rocket propulsion didn't succeed, he was headed for a dead end, but if it did, there were no limits to how far the field could go.

I met Del Tischler shortly after he'd moved to NACA's rocket lab, when I was working at Princeton University on one of the knottiest problems faced by rocket engineers: combustion instability. I had been touring the nation's rocket test facilities: Bell Aircraft in Buffalo, New York; General Electric in Ballston Spa, New York; Reaction Motors in Rockaway, New Jersey; Aerojet in Azusa, California; North American Aviation in Santa Susanna, California; Purdue University in Lafayette, Indiana; and others. When I got to Cleveland, I found one of the best-organized test setups and what was then by far the most comprehensive data yet compiled (in the form of high-speed strip-camera photos and fast-response pressure recordings) on the elusive phenomenon we were all studying so intensively. Del Tischler, with his round sober face and large round glasses, resembled a wise, impassive owl sitting at the head of our conference table, carefully and precisely describing in his clipped, dry voice the results and implications of his tests. Clearly a man to rely on for accurate, conservative (a plus, for engineers), impartial but complete information, Tischler was checked off in my mental memo book as someone whose judgment I could rely on.

When he moved to Washington in March 1958, he was one of twenty or so handpicked people Silverstein selected from NACA's Langley (Virginia) and Lewis laboratories to set up the space program for the new agency, NASA. "Those twenty people, in the course of the four or five months before NASA was set up and in the six months afterward, outlined the substance of every major program decision made by NASA for the next ten years," Tischler said recently. "Furthermore, most of those decisions were right. The few wrong ones—and there were a few—were quickly corrected, because there was no bureaucratic paper jungle.

"The twenty people could all meet in one room, so that once we recognized that some project was going wrong, Abe could simply and abruptly stop it. And he did, on a number of occasions. Furthermore, since none of us knew how long things were supposed to take, we did them about ten times faster than now. For example, in October 1958, with the telephone assistance of the Air Force Propulsion Laboratory, I wrote the complete specification for the F-1 engine in one twenty-hour stretch. Less than three months later it was under contract—NASA's first major development project. Today it takes longer than that to prepare the procurement request!"

Tischler had been appointed chief of large booster engines by Silverstein. "But since I was practically the only one at NASA headquarters at the time who had any real liquid-rocket experience," he said, "I absorbed much of the rocket-propulsion effort for NASA. Whenever someone was needed to start up a propulsion development, I was that guy. And since nobody goes into space without propulsion, I was involved in almost every project."

The formative years for NASA saw many critical decisions and actions, like those made by Silverstein's famous twenty, which wove the fabric of the present U.S. space program. Significant early events were the assimilation into NASA of the Vanguard program (in November 1958), the transfer into NASA of the Air Force's lunar-probe project and five Army satellite projects, and the acquisition of Cal Tech's Jet Propulsion Laboratory. But the Army balked at losing its prestigious Army Ballistic Missile Agency at Huntsville, Alabama, headed by von Braun; besides, as von Braun told Glen Wilson at a meeting in San Antonio in 1958, he didn't want to go to NASA, because in his experience you could get "big-money" funding only if you were connected with the military.

But it was clearly recognized even after the acquisition of the JPL and numerous Department of Defense (DOD) space programs that NASA continued to lack a substantial capability in launch vehicles—the carriers for its spacecraft program. NASA needed ABMA's large launch-vehicle know-how and hardware, which incorporated all the von Braun team's accomplishments since World War II.

The Department of Defense, in its fiscal year (FY) 1961 budget (filed in 1959), had requested $140 million for the large Saturn rockets von Braun was developing at Huntsville. The first NASA administrator, Keith Glennan, was well aware of his new agency's desperate need for launch-vehicle capability, particularly the Saturn. He offered President Eisenhower a "deal": NASA would run the Saturn project *and* set up a new NASA facility at Huntsville for only $67 million. Glennan's ploy was successful; the Saturn transfer was made on October 20, 1959. However, it put NASA into a severe budget squeeze (Glennan's $67 million wasn't anywhere near enough), which forced NASA to "return to the well" twice later, for a total *supplemental* request of $162 million.

This pattern, in which NASA offered to do too much for too little in order to obtain vitally essential approvals, was to recur time and again in later years. It was admittedly a tough decision: Do you "tell the truth" and risk the possibility of rejection, or do you present an overoptimistic budget picture, get the job, and then work your way out of the subsequent loss in credibility as best you can? This type of decision is a close parallel to the practice known in industrial contracting as "buying in." More often than not, NASA people created sizable future problems for themselves by "taking the plunge": they would show the rosy picture and hope for the best in the future. It's truly difficult to tell whether they were right or wrong.

Unquestionably the best known of NASA's early projects was Mercury, the first manned flight program. Another, less well-known but of comparable importance, was the development (with Del Tischler's specifications) of a 1.5-million-pound-thrust rocket engine, the F-1, by North American Aviation's Rocketdyne division. Both programs started in late 1958; they came together a decade later to put Neil Armstrong and Buzz Aldrin on the moon.

These two major program decisions now seem almost impertinent, given the circumstances at that time: the first four NASA-sponsored space launches (in 1958) were failures, and it wasn't until August 1959 that NASA achieved its first fully successful satellite launch. Meanwhile, the Soviets had in 1958 launched the two-ton Sputnik 3; in 1959 they had landed Lunik 2 on the moon and had taken TV pictures of the backside of the moon with Lunik 3; in 1960 they had orbited and recovered space capsules carrying live dogs, as well as a 14,300-pound operational satellite. By the end of 1960, NASA could tote up only eight successful satellites (all much, much smaller than the Russians'), three in 1959 and five in 1960, out of a total of twenty-five attempts. The percentage improved to slightly better than one out of two in 1961, but it wasn't until 1962 that NASA could really begin to rely on its launch vehicles.

The Soviets' live-dog tests included Korabl Sputnik 2, which made seventeen orbits around the earth before its safe return; it carried mice, rats, and insects along with the dogs. Korabl 3 and 4 added guinea pigs, frogs, and mannequins—and stayed up for one orbit. These "menagerie" satellites had obvious significance: on April 12, 1961, Yuri Gagarin was launched in a Vostok spacecraft, made one orbit around the earth, and landed. On August 6 Gherman S. Titov, in Vostok 2, stayed up for seventeen orbits before parachuting back safely.

Meanwhile, the U.S. "catch-up ball game" in the manned-space-flight olympics had finally resulted in the relatively puny, fifteen-and-a-half-minute "suborbital" flight of Alan Shepard, America's first man in space, on May 5, 1961. Shepard's 302-mile trip, which lofted him to only 116 miles and kept him "weightless" for only five minutes, scarcely compared with Gagarin's full orbit around the earth. One administration opponent of Project Mercury derided the whole experience as "no more than the circus lady who gets shot out of a cannon."

However, Shepard's "anticlimactic" flight did give the United States a small but much-needed psychological boost (it was, after all, totally successful). But perhaps more important, it illustrated an extremely important feature of the U.S. space-program philosophy: the almost single-minded dedication to manned-flight safety. This aspect was nearly obscured by the massive national "too little and too late" recriminations that followed Gagarin's and Shepard's flights, but it is one of the key factors in the later U.S. ascendancy as the world leader in space flight. It is not widely known that the United States *did* have the capability to launch Shepard's flight in January 1961, as proven by a full suborbital "dress rehearsal" with the famous chimpanzee Ham (named not for his considerable personality, but to honor the *H*olloman *A*erospace *M*edical Center, which trained him). But despite Ham's success, the Redstone launch rocket had shown a few quirks that bothered von Braun and his crew, so they postponed the first manned flight and launched instead an unmanned MRBD (Mercury Redstone Booster Development) flight on March 24, 1961. It flew perfectly. Shepard could have been on board, and would have been in space three weeks ahead of Gagarin.

The Soviets, on the other hand, although they had run far more extensive animal tests than the United States, apparently employed a "go for broke" philosophy. Gagarin's orbital flight had *not* been preceded by a suborbital flight-test; his capsule was *not* designed, like Shepard's, to sustain him in landing—he had to parachute out of it;

and he had no global tracking-station network, as was painstakingly set up by the United States for its manned space flights. Further, the total secrecy that enshrouded Soviet space flights until success had been achieved (in contrast to the circuslike national TV coverage of U.S. events), would not have revealed prior failures, rumored to have killed one or more early cosmonauts. So despite the public outcry at being behind the Russians again, the U.S. Mercury project laid a solid and, in the long run, superior groundwork of technical capability for the United States in space. It's always tough to "lay back" while the front-runner gets all the glory, but in this case the young NASA organization apparently picked the right course.

That course was firmly established in the public view only two weeks after Shepard's flight with President John F. Kennedy's historic announcement of the Apollo program on May 25, 1961. Precipitated mainly by Kennedy's need for a U.S. prestige boost after the abortive Bay of Pigs invasion, as well as by Gagarin's achievement a month earlier, the plan had been under study by NASA for several years. The unequivocal statement of a U.S. lunar-landing goal, as Kennedy had undoubtedly intended, electrified the world. Interestingly enough, it was the need for an improved national image rather than science or military dominance (which had totally motivated all early U.S. space efforts) that generated what will undoubtedly turn out to be one of history's boldest decisions.

It is necessary to recognize, however, that although the attainment of Apollo's stated goal had its greatest impact on the United States' political prestige and, to a lesser degree, on the pioneering spirit of exploration, by far the most significant result of the Apollo program was in the enormous organizational, technical, and operational space capability it developed. The Apollo program indirectly nurtured a global electronic-communications industry, a totally new type of weather information service, a scope of scientific discovery unmatched by any prior "golden age" of science, methods for exploring, examining, and monitoring the earth's surface in previously impossible ways, and an essential tool for ensuring peace through incredibly accurate and comprehensive military surveillance. So Apollo gave the United States far more than a few hundred pounds of moon rocks, although even they in themselves have considerable importance to a number of future prospects for the massive utilization of space.

I will not attempt to recount the innumerable milestones and crises that comprise the Apollo saga; they have been exhaustively documented elsewhere. However, a few events that bore significantly on later developments are worth noting.

As early as the summer of 1961, William Proxmire, who was then the junior senator from Wisconsin, began to flex his muscles in a role that later was to establish him as NASA's most powerful and effective critic. In the final hearings on the NASA budget for fiscal year 1962, Proxmire tested Senate Space Committee Chairman Kerr's unquestioned power by attempting to insert two amendments that would reduce the scope of NASA's activities. Kerr (with NASA deputy administrator Robert Seamans relaying information into his right ear) engaged in a vigorous floor debate with Proxmire, and predictably won a favorable final vote. Such was not always the case in later years.

Congressional politics dominated space activities far more than those of most other federal agencies, partly as the result of a unique amendment to the Space Act of 1958, inserted by Lyndon Johnson in 1959, which required *annual* congressional reviews of all NASA programs. This gave Congress the opportunity to impose sudden death (or the slow death of a stretch-out) on any NASA project, thus keeping NASA administrators somewhat nervous and highly sensitive to the impact on Congress of any adverse occurrences in their programs.

"Politics as usual" also affected the space effort, just as it does any federal "public works" program that spends money and creates jobs. The political infighting became most intense over the establishment of new NASA centers, whose long lifetimes generated the steadiest and most desirable local economic benefits. It was no surprise that the biggest NASA plum, the Manned Space Flight Center which serves as the nerve center of all U.S. manned-space-flight development and control (as well as the astronaut training base), went to Houston, Texas, the home town of Albert Thomas, then head of the House Appropriations Subcommittee that approves the NASA budget and who, up to that point, was wholly unsympathetic to space spending. It didn't hurt, of course, to have Vice-President and National Space Council Chairman Lyndon Johnson, a well-known Texan, proclaim publicly, "I'm going to see that Houston gets its fair share of the space budget." It was also no surprise that the center was later named the Lyndon B. Johnson Space Center. However, NASA's Electronics

Research Center went to Boston, an inappropriate choice since it never really got organized before it was closed down as part of a 1969 economy drive. Again, it was no coincidence that Massachusetts Senator Edward M. Kennedy was one of NASA's staunchest opponents.

Aside from politics, a number of sensitive issues were inflamed by key operational decisions. The big question in 1962 was the methodology of getting to the moon: Should we use an enormous new booster (originally called "Nova") capable of placing a spacecraft and its return booster on the moon in a single shot? Or should we launch two Saturn V boosters into earth orbit, one carrying the moon lander (with its return booster), the other loaded with propellant that could be transferred to the spacecraft in orbit? Or, as was finally decided, should we use only a *single* Saturn V to do the whole job, employing a daring maneuver known as "lunar-orbit rendezvous" (LOR)? For LOR, the main spacecraft is sent directly into an orbit around the moon. The lander is sized just large enough to get from *lunar* orbit to the moon's surface and back, where it rendezvouses with the main spacecraft, which then returns to earth. This idea, suggested by a NASA Langley engineer named John Houbolt, was so "way out" that it took him two years to convince NASA management that not only would it work, but that it was probably the only way NASA could meet the tight schedule imposed by President Kennedy's announcement.

But because it took considerable study and engineering insight to appreciate so unconventional an approach, the leader of the scientific community, presidential science adviser Jerome Wiesner, strongly opposed the lunar-orbit-rendezvous approach. He also felt that military needs would eventually call for the more costly and lengthy but, he believed, less risky *earth*-orbit rendezvous. The debate created a major schism between the nation's space scientists, who backed Wiesner, and the engineers, represented by NASA launch-vehicle czar von Braun. The argument was so intense that it erupted during a presidential inspection of the Marshall Space Flight Center, with von Braun and Wiesner quarreling heatedly in front of an embarrassed President Kennedy. Kennedy finally decided to back NASA administrator James Webb, whom he trusted implicitly, and publicly stated that since the lunar-landing task had been assigned to NASA, it was NASA's province to select the flight plan.

Lunar-orbit rendezvous proved itself by its unequivocal success, not only in the six successful moon landings, but also on the aborted *Apollo 13* flight, in which the crew was able to return safely only because of the particular nature of the lunar-orbit-rendezvous spacecraft configuration. But the battle over the decision left a deep scar in the relationship between space scientists on one hand and space-program managers and engineers on the other. Further outbreaks of the scientist-NASA controversy were successfully averted by NASA administrator James Webb (who succeeded Glennan when Kennedy took office) with his adamant refusal to reduce NASA's unmanned space science and exploration project budgets to accelerate the manned space-flight program. Webb's insistence on a "balanced" space effort worried congressional space "hawks" and others, including his own program managers, but with Kennedy's support, Webb was able to stand firm. Apollo *did* make its deadline, and Webb's position established a permanent policy, insuring a place for science, technology, and applications in the total NASA program, although serious criticism of NASA by both scientific and applications interests did recur later.

Webb's "balanced space program" generated a broad phalanx of solid achievements in the 1960s, and established the basis for the commercialization of space. Enormous strides were made in the gathering of scientific data on the earth, its atmosphere, the sun, the moon, and the planets Mars and Venus. Weather forecasting by satellite became an accepted practice. Communications satellites, pioneered by NASA, were turned over to private industry and rapidly brought the world's people into closer contact with each other than had ever been dreamed possible as witnessed by Syncom 3's "live" television broadcast of the 1962 summer Olympic games from Japan. The "industrialization of space," long proclaimed by science-fiction writers as a hopeful prospect for the twenty-first century, actually came into being in the 1960s, with the establishment of the COMSAT Corporation and the Intelsat world network of communications satellites.

But by the mid-1960s, with the moon landing still to come, the harbingers of doom were already gathering their forces. Growing social problems in the United States, the escalation of the Vietnam war, and the lurking specter of double-digit inflation forced a reevaluation of America's expenditures. Even space-hawk President Lyndon Johnson, in view of his vaunted Great Society program and his sensitivity to public outrage over Vietnam, was compelled to begin reducing NASA budgets. But because Apollo was by then in the "home stretch," the budget cuts had to be absorbed by the balance of NASA's programs.

This brought the still-smoldering scientists' concerns leaping into flame. And liberal senators and congressmen, itching for opportunities to transfer space allocations to social programs, complained that Johnson had cut "the only useful parts of the space program"—the earth applications.

NASA had, of course, begun its planning for post-Apollo projects well in advance of the historic *Apollo 11* flight to the moon, actually starting (abortively, however) in 1963. These plans were finally crystallized by a special presidential Space Task Group shortly after the first lunar landing. The national euphoria of that incredibly successful flight had an obvious effect on the three options they came up with:

• Establish a fifty-man space station orbiting the earth, an orbiting lunar space station, a lunar-surface base, and launch a manned flight to Mars by 1985. A reusable carrier would be needed to "shuttle" between the earth's surface and the earth-orbiting station, and a reusable "space tug" would be needed to service the lunar orbital station. (This option required a long-term commitment to a substantially increased NASA budget.)

• Establish the earth-orbiting space station, along with the reusable shuttle, but eliminate the lunar projects and postpone the manned Mars launch to 1986.

• Develop the earth-orbital space station and the shuttle, but defer any decision on the manned Mars landing, keeping it only as a goal to be realized before the end of the century. This minimal of the three options still required a commitment to a $4 billion annual NASA budget.

The national reaction to the Space Task Group report, presented to the White House in September 1959, was violent. New NASA administrator Thomas Paine (who had been named by incoming President Nixon to succeed Webb in March 1969) had received most of the media brickbats after a speech he gave in August 1969, urging an immediate commitment to the manned Mars flight.

The brief glory of *Apollo 11* had not changed the country's basic concerns about Vietnam and mounting domestic problems. Liberal senators and congressmen seeking more funds for desperately needed social programs, space scientists who continued to stress the enormous cost-effectiveness of unmanned missions compared to manned flights, and even "stay-ahead-of-the-Russians" advocates (who now realized that it would be years before the U.S.S.R. could overcome the United States lead garnered by Apollo)—all jumped on the bandwagon to urge cuts in the space budget, and almost unanimously (and quite properly) blasted the expenditure of vast sums "just to go to Mars." The only part of the Space Task Group report that received public support was its stress (inherited from the Webb era) on maintaining a balanced effort in science, applications, and international cooperation.

President Nixon carefully monitored all reactions to the report for several months before making any decisions. The space program had always been popular with middle America, whom he courted in order to maintain his political strength. Space cuts did not seem appropriate to satisfy this "silent majority." Yet the overwhelming cries of negativism generated by far-from-silent public-opinion makers demanded his attention and his action.

Nixon's comprehensive space-policy message, finally issued in March 1970, was considerably less ambitious than even the third option offered by the Space Task Group. It did not include commitments to a large space station, a shuttle, or a manned Mars expedition. The statement identified three "general purposes which should guide our space program—exploration, scientific knowledge, and practical applications." *Studies* of a space station and a shuttle were indicated, but no specific new projects were detailed. NASA budgets were pegged at well below the $4 billion minimum needed to begin realizing even limited goals.

The "aerospace depression" had clearly begun.

One of the men who left NASA that year was Dr. George Mueller, who as NASA's associate administrator for manned space flight since 1963 had guided Apollo to its unprecedented success. At Mueller's insistence, the Space Task Group had included a reusable space shuttle in all three of its options. Mueller saw the need for massive cost reductions in space operations as the single most important ingredient in the acceptance of large-scale space activities by the American public. He correctly recognized the fact that despite Apollo's great success, it was strictly a "stunt"—a one-of-a-kind, gold-plated extravaganza—and not the kind of day-in, day-out airlinelike operation that could ever become commercially successful.

Mueller left NASA in 1969, but fortunately he had implanted his seed well. When the space shuttle became a reality in 1972, George Mueller was clearly recognized as its father.

Joy in the blockhouse on July 16, 1969, soon turned to gloom when NASA's grandiose post-Apollo plans were squelched. Von Braun (with binoculars) and NASA's associate administrator of manned space flight, George Mueller (wearing eyeglasses), applaud the letter-perfect launch of Neil Armstrong, Edwin Aldrin, and Michael Collins to the moon. Although Mueller left NASA shortly thereafter, he left a legacy to prosper after him: the germ of the space shuttle.

3

THE GENESIS

"Everything is hard to predict—especially the future."

—*Oskar Morgenstern*
(Testimony before Aeronautical and
Space Sciences Committee, U.S. Senate)
April 12, 1972

SPACE-SHUTTLE DESIGNERS AND ENTHUSIASTS KEEP TRYING TO PRE-dict the future—generally quite unsuccessfully, as so eloquently expressed by econometrician Morgenstern. Because when you get right down to it, the past (and present) practice of using a "throwaway" rocket to launch payloads into space is a method that leaves a lot to be desired, despite the brilliant successes of Apollo and other space activities to date. Thoughtful engineers often look to our air-transport system for comparisons: commercial airplanes, highly complex machines, boast excellent safety records (currently better than any other form of public transportation) and carry freight and passengers for tiny fractions of the energy-equivalent space transports. So essentially all post-Apollo space-program planning, starting in 1963, has included some form of reusable transport to get from earth to space and back.

The idea of reusable spaceships goes back as far as the idea of space flight itself. Even Lucian's second-century moon voyager used a reusable (although not too practical) sailing ship for his "true history" journey. The first practical concepts for reusable spacecraft began to show up in the 1940s. A two-stage returnable moon rocket was described in the *Sacramento Bee* in 1947; the idea hit the mass-circulation market in 1952 in a *Colliers'* cover story describing von Braun's speculations on a manned flight to Mars.

The intense military concentration on intercontinental ballistic missiles (which were by their very nature expendable) and the equally intense space race with the Soviets in the 1960s barred any serious efforts on such frills as reusable spacecraft carriers, at least until the Apollo goal was in clear sight. Even then, the reusable space shuttle visualized by the post-Apollo NASA planners in the late 1960s was simply a stepping-stone—a necessary adjunct to reduce the costs of such grandiose schemes as one-hundred-man space stations, lunar colonies, and manned flights to the planets. The early designs for reusable boosters reflected this optimistic view of the nation's space future: most of them envisioned payload weights even greater than those of the Saturn V launcher (200,000 pounds into low earth or-

The first "staged flight"—the British "mother" flying boat *Maia* boosts the *Mercury* on a nonstop Ireland-to-Montreal flight (February 6, 1938). This combination achieved the still-standing seaplane world's distance record: 5,997 miles.

bit). Concepts ranged from Truax's Sea Dragon, a simple, pressure-fed liquid-propellant rocket, sea-launched from a vertical floating position and recovered from a parachute landing in the sea, to Krafft Ehricke's Nexus, a monstrous, scaled-up version of the Saturn V that could deliver up to a thousand *tons* of payload to a Mars orbit and was recoverable by means of a rocket-controlled "soft" landing back on earth. Most of the reusable designs, though, concentrated on airplanelike launchers that took off and landed horizontally, but used advanced ramjet engines and/or rockets to reach the high flight speeds required of a spacecraft launcher.

It was no surprise, therefore, that NASA's preliminary studies came up with various forms of *totally* reusable launchers. By the late 1960s, the scope of possible configurations had narrowed down to two-stage concepts using a manned, airplanelike "flyback" booster (one that "flies back" to its base) to launch a smaller, manned airplanelike flyback orbiter. These designs were clearly aimed at minimizing the enormous operating costs associated with the ambitious manned space station and lunar and planetary programs. The fact that these totally recoverable launchers would require massive infusions of "up-front" dollars for their development and initial hardware costs was not considered nearly as important as reducing the day-to-day costs of "routine" space operations.

This implicit trade-off of low recurring costs for high nonrecurring costs certainly made good economic sense—but *only* if the "markets" for the launchers, throughout their useful lifetimes, were sufficient to justify—that is, to write off—the high initial investment. Manned space stations, lunar bases, and planetary expeditions represented excellent markets for such expensive launchers. So when NASA awarded its first contracts for "Phase A" studies of "reusable-rocket transportation systems," in January 1969, their purpose was to assess the feasibility, project the costs, and define project objectives for a totally reusable shuttle system capable of "*routine* access to space."

Access to space can mean many different things. Most satellite missions require only "low earth orbits," whose altitudes range slightly above the fringes of the earth's atmosphere—150 to 300 miles. Satellites can stay in stable orbits when their centrifugal force—the force (due to their speed) that tends to make them fly off into space—exactly balances the earth's gravitational force pulling them toward the center of the earth. The rocket launcher's sole function is to accel-

The conceptual period for the space shuttle brought innumerable ideas to light. These early sketches (1969) show two variations on a popular scheme known as the "stage-and-a-half."

erate the satellite (the launcher's payload) to the necessary speed. The launcher has to impart to the payload not only the energy associated with the orbital speed itself (which for a 200-mile orbit is about 17,000 miles per hour), but also the energy needed both to climb *up* to that altitude against the earth's gravity and to overcome the aerodynamic "drag" forces imposed on the climbing spacecraft by the atmosphere. Translating this additional energy into an equivalent velocity (that is, the speed the rocket would have to deliver to the payload if the earth and its atmosphere *were not* there), we say that the total "velocity increment" a rocket has to generate in order to deliver a payload into low earth orbit is typically about 20,000

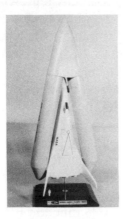

One of many early concepts for a space shuttle—a small spacecraft boosted up to high speed by a much larger aircraft.

This particular configuration (mid-1970), is quite reminiscent of the *Maia-Mercury* seaplane pair.

Still another variation (mid-1969), based on the so-called lifting body concept. Both stages are fully reusable.

miles per hour. Of that 20,000 miles per hour, only 17,000 shows up as actual speed in orbit; the rest is used fighting gravity and drag on the way up.

A small but significant energy saving can be realized by launching eastward to take advantage of the speed of the earth's rotation on its own axis (about a thousand miles per hour at the equator; slightly less at Cape Canaveral). The energy that needs to be supplied by the rocket launcher is thereby lessened. If a "polar" orbit is desired, this benefit is no longer available, and the launcher has to provide the full orbital speed requirement all by itself.

To reach higher orbits, or to change orbital directions (from, say, an orbit parallel to the equator to one inclined at twenty or thirty

The penultimate shuttle: a single-stage-to-orbit spacecraft that takes off and lands just like an airplane.

degrees to it), or to escape from the earth's gravitational field altogether (to go to the moon or the planets), the launch rocket has to supply considerably greater energy. To escape from the earth, for example, a fast-burning rocket (operating much like Jules Verne's cannon) would have to accelerate its payload to 25,000 miles per hour, *not* including atmospheric drag. With the "gravity loss" of a finite rocket-burning time, and including the retarding effect of the atmosphere, the escape-rocket's velocity-increment requirement is likely to range up to as much as 30,000 miles per hour. And since the energy expended by the rocket goes up by the square of its speed (the speed multiplied by itself), it takes around twice as much energy to escape from the earth as it does to reach a 200-mile orbit. Now, the expenditure of at least thirty pounds of the highest energy propellants is needed to accelerate one pound of hardware (leftover rockets, tanks, etc., as well as payload) to "escape" speed. Engineers call the propellant mass divided by the total takeoff mass of the rocket the "mass ratio"; in this example the mass ratio would be thirty over thirty-one, a totally unachievable 0.968 (for comparison, an *egg's* "mass ratio" is about 0.92). This is the reason Tsiolkovsky and Goddard quickly recognized the need for multistage launch rockets, where each successive stage is the payload for the previous one.

It was established very early in the game, therefore, that at least two different kinds of reusable carriers would be needed for space operations: an earth-to-low-orbit booster, which simply "shuttles" back and forth between the surface and the lowest practical "parking" orbit, and a space tug, for operations between the parking orbit and the higher earth orbits or interplanetary trajectories required by various payloads. The reason for using two kinds of carriers is that the tasks required of each, and the environments in which they operate, are vastly different, and the design compromises needed for an *all*-purpose carrier would severely curtail its performance. The shuttle, for example, must lift itself off in a high gravitational field, so it must be built to withstand acceleration forces of at least several earth-gravities, or "g's." It must be streamlined for high-speed flight in the atmosphere, and it must use massive thermal protection measures to keep it from burning up when it reenters the atmosphere at high speed. The tug, on the other hand, is never used in the atmosphere, so streamlining and atmosphere-entry thermal protection are not needed. Besides, it always operates in close balance between orbital (centrifugal) forces and gravity forces, so it does not need much thrust. Some electrically propelled tug designs accelerate at only a ten-thousandth of a g. Moreover, a space-based tug never even has to support its own weight against normal earth gravity, so its structure can be almost literally like that of a spider web.

As the first Apollo landing approached, NASA turned more and more to thoughts of follow-on programs like shuttles and tugs. As might be expected when a multibillion-dollar federally supported project was in the offing, there were many factions vying for lead roles. Although overall project management for the United States' post-Apollo space program would unquestionably go to NASA, the various options and suboptions brought out of the woodwork practically everyone who had ever been involved in space activities, plus a whole host of new entries eagerly seeking their cut of the expected federal largess. It is not easy to characterize so complex an under-taking, but most activities fell into one of three categories: defining and developing the market for space operations; establishing the technology capabilities, requirements, and costs; and, of course, responding to the ever-present political maneuvering.

Although there was a great flurry of activity in developing paper studies of space-market prospects and both spacecraft and launcher technology, the bottom line in the late sixties turned out to be political. The national euphoria following the July 1969 lunar landing scarcely lasted through the summer. Although NASA had let its Phase A study contracts on the space shuttle early in 1969, it soon became evident to everyone that the battle for any major new space development would be a tough one, especially after Nixon's space message of March 1970 confirmed the expected cutback in program scope.

During this period NASA administrator Paine, recognizing the changing mood of the nation's decision makers, conducted an extensive campaign for cooperation (including partial funding) with foreign nations, particularly in Western Europe and Japan. Paine hoped to obtain firm international agreements, which he could then use to secure favorable congressional actions. The Europeans were eager to cooperate with the United States in order to gain both technical and economic support for their floundering space programs. These early efforts laid the groundwork for substantial later cooperative space activities, but produced little of the help that Paine needed in early 1970.

Opposition to the entrenched NASA view, that "routine" access to space was essential for all future space activity, grew rapidly in this period. The President's Office of Management and Budget (OMB), the old Bureau of the Budget, whose principal function is to keep federal expenditures in line, saw in the completion of the Apollo program a superb opportunity to cut NASA's priority (and funding) from the almost open-ended budgetary largess established early in the space race. This was further strengthened by the ever-present need to reduce inflation, by the change in political climate due to escalation of the Vietnam war and at-home social issues, and by skepticism as to whether NASA was truly revealing the full costs of its projected space programs; that is, OMB suspected another NASA "buying-in" ploy. The resulting cut in NASA FY 1971 budget requests (even before going to Congress) forced NASA to drop two of the remaining scheduled Apollo moon flights and delay several space-science and -applications programs rather than delete its beloved shuttle and space station studies, even though they had not yet been approved by Congress.

Nixon's space message in March did, however, strike a limited but promising blow for the shuttle, despite its implications of a NASA budget cut and its pointed omission of any of the Space Task Group's recommended projects: "We should work to reduce substantially the cost of space operations. . . . We are currently examining in greater detail the feasibility of reusable space shuttles as one way of achieving this objective."

With these favorable passages in the Nixon message shining brightly in their tunnel vision, NASA failed badly in assessing the Congress's reaction to another large-scale technological program. It blithely entered the congressional hearings in 1970 with the shuttle (still budgeted for $80 million in FY 1971, even after OMB's slash of $110 million) as an integral part of a space station and with the Mars landing fully visible as a potential prospect. The considerable value of the shuttle for unmanned scientific and applications missions, so clearly the principal feature of Nixon's space message, was barely mentioned.

The resulting fireworks were spectacular. NASA came within a hair of cooking its own goose.

A war-weary, inflation-scarred Congress, besieged by voluble lobbyists and constituents clamoring on all sides for desperately needed at-home social reforms, quickly developed an almost knee-jerk negative response to anything so costly and politically unpopular as an extensive manned-space-flight program.

In previous years a group of liberal senators—Walter Mondale, Clifford Case, Jacob Javits, J. W. Fulbright, William Proxmire, George McGovern, Edmund Muskie, Birch Bayh, and Edward Kennedy—had made a practice of opposing space budgets mainly as a gesture to demonstrate their liberal views to their constituents, with little real hope of actually achieving anything, given the Apollo commitment and the enthusiasm of their colleagues. But in 1970 they suddenly found their quixotic position bulwarked by strange and powerful bedfellows—members of the almost addictively pro-space Subcommittee on Space Science and Applications of the House Committee on Science and Astronautics, including, of all people, the subcommittee chairman, Minnesota's Joseph E. Karth.

Karth's ire (and that of a half dozen other members of his subcommittee) was raised by NASA's decision to delay several important science and applications missions in order to make room for the shuttle/space station budget item. He also believed NASA was back to its old game of not telling the whole truth about future cost projections. "In my judgment these decisions were unwise," he said. "I oppose rushing into development of expensive shuttle/station hardware during these years of declining space budgets." Karth was not opposed to the relatively modest *research* effort on shuttle-related technology, then going on under Del Tischler's direction in NASA's Office of Advanced Research and Technology, but he saw the $80 million shuttle project money as the first step in a precommitment to a $50 to $100 billion manned Mars landing. This, he claimed, was NASA's real goal, and he was unalterably opposed to it.

Karth was further burned when his parent Committee on Science and Astronautics chose to ignore his recommendation and restore the full $80 million shuttle item in the FY 1971 budget. He therefore revived the question on the floor of the House, proposing an amendment to the NASA budget bill that would eliminate the shuttle/space station allocation.

With the comprehensive knowledge of the space program afforded by his subcommittee chairmanship, he came within a hairsbreadth of wiping out NASA's most cherished hopes. The House vote on his amendment was a tie—fifty-three to fifty-three—the closest Karth could come without winning.

But Karth's almost-successful campaign provided welcome ammunition for a fellow Minnesotan, Walter Mondale, who gladly took up the cudgel in his perennial Senate battle to squelch space expenditures. Mondale had secured considerable additional support from another sector. Disgruntled space scientists saw their hopes for space-science programs, finally ready to expand now that Apollo was nearing completion, in danger of being promptly submerged again in favor of another large manned project. This was another manifestation of the early schism that had developed during the Wiesner/von Braun clash over lunar-orbit rendezvous back in 1962. Held in check by Jim Webb's insistence on a balanced space program in spite of Apollo's high priority, the schism had developed ominous rumbles when NASA's space-science program had been buried by shuttle/space-station proponent George Mueller in the original NASA recommendation to the Space Task Group. The bitter 1969-70 public debate on manned space activities had brought the clash out into the open, and many scientists were quick to give their support to Mondale and his shrewd and vocal colleague, Bill Proxmire. Even James Van Allen, prestigious discoverer of the vast radiation belts that bear his name, enriched Mondale's arsenal with a letter stating unequivocally that scientific purposes could be served by an unmanned space program at least as well as—and considerably cheaper than—manned flights.

But Mondale's most prized weapon was the U.S. Air Force's position on the shuttle. The Air Force had suffered a cancellation of *its* space-station counterpart, the manned orbital laboratory, in 1969. An earlier program, appropriately titled Dyna-Soar, had developed much of the technology base from which the shuttle later drew. It was a weapon system that used rockets to boost a manned glider to the fringe of space, from whence it could skip-glide in and out of the atmosphere at near-orbital speed and reach virtually any target on earth. Dyna-Soar had gone the way of its namesake several years earlier, when perfection of the intercontinental ballistic missile made its mission obsolete.

So the Air Force in 1969 was left with no manned space projects, but with considerable present and projected future traffic in unmanned spacecraft for reconnaissance and other military purposes. This traffic,

supported by virtually sacrosanct defense budgets, was quite satisfactorily served by expendable launchers like Atlas and Titan. The
Air Force position on the shuttle, therefore, could be summed up
quite briefly: "Who needs it?"

NASA, of course, needed it, but it also desperately needed that considerable Air Force space traffic to bolster the shuttle "market"—the
basic justification for the high initial shuttle investment—a point that
later became the fulcrum of the final shuttle decision. NASA actively
courted Air Force support, but with little success. The Air Force was
quite satisfied with its current stable of launch vehicles—unless, of
course, NASA would be willing to redesign the shuttle so that it would
give the Air Force *better* launch performance than could be obtained
with expendable rockets, perhaps? Cost advantages, if indeed they
did exist, were not a primary sales argument for the military; the
ability to retrieve both unmanned and manned spacecraft *was* extremely interesting to them, though.

The Air Force was not averse to using its long-standing and effective lobbying potential in Congress to achieve its ends. NASA found
itself being pressured by powerful congressmen to accommodate the
Air Force requirements into the shuttle design. These requirements
were considerable: the Air Force wanted a 65,000-pound payload
and a fifteen-by-sixty-foot payload bay instead of the smaller NASA
design, which would make the whole shuttle bigger and heavier. Even
more important, though, the Air Force wanted 1,500 miles of "cross-
range" capability; that is, the ability to maneuver the orbiter so that
it could land anywhere within a 3000-mile-wide "footprint" bracket-
ing its return trajectory. This requirement would mean changing the
basic shape of the shuttle from NASA's preliminary designs, and
would impose severe additional requirements on the thermal protection system. As might be expected, the cost implications were
sizable, adding well over 20 percent to both development and operations costs of the shuttle.

Despite NASA's reluctance to change its design (in no small part
due to the additional funding that would have to be sought from
Congress), the fat Air Force contribution to the shuttle's payload
"market," plus the pressure from Congress, were irresistible. As early
as 1969, before he left NASA, George Mueller negotiated a "deal"
with the Air Force. As Mike Yarymovych (then deputy assistant
secretary of the Air Force for space) put it, "NASA needed Air Force

support, both for payloads and in Congress. I told Mueller we'd support the shuttle, but only if he gave us the big payload bay and the cross-range capability, so we could return to Vandenburg [the Air Force space-launch center in California] after a single orbit. Mueller knew that would mean changing Max Faget's beloved straight-wing design into a delta [triangular] wing, but he had no choice. He agreed."

The "deal" Yarymovych negotiated went via Mueller to the Space Task Group study and then into NASA's Phase A shuttle-study specifications, along with its severe technical requirements and high cost implications. But despite these stringent demands, the Air Force was in no rush for the shuttle. "Sure, NASA needs the shuttle for the space station, so they need an early IOC [initial operational capability]," said Air Force assistant secretary for research and development Grant Hansen in the spring of 1970. "But for the next ten years expendables can handle the Air Force job. We won't seek shuttle funds even if NASA doesn't. We don't consider the shuttle important enough to set money aside for it."

With that attitude, Senator Mondale wanted to know, why should NASA ask for a substantial budget increase just to meet Air Force needs? Mondale reasoned (and with sound logic) that if NASA, a civilian agency, developed a system with definite military uses, why shouldn't the Department of Defense pay part of the bill? Certainly, at the very least, that part of it that resulted from their own specific needs?

NASA had obviously hoped that the Air Force's strong congressional ties would help them with the shuttle budget battle. But once the Air Force got the shuttle design change it wanted from NASA, there was no reason for it to support the shuttle any further. So, armed with this weak, inconclusive, and generally damaging Air Force position, as well as the strong views of the space scientists and the unusual opposition by House of Representatives space stalwarts, Mondale sponsored an amendment to the Senate's NASA FY 1971 budget bill to eliminate the shuttle and space station. The amendment had the usual liberal support—Senators McGovern, Kennedy, Fulbright, and the other perennials—but this time NASA had a real battle on its hands. The Aeronautical and Space Sciences Committee, NASA's champion in the Senate, was headed by Clinton Anderson of New Mexico, who was physically ailing (he retired shortly thereafter) and took little interest in the debate or in the essential pre-vote politicking.

The main responsibility for garnering Senate support for the NASA shuttle program, therefore, fell on the committee staff.

Glen Wilson by this time had become an old hand in the behind-the-scenes maneuvering of the Senate. He had cut his political teeth at the knee of Lyndon Johnson, one of the most adept operators ever to steer a critical program through the congressional maze. Through his position on the Aeronautical and Space Sciences Committee staff he had been involved in every aspect of the space program since Sputnik. He not only knew all the ins and outs of the political process, but had become a fervent "space buff." As counsel to the committee's staff leader, Jim Gehrig, he was an ardent and effective instrument in combating the suddenly powerful anti-shuttle movement.

Wilson, freckled and redheaded, had a feisty, table-pounding style that belied his classic Texas drawl. His dedication to space was total, but he had no illusions about how programs got funded in our vaunted democratic system. "This is a tough town," he told me once while we sat in his Washington town house. "If you want that money for the space program, you've got to organize yourself and your team and get in there and slug it out with all those other guys who're fighting for *their* programs."

The Senate shuttle authorization vote of 1970 took every bit of fight Glen Wilson and the Space Committee staff could muster. "We came awfully close to losing the damn thing," he said. "We won that first shuttle go-around by four votes. [It was 32–28.] There were four people really responsible for that vote: Jim Gehrig, Charlie Lombard, Craig Voorhees, and me [the four key Space Committee staff members]. Senator Anderson was physically out of it; he couldn't even make a speech from the floor, although many senators supported the program out of long-standing respect for him. The only one we could get to stand up there was Senator Cannon. Although a consistent supporter of the space program, he hadn't been following things closely that year and really wasn't up on the details. It was almost totally up to us."

Wilson and the staff knew their own Space Committee members well; they had studied all the testimony and had been thoroughly briefed by the key NASA engineers. But in marshaling their support on the Senate floor (where only senators, of course, could be heard), it was necessary to use every scrap of politically useful information they could glean from their many collective years of space-program activities. Wilson told me, for example, that Mondale, the leader of the Senate opposition, had been a former member of the Space Committee. He had become NASA's implacable foe as a result of the hearings held after the tragic Apollo fire in 1967, in which three astronauts lost their lives during a ground test of the space capsule. "He believed he'd been lied to by NASA," Wilson said. "That's what started his negativism on space. Now Proxmire," Wilson chuckled, "he's something different. Hell, he was *born* negative!"

The Space Committee won that fight. But even though the Mondale group lost the Senate authorization vote they kept at it. There was still the appropriations vote, and then, because President Nixon that year vetoed the omnibus appropriations bill (for reasons totally unrelated to space), a *second* appropriations vote. It is rare that a Senate floor vote is called for more than twice on any one program; that year the shuttle approval came up for an unprecedented three roll-call votes. But Wilson and the Space Committee staff had done their work well. The shuttle made it through.

Fortunately, the tough 1970 debate finally alerted NASA to the fact that the old days of "gung ho for space" were gone, and that a constant assessment of the nation's and the Congress's mood was essential to the achievement of valid space goals, along with careful and thorough "homework" on all aspects of future budget requests.

As soon as the smoke had cleared from the 1970 congressional battlefield, NASA began to play down the fact that the shuttle would be manned and to play up its important (and heretofore de-emphasized) role in supporting unmanned space programs and military satellites. Under Senate pressure, NASA finally agreed that any manned-flight program projections beyond the shuttle would be too expensive, and when they realized that there was little chance of getting funds for *both* the shuttle *and* the space station, they dropped the station from project status, on the obvious grounds that there could be no space station without a shuttle. One relatively minor "goof": NASA ill-advisedly placed its Space Shuttle Task Group in the Office of Manned Space Flight, on the rather thin basis that the shuttle, although *not* directed toward any manned-flight goals, required people to operate it. This rankled a sensitive Congress, which because of NASA's loss of credibility during the 1970 budget hearings thought NASA might still use the shuttle as the opening wedge in a large and expensive manned-flight program.

By January 1971 the shuttle's preliminary design was relatively well fixed as a fully reusable, two-stage airplanelike system using a manned flyback booster to carry a manned flyback orbiter. Air Force requirements were accommodated, as agreed. The system was still based on the principle that low operating costs were more important than low initial system-investment costs, a philosophy that was economically sound *if* the projected space traffic were high enough. But the new NASA administrator, James Fletcher, who came on board in March 1971, was quick to realize that Congress could in no way be convinced to spend the more than $10 billion then estimated for development of the fully reusable shuttle, especially after the near-debacle in 1970. He sent NASA's shuttle designers back to their drawing boards, and told them to see what alternatives they could come up with.

NASA had been prompted by OMB back in 1970, when OMB had slashed NASA's original budget request from $190 million to $80 million, to study the economics of the shuttle in considerably greater detail to see whether or not it really was worth the investment. In May 1970, NASA let a contract for such a study to a Princeton company, Mathematica, Inc., headed by renowned econometrician Oskar Morgenstern. Morgenstern assigned the day-to-day conduct of the analysis to his former graduate student, a brilliant young Viennese-born economist named Klaus Heiss.

The Mathematica study, delivered to NASA in May 1971, was probably what prompted Fletcher's decision to restudy the whole shuttle concept. Mathematica's work was a key element in all subsequent shuttle decisions, and helped shape much of the present national space program. Heiss's analysis, under Morgenstern's sage guidance, created a whole new approach to the economic assessment and evaluation of major federally supported undertakings, and Heiss later became the senior statesman of space-program benefit/cost analysis.

But despite the elegance of the mathematical methodology, no analytical result can be any better than the initial data and assumptions that are fed into it (the basis of the popular computer axiom: "garbage in, garbage out"). The main inputs to Heiss's study consisted of launch-vehicle designs and estimates of their costs, provided by the Aerospace Corporation; payload designs and cost estimates, provided by Lockheed; and projections of the future payload "mar-

Senate Space committee staff counsel Glen Wilson tells a rapt audience how things get done in Congress. Wilson and the other staff members of the Senate Committee on Aeronautical and Space Sciences were instrumental in guiding the space-shuttle authorization bill through the Senate. Photograph courtesy of *Astronautics and Aeronautics.*

Oskar Morgenstern and Klaus Heiss (left) of Mathematica, Inc. present their economic analysis of the space shuttle to a Senate committee. Photograph courtesy of *Astronautics and Aeronautics.*

ket," provided by NASA and the Department of Defense. Mathematica's technical consultant—mainly to keep Aerospace and Lockheed "honest"—was Pres Layton, by then director of the Aerospace Systems Laboratory at Princeton University.

The basic question the study intended to answer was, will the cost reductions afforded by the space shuttle during its useful life (as compared with expendable launchers) more than offset the initial investment for development and purchase of the shuttle system? That answer clearly could not be a simple yes or no; it depended on a host of options and parameters whose probable values were still unknown. Skipping the details, Heiss's bottom-line conclusions were as follows:

• Based on the best estimates and projections available, the fully reusable shuttle would be *marginally* cost-effective. The dominant factor would be the total number of flights, which depended on the future demand for payload launchings; whether or not the payloads were manned or unmanned made very little difference.

• The principal savings would come, surprisingly enough, not from reducing the cost of transportation itself, but from reducing the stringent *payload* specifications required by expendable launchers. That is, the big shuttle payload bay and low-acceleration launches (compared with expendable rockets) allowed much cheaper payload construction; further, the ability to repair payloads in orbit, replace worn-out or defective parts, or to return them to earth for modernization or salvage offered considerable overall cost reductions. (The example that best illustrated this point was NASA's first Orbiting Astronautical Observatory, launched in April 1966. It went dead upon reaching orbit, and was a total loss. Arthur C. Clarke later wrote, "A man with a screwdriver could probably have fixed it in five minutes, and saved fifty million dollars!")

Because the Mathematica report revealed such barely marginal cost benefits (the "most probable" estimate calculated by Heiss showed scarcely $100 million savings from a $12.8 *billion* investment), the highly likely event of even a minimal cost overrun could wipe out the entire economic rationale for the shuttle. As a result, OMB was, not unexpectedly, wholly negative. Nevertheless, the President's final budget request to Congress for FY 1972 still included $100 million for the shuttle—up $20 million from FY 1971. Total development cost for the shuttle was not yet well defined; NASA informally pegged it at somewhere between $6 billion and $10 billion (the Mathematica estimate of $12.8 billion had included flight hardware and ground facilities as well as development costs).

Budget authorization in the House of Representatives that year was relatively smooth sailing: this time NASA had done its homework well. Deputy administrator George Low had flatly and publicly stated that "no Mars landing plans exist." Major space-station efforts had been postponed indefinitely—Skylab, using mainly leftover Apollo hardware, would verify whether or not man could function for long periods in space and define potential space-station benefits. It was to be strictly a "shoestring" operation. Emphasis was on "the shuttle mission model"—all the *unmanned* payloads to be launched by the shuttle from 1978 to 1990—not only NASA's, but the Department of Defense's, the commercial Intelsat communications satellites, the National Oceanic and Atmospheric Administration's weather satellites, payloads for foreign nations, and so on.

But even though subcommittee chairman Karth "went along" with NASA that year (thereby defusing any real House resistance to the budget proposal), he had carefully read the Mathematica report and was openly skeptical of NASA's cost projections. "Before the shuttle flies operationally," he predicted, "it will probably have cost closer to twenty billion dollars than six billion." He also doubted that efforts to obtain significant European financial cooperation, started in 1969 by Paine and still being actively pursued by NASA, would bear any fruit, citing the difficulty of multinational cooperation on so complex a project, as clearly evidenced by the mess the European Launcher Development Organization had made of itself. "Besides," he said, "it appears unlikely that the Europeans can raise a meaningful share of the money."

Karth also discounted Russian competition in space as having "not only subsided, but evaporated." He worried most about the continued erosion of public support. A recent survey in his own home district had revealed only 9 percent of the interviewees wanting the space program accelerated; 58 percent wanted it cut. "The only way to get increased support," he insisted, plugging away at an old theme of his, "is to apply the space technology to benefit the man in the street. There's not one penny in the budget for that purpose."

The Senate opposition, again under Mondale's leadership, was well organized. The taste of near-victory in 1970, after all the frustrating years of bucking the too-popular Apollo budget, had whetted the liberals' appetites, and the experience had sharpened their tools. Again, they brandished all of Karth's cautions (although the loss of his out-and-out negative vote clearly damaged Mondale's case), resurrected the old but still valid reluctance of the Air Force to kick in development funds (although they still planned to use the shuttle extensively), and again trotted out a battery of negative letters from scientists. In addition to Van Allen and well-known Cornell astronomer Thomas Gold, Mondale cited a strongly negative letter on the shuttle from a new source: disgruntled ex-astronaut Brian O'Leary.

O'Leary, a boyish-looking but highly imaginative Ph.D. astrophysicist, had leaped at the opportunity to explore the moon firsthand, and had been accepted by NASA as one of the first civilian scientist-astronauts. After some eight months in the astronaut corps, he realized that not only would he not get to the moon, but that the astronaut office leaders, Alan Shepard and Deke Slayton, were not really interested in scientific activities. They were old-line test pilots, and at that time in a brand-new manned-space-flight program test piloting seemed more important to them than studying the stars from space. So O'Leary quit the corps, wrote a revealing and popular book, *The Making of an Ex-Astronaut*, in which he described his experiences, and lambasted the manned space program whenever he could. Mondale's crusade against the shuttle provided a likely opportunity for O'Leary to gain national publicity for his views. He wrote to the senator expressing his strong support of Van Allen and his belief that NASA was developing the shuttle because it was a big, advanced-technology, "make-work" program that could fill the gap left by Apollo.

One of the most negative of the scientists who opposed the shuttle in 1971, O'Leary was later to become one of its staunchest proponents, providing an illuminating example of the thesis that "once the shuttle is flying, we'll find all sorts of uses for it that we'd never imagined." O'Leary's turnaround came because he later realized the shuttle to be an essential element in accomplishing one of the most imaginative scientific opportunities of the century: capturing an asteroid. But that's a story for another chapter.

Mondale's mainstay of support for his 1971 amendment to kill the shuttle was Van Allen's interpretation of the Mathematica report. Van Allen, unfortunately, did *not* do his homework well, and his misinterpretations of Heiss's analysis were relatively easy for the opposition to ridicule. This was certainly one of the contributing factors to the final result, but again, it was dogged plugging by the dedicated Space Committee staff that probably had the biggest impact on the final vote. If Mondale's group had been sharpened by the close call in 1970, Glen Wilson and the other committee staff members had really learned how to flex *their* muscles. Chairman Anderson was still unable to participate, but the staff marshaled its arguments (including a devastating rebuttal of Van Allen's misinterpretations) and with them, the necessary votes. Mondale and the liberals, whose position finally degenerated into their old saw of "anti-technology for technology's sake," were badly defeated: sixty-four to twenty-two.

It is entirely possible that the unexpectedly strong supportive vote on the shuttle owed something to two hapless fellow programs: the ill-fated supersonic transport (SST) and the antiballistic missile (ABM). Both were killed during the same session, and it is conceivable that a number of senators did not want to be classed as *too* liberal or *too* anti-technology. After all, they had satisfied their liberal constituents by the nationally publicized SST and ABM votes; why not pick up whatever pro-technology public support they could by a favorable vote on the relatively little-known (and still only $100 million) shuttle?

Whatever the reason, the shuttle made it through again—but now NASA administrator Fletcher was faced with the same tough problem: how to convince both the White House and Congress that he could bring the *total* shuttle-program cost down to a level they would accept. OMB had flatly made it clear that Fletcher's limit would be one billion dollars per year for the then-projected five-year shuttle development—far less than the most recent ten-billion-dollar estimate for the fully reusable shuttle design.

So Fletcher first redirected the industry contractors, who were already into their Phase B studies, to develop preliminary design configurations examining alternative options that would cost no more than $5 billion, and he extended their contracts by four months to do so. He also let a new contract to Mathematica to develop an analysis similar to their previous one, but this time to include the cheaper designs the Phase B contractors were in the process of formulating.

Morgenstern gave Klaus Heiss almost full responsibility for this second report. But the data Heiss got from Aerospace and Lockheed, still preliminary in most cases, again made it difficult for him to identify very accurately his input costs. Further, NASA was faced with what it believed was an almost impossible task of developing an extremely advanced and complex system on a veritable shoestring—the $5 billion limit. So, knowing from the previous report that the key factor in the economic analysis was likely to be market demand— the number of flights—the agency turned itself inside out to drum up a "mission model" having the maximum possible number of flights. Almost like the hen laying a square egg, they finally squeezed out an incredible, but barely justifiable, 714 flights during the projected twelve-year shuttle write-off period (1978-90): almost 60 flights per year.

Pres Layton, again consultant to Mathematica on the second contract, clearly recognized the quicksand into which Heiss was about to step. NASA had not wanted the first Mathematica study—it had been forced on it by OMB—but it now desperately needed to find and justify a "cheap" but practicable shuttle program. Bob Lindley, Heiss's NASA contract monitor, saw the agency's answer in Mathematica's study, and pushed Heiss for an early release of his results.

But Layton pointed to numerous flaws, again not so much in Heiss's analysis as in the input data he was getting. First of all, Layton said, NASA's 714-mission projection was overly optimistic, particularly in its early-year projections. More important, the key justification for all the shuttle configurations seemed to be in payload cost reductions, as in the first study. But Layton thought these estimated reductions were overemphasized. He couldn't accept, for example, Lockheed's insistence that the relaxation of specifications made possible by the benign shuttle environment would permit the use of ordinary commercial electronic components. He also checked with some of the potential customers, particularly the existing communications satellite market, and found very little interest on their part in repairing, refurbishing, or retrieving payloads. If that really were the case, much of the shuttle's cost advantage disappeared. In addition, Layton told Heiss that the technology and system-design aspects of the new "cheap" configurations were not yet well-enough established to define costs adequately, and he thought Aerospace had, as usual, given Heiss highly optimistic estimates.

The most appealing shuttle design studied by Mathematica was a winged flyback orbiter based on the previous fully reusable concept, but now boosted into orbit by large unmanned rockets that would be recovered and reused after falling back into the sea (shades of Bob Truax's Sea Dragon!). But to keep the orbiter small enough for the projected cost reduction, it would be necessary both to store its propellants in a big external tank, which would be thrown away after being emptied, and to run its engines right from the start, in parallel with the booster rockets. This mostly reusable configuration (which later developed into the space shuttle now flying) was dubbed TAOS —Thrust-Assisted Orbiter System. Mathematica also correctly observed that an additional element would be needed—a reusable space tug for transport to higher orbits or escape trajectories—since the TAOS was strictly a low-orbit shuttle.

Layton's concerns about this design, only newly conceived by McDonnell Douglas during Phase B studies, revolved around his own area of expertise, the rockets. He predicted much higher costs for the orbiter's main engines than did Aerospace and, even though he was an old buddy of Truax's, he did not believe that *either* big solid-propellant or big self-pressurized liquid-propellant rockets (the boosters) could be retrieved and refurbished as cheaply and as reliably as had been projected. Further, as a consultant to Aerojet (manufacturer of the Titan missile engines) and Martin Marietta (builder of the Titan missile), he was quite familiar with what could be done in the way of designing a new family of *cheaper* expendable launchers that could compete well with the "compromise" TAOS shuttle. He recognized that the Aerospace study of such new systems had been only perfunctory—in effect, a "straw man" to be knocked over to show how good the reusable shuttle was—and that the systems should be reexamined to make the Mathematica economics valid.

However, Heiss, a brilliant economist but by no means a competent space engineer, was simultaneously having his ear bent by NASA's knowledgeable Bob Lindley, who persuasively countered most of Layton's arguments—and was, after all, Heiss's contract supervisor. Heiss therefore agreed to have Morgenstern (whose reputation carried a great deal more weight than his own) coauthor a letter to Fletcher outlining his preliminary (and highly favorable) findings. It was Morgenstern and Heiss's letter of October 28, 1971, which tipped the scales that eventually launched the shuttle.

Actually Lindley's motivation for pressuring Heiss was a valid one. OMB, in its single-minded emphasis on reducing investment costs, was pressing very hard for NASA to adopt a Dyna-Soar-like manned glider boosted into orbit by an existing Titan III missile—a real investment bargain at about $3 billion total development costs. But the preliminary Mathematica analysis clearly showed that the high operating cost ($30 million per flight compared to TAOS's $10 million) made it a very expensive alternative over its total useful life. Another valid point favoring early release of the Mathematica letter was that many in NASA were reluctant to give up their "baby"—the fully reusable, flyback two-stage design, and as long as there was no decent compromise available, they would stick to their expensive guns and be shot down altogether, if not by OMB then certainly by Congress.

So, whereas Layton's concerns all turned out to be quite accurate, Heiss's decision to send the letter anyway *did* get the shuttle effort moving in the proper direction—toward a reasonable compromise between unacceptably high investment costs and unacceptably high operation costs. The decision cost Heiss his friendship with Layton (who promptly, and properly, quit Mathematica as a consultant when his advice was ignored), but it set him up as NASA's primary source for benefit/cost analyses of space programs. In fact, he too quit Mathematica shortly after the shuttle study was completed to set up his own econometric analysis firm, ECON, Inc., also in Princeton and, like Mathematica, highly successful in space-oriented economic studies.

The Mathematica letter eventually brought powerful forces into play on NASA's side. Even NASA, after much soul-searching, concluded that it would have to give up its dearly beloved fully reusable shuttle. It simply would cost too much. It was NASA administrator Jim Fletcher who, armed with Mathematica's analysis, convinced the President of this during a face-to-face meeting in late December 1971.

On January 5, 1972, President Nixon announced his decision to go ahead with the compromise TAOS shuttle. The final Mathematica report came out on January 31, but its conclusions were already well known. Morgenstern, fortunately for Mathematica's future reputation, *had* listened to Layton and had inserted into the final report all the necessary caveats to cover Mathematica on the weakness of its input data. But the final compromise decision, arrived at in relative haste for so large an effort, constrained NASA to proceed with a decade-long multi-billion-dollar program on the basis of some rather sketchy technical data. Again, they had "bought in" to a complex-technology program and were stuck with it. And they *were* stuck. Congress, in the FY 1973 budget approval process, nailed down the lid on what NASA had agreed to: a first orbital flight in 1979, at a total development cost of $5.22 billion (in 1972 dollars), and a total program cost (including the development costs, five orbiters, the necessary boosters and tanks, and launch facilities) of $7.5 billion (1972 dollars). The congressional debate also put an absolute limit of 20 percent on cost overruns (one billion dollars), which NASA was forced to accept, despite the high level of technological risk implied by the shuttle's performance. The compromise also did not allow sufficient funds for development of the reusable tug needed for high-orbit transfers, a point that did not receive much attention at the time, but that later came back to plague NASA's shuttle marketing effort.

During all this political hullabaloo, Del Tischler was proceeding with the development of the advanced technology needed for reusable space shuttles, whatever their detailed configurations. His shuttle-technology office and its relatively small budget, comfortably ensconced in NASA's headquarters research arm called the Office of Advanced Research and Technology (OART), was not on the congressional block as was the shuttle *program* office, which was part of NASA's highly visible Office of Manned Space Flight (OMSF). (NASA soon changed *that* "red-flag" name to Office of Space Flight, and then in 1978, the year before the first shuttle flight, to Office of Space Transportation Systems.)

The circumstances surrounding Tischler's transfer to OART back in 1964 had a significant impact on the serious developmental problems NASA later experienced with the shuttle's main rocket engines. When Tischler had been at NASA headquarters monitoring the Apollo propulsion effort (prior to 1964), he had handpicked his staff for competence; he'd spirited them away from top positions in industry and universities. No NASA field center, even von Braun's highly touted Marshall Space Flight Center in Huntsville, could match them, man for man. Von Braun and his people resented having this group ride close herd on them and their contractors. "There was no way those guys could snow my people," Tischler told me, "either technically or managerially."

But von Braun had established himself and the Marshall Center as the hub of the space-program universe—openly proclaimed by signs at the boundaries of Huntsville—and Tischler's group represented a thorn that might pierce his balloon. So when George Mueller became NASA's director for manned space flight, von Braun got his chance. He convinced Mueller to break up Tischler's team. Tischler and one of his top combustion experts went to OART; the others scattered to various NASA centers and contractors.

But Mueller was shrewd enough to recognize his error and shortly thereafter invited Tischler to sit in as a critic of the Office of Manned Space Flight's Apollo program, even though Tischler worked for a different NASA office. The new team Tischler assembled for this task

Adelbert O. "Del" Tischler (center) describes a shuttle booster model in a static test stand (April 1971).

was fully as competent as his old one, and made significant contributions to Apollo engine development. But without the necessary support in his own organization, he was unable to keep his team together. His entire propulsion group, for example, was transferred to another OART division; the best ones promptly left for greener pastures. "If only I could have somehow retained these people that once worked for me," Tischler ruminated many years later. "I'd bet my pension there wouldn't have been any shuttle main-engine problem."

Nevertheless, during this period he was instrumental in moving NASA (with Air Force cooperation) into the extremely advanced liquid-propellant engines that later formed the basis for the shuttle orbiter's main propulsion, and also, almost single-handedly, into the development of very large solid-rocket boosters (again with substantial Air Force help). "For a long time I was one of the few in NASA who saw the potential value in large solid boosters," he remembered. "I had lots of support from Congress, but von Braun's Marshall Space

Flight Center was too imbued with liquids." In 1967 NASA dropped the entire large-solids program like a stone, and it wasn't until the final shuttle compromise came along that it was resurrected.

That resurrection was due in no small part to Tischler's influence. He had spent considerable personal effort attempting to project the future of space activities after Apollo. In August 1969, he published an extensive "Commentary on Low-Cost Space Transportation" in *Astronautics and Aeronautics* magazine. In that article he accurately forecast the trade-offs that later were detailed by Mathematica (investment cost versus operational cost), as well as the fact that the traffic rate dominated that trade-off; in fact, he specifically identified the final shuttle compromise configuration, although, in his own words, only as "a step along the way to the ultimate low-cost space transportation system."

Early NASA shuttle-technology efforts were fragmented. Some of them were in George Mueller's Office of Manned Space Flight; some were in the various NASA research discipline divisions—"hobby shops," Tischler called them—of Bruce Lundin's Office of Advanced Research and Technology. Tischler recognized the need for a coordinated activity simply because he foresaw that piecemeal efforts would not create the enormous technical advancement the shuttle would eventually require, and he sensed its significance to the nation's space future. He talked to OART head Lundin and to OMSF head Mueller, and secured an agreement from them. Two letters were written, one from Lundin to Mueller, suggesting that all recoverable-launcher-technology efforts be coordinated under a new office to be headed by Tischler and supported jointly by OMSF and OART; the other was Mueller's response accepting Lundin's suggestion. "The fact of the matter is," chuckled Tischler, "that I drafted both letters. I slipped up on one point, though: Mueller's reply is dated a day earlier than Lundin's suggestion!"

Tischler gives "the father of the space shuttle" full credit:

> Mueller was very astute. He was able to make major decisions and make them well. He recognized that this arrangement, in effect, doubled his money; and that funds contributed to OART were not readily visible under a "shuttle label." He also recognized that because I had worked at OMSF before transferring to OART, there was no one else in NASA at that time who knew both OMSF developments and the research activities at OART as well as I did.

And once Mueller had given me that responsibility, he was perfectly willing to let me run the whole thing pretty much as I chose. I had more trouble with Lundin, my boss; Mueller accepted almost everything that I did.

Mueller's faith in his own good judgment paid off: Tischler's Shuttle Technologies Office came up with an absolutely unprecedented 42 percent applicability; that is, 42 percent of the efforts in what was then a wholly new battery of technologies were eventually used in developing the shuttle. Rarely is an applied research or technology effort more than 5 percent to 10 percent applicable to its ultimate goal.

The phenomenal success of the Shuttle Technologies Office was no mean achievement. When Tischler first received his assignment he

NASA Administrator James Fletcher finally convinced President Richard M. Nixon that the space-shuttle program was needed, based in good part on the economic arguments provided by Mathe-matica's Morgenstern and Heiss. Here they discuss the project in San Clemente on January 5, 1972, the day the President announced that the United States would proceed with the program.

used an apt phrase to describe it: "This is going to be a nasty job . . . somewhat like putting a ring in a bull's nose from the wrong end of the animal. But [and here the eternal optimism of the space enthusiast shines brightly through] I'm imbued with the conviction that it can be done—if we can work our way through the bull." He considered his task to be midway between the *inspirational* phase of the shuttle, where the ideas were conceived, and the *perspirational* phase, where those ideas became transformed into real hardware. He called it the *transpirational* phase—"shaking down" the myriad technical approaches that are possible into the ones that are practical, achievable, and economical. Rule number one in his book was, "There is no substitute for knowing what we're doing."

One of Tischler's problems in coordinating the diverse elements of technology that were needed for the shuttle was that the principal

George Mueller, NASA Associate Administrator for Manned Space Flight, describes the key role a reusable space shuttle will play in the world's future. His insistence paid off: the shuttle program was the only one of NASA's three big post-Apollo "dream projects" that actually came about. Photograph courtesy of *Astronautics and Aeronautics*.

spacecraft manufacturers had been spawned by aircraft companies, but aircraft and spacecraft were so totally different that the progeny, a decade or so later, no longer designed, built, or even thought the way their forebears did. But the shuttle required a wedding of the talents of these dissimilar corporate segments—a reunion process that Tischler remarked was ". . . somewhat like unfrying an egg. But at the same time," he continued, "it is necessary to acknowledge that something shaped like a flatiron cannot be expected to fly like an airplane." Hence the already difficult amalgamation process required plentiful salting with brand-new technology—Tischler's job. Achieving his enviable record in developing that technology took a great deal of something Tischler was not afraid of—hard work. His concept of what that meant was best put in a talk he gave at a space-shuttle symposium at the Smithsonian in October 1969: "I don't mean the kind of work represented by fellows like me addressing audiences like you to enthusiastically project optimistic views about future space systems. That kind of presentation always reminds me of the reason given by a wife of one of our research engineers when she divorced him to marry a plumber. She told the judge that her husband was always telling her how wonderful it was *going* to be."

Despite the excellent technical accomplishments of Tischler's Shuttle Technologies Office, when the politics of 1971 forced NASA's retrenchment from a fully reusable two-stage shuttle to the "stage and-a-half," partly reusable TAOS compromise, much technological backing and filling was necessary. There just wasn't enough time. The resulting ironbound commitment implied by Nixon's January 1972 announcement and the subsequent congressional budget debate locked NASA into the manacles of a bare-bones development budget. The nation's most important space project, on the basis of only a few months' technical integration of truly advanced technologies, was going to have to be done on a literal shoestring. There was practically no margin for error—for the next nine years.

Many serious supporters of the space program were deeply concerned. Among them was the professional society that represented the nation's aerospace engineers and scientists, the American Institute of Aeronautics and Astronautics (AIAA). The AIAA had been created in 1963 by an amalgamation of the old high-flying American Rocket Society and the relatively stodgy Institute of Aerospace Sciences. Up to 1971 the institute had pretty much "tended to its knitting," publishing several monthly technical journals of interest only to aerospace researchers and designers and holding a dozen or more technical meetings each year on subjects like laser fluid dynamics, mechanics of noise generation in fluid flows, and space instrumentation for atmospheric observation.

But in 1971 the supersonic transport project was terminated by the United States Senate. There were a fair number of AIAA members—qualified aeronautical engineers—who agreed that an American SST should not have been developed at that time. But I doubt that you could find a single one who wouldn't agree that the program had been killed for the *wrong* reasons. The AIAA's board of directors, therefore, pulled its collective head out of the sand of nonpublic involvement and decided to "mix it" in the national scene, along with all the other special-interest groups who made their voices and their positions heard in the halls of government. But the AIAA was a highly conservative organization. In July 1971 its president, Martin Goland of the Southwest Research Institute, established the AIAA's guiding principle in the new public-policy arena: "Inform but do not persuade." One of the first activities to be started under that far-from-rampant banner was the preparation of assessment papers on national issues affecting aerospace. After a great deal of acrimonious debate as to "the proper role of a technical society," the title of the first paper was selected: "New Space Transportation Systems—An AIAA Assessment." The board's concern was the madly whirling political merry-go-round the shuttle was then riding. The board's nominee for assessment leader: J. Preston Layton.

Layton assembled a blue-ribbon team of university, industry, and government engineers and began hammering out his assessment. It took a year and a half, not so much because of the technical difficulties or the problems of developing a responsible publication from among a group of volunteers already committed to heavy overtime hours at their regular jobs, but mainly because of political problems. As a member of Layton's committee, I remember what were supposed to be working sessions turning instead into debates that raged far into the night. The most common altercation revolved about the obvious dilemma: how could the committee—all of whose members depended for their jobs either on NASA programs or on companies bidding for them—generate an assessment whose conclusions might not agree with NASA's "party line"?

That dilemma, incidentally, is peculiar not only to the AIAA's shuttle assessment, but to all large technologically based programs; the best current example is commercial nuclear power. The dilemma is, of course, that the only people who really understand the project and by their training are best equipped to assess it, are the ones most likely to be unduly favorable to its development because their livelihoods depend on it. Hence their assessment is necessarily suspect.

Pres Layton was one of the very few people stubborn enough to resolve the dilemma. Sitting at the head of the seething conference table, an implacable blond Buddha, he laid down Layton's law: "Do it as I say, or else get off the committee." There's no way to count the hours Layton and I spent together drafting and redrafting sections of the report, only to elicit howls of rage from a committee member concerned about what his company management would do to him.

One of the *minor* problems we faced, of course, was that the period during which the assessment was being assembled was NASA's bid evaluation period for the shuttle's prime contract—and people on both sides of the fence got very, very nervous at the remotest prospect that a technical society might do something to upset a five-billion-dollar applecart.

Even when the draft was finally done, the battle continued: the AIAA board of directors—mostly high-up aerospace company executives and government agency leaders—had to approve it. Pres Layton suffered from gout in his later years; I think it must have come from the hours he spent on his feet at AIAA board meetings, defending, parrying, explaining, and not infrequently pounding the big table to emphasize his point: unless the AIAA turned out an honest assessment of the shuttle, whether or not it agreed with NASA's position, the whole exercise (and the AIAA's entire new public involvement effort) might as well be flushed down the drain.

Layton won. In January 1973 the AIAA's assessment, edited by Layton and Grey, was released to the Congress and to the public. As might be expected, it was unquestionably bullish on the need for a reusable space-transportation system, and it supported the flexibility, potential usefulness, and technical basis of the final NASA compromise design. But it clearly pointed out the fallacy of projecting shuttle cost savings without sufficient space traffic (and noted the inadequacy of the then-current NASA mission "model" that defined that traffic). It also reiterated the inadequacies in the payload-savings analysis on which the January 1972 Mathematica cost-effectiveness analysis was based, and highlighted the need for a space tug (which NASA had to delete from the program in order to meet its too-tight budget) as an essential element for a major portion of the payloads to be carried by the shuttle in the 1980s and beyond.

The AIAA's assessment was the basis for the institute's first appearances at congressional hearings in February 1973. Pres Layton's dogged insistence on presenting the facts—even though some of them were readily construable as not being favorable to the biggest space project since Apollo—paid off. The AIAA was recognized as a knowledgeable, yet credible voice for aerospace technology, an image which the institute jealously guards to this day. In the long run (again, with our impeccable hindsight) that first assessment has stood up quite well: all its major points turned out to be accurate and, in some instances, prophetic.

Incidentally, the shuttle program had few problems in getting through Congress, either in 1972 (for the FY 1973 budget) or in 1973. The excising of the Mars landing and the space station, the massive shuttle compromise imposed on NASA by the Nixon administration, and especially the strong support developed during the two tough prior years of intensive campaigning by the authorizing committees and their indomitable staffs, had easily overwhelmed the token liberal vote. Mondale's half-hearted amendment in 1972 was roundly defeated by a roll-call vote. It was the last roll-call vote ever on the shuttle budget.

But in February 1973, one senator listened attentively to Pres Layton and to Klaus Heiss when they presented their views on the shuttle during testimony before his subcommittee of the Senate Appropriations Committee responsible for HUD, the Veterans Administration, and the independent agencies (one of which was NASA). He was the subcommittee's new chairman; his name was William Proxmire. He had recently licked the whole aerospace industry on the SST, and he was not yet willing to give up on the shuttle.

CHAPTER

4

THE DEVELOPMENT

"Every revolutionary idea . . . seems to evoke three stages of
reaction. They may be summed up by the phrases: (1) It's completely impossible—don't waste my time; (2) It's possible, but it's
not worth doing; (3) I said it was a good idea all along."

—Arthur C. Clarke
in The Promise of Space
September 1967

IN 1967 ARTHUR C. CLARKE SAID THAT ASTRONAUTICS WAS IN THE
second of his three stages, catapulted dramatically therein by John F.
Kennedy's decision to "go for the moon." President Nixon's scarcely
noticed announcement on January 5, 1972, eased the world gently
into Clarke's third phase:

I have decided today that the United States should proceed at
once with the development of an entirely new type of space-
transportation system designed to help transform the space frontier
of the 1970s into familiar territory, easily accessible for human
endeavor in the 1980s and '90s. . . . It will take the astronomical
costs out of astronautics.

But now those who "said it was a good idea all along" had to put
their technology where their mouths were. It wasn't all that difficult
to develop new and complex space systems when all NASA had to do
was hold its tin cup up to Congress and say, "More!" But this time
the space agency had "bought in" to a closed-end deal: the terms had
been clearly spelled out, and OMB and Congress were going to hold
NASA to them.

One of the problems was that the switch from a fully manned, two-stage flyback system to the compromise thrust-assisted orbiter scheme, although it did reduce overall technology demands as well as investment costs, came about so quickly that there were many technical decisions still unmade. As late as August 1971 the bulk of NASA's design efforts were still concentrated on the all-reusable, two-stage flyback configuration, "Because," as Del Tischler put it, "of the lack of sufficient funds to do much else." In the few months before the switch was made, even though Tischler insisted that much of his technology could be applied to a broad range of flyable reentry concepts, there just wasn't enough time to tie down all the details of the new system, and many of the cost estimates on which NASA had agreed to mortgage its future were based on the sketchiest of preliminary design data.

At the time of Nixon's decision, the shuttle "compromise" configuration had evolved into a flyable orbiter having a triangular (delta) wing and using liquid-propellant (hydrogen-oxygen) rockets for take-off. Its big sixty-by-fifteen-foot payload bay was to be able to carry 65,000 pounds into low earth orbit. The orbiter was to be boosted in a vertical launch by one of two possible schemes, depending on costs and technology still to be evaluated. One was a simple, unmanned, pressure-fed liquid-propellant booster, not flyable but recoverable Sea-Dragon style from the water after burning up its propellants. The other was to be a totally expendable, inexpensive solid-propellant booster. The orbiter's rocket engines would fire right from the beginning, along with those of the booster, but would continue after the booster had burned out and been jettisoned. The propellants for the orbiter's engines would be carried in a big tank that was to be discarded just before orbital altitude was reached. In falling back to earth, the tank would be torn to pieces, which would mostly burn up like meteors in the upper atmosphere before dropping into the ocean halfway around the world from the launch site. The orbiter would then "insert" itself into orbit with an extra "kick" from its small onboard maneuvering rockets, perform its mission, "deorbit" by a reverse-thrust "kick," and coast back into the atmosphere. It would then fly back to base using airplanelike, air-breathing turbojet engines.

The hurriedness of the budgetary decision-making process that led to this compromise became evident almost immediately. By March 1972 the booster decision was made, but *neither* of the original options that had formed the basis for the already locked-in budget was selected. Instead, NASA decided on another compromise dictated almost wholly by cost and reliability considerations: recoverable solid-propellant booster rockets.

A few months later, as more and more data on thermal protection systems and other hastily estimated components became better defined, the design weight of the shuttle began to grow to the point at which its 65,000-pound payload capability was endangered. The simplest expedient was to eliminate the jet engines; technological progress permitted the orbiter to be maneuvered sufficiently well in the upper atmosphere so that it could glide, unpowered, to its base—a "dead-stick" landing. The jet engines could be "tacked on," using a special kit, for ferrying the orbiter around in the atmosphere—for example, from Cape Canaveral in Florida to the Air Force launch site at Vandenberg Air Force Base in California. Later, further shuttle design-weight growth forced the elimination of even the ferry "kit"; the orbiter had to be hauled around on the back of a specially modified Boeing 747 airliner. Also, in the course of making these cost-compromising decisions, the fifteen-hundred-mile cross-range capability originally demanded by the Air Force had to be compromised to eleven hundred miles. All these retrenchments, incidentally, provided NASA with much-needed cost savings that could be applied elsewhere whenever unpredicted cost excesses popped up, like slapping patches on leaks in a dam.

So the shuttle configuration finally evolved. Its far-from-sleek appearance, so different from the beauteous all-reusable early concepts, was the result of an almost continuous juggling of compromises. The appellation "camel" (an animal obviously designed by a committee) was often hung ignominiously on the ungainly craft, but it *did* come close to meeting the staggering array of cost trade-offs, payload requirements, cross-range specifications, schedule constraints, and operational conditions that shaped it. Here's how it works:

The airplanelike shuttle orbiter (the first of which, number 101, was named *Enterprise*) is hauled up to a vertical position in the assembly building at Cape Canaveral and is mated to its big aluminum propellant tank, over 27 feet in diameter and 154 feet long (considerably longer than the 122-foot orbiter). Two large solid-propellant rockets are fastened to the tank. The whole assembly is then moved out to the launch pad on an enormous "crawler," and the tank is filled

The space shuttle as it finally evolved in late 1972 from the economic and technical trade-off studies. The big central tank carries the liquid rocket propellants for the airplanelike orbiter. The two long solid-propellant rockets on opposite sides of the tank help boost the shuttle into orbit, and are then dropped into the ocean to be recovered for reuse.

with almost eight hundred tons of liquid hydrogen and liquid oxygen. When all systems are checked out, the crew members climb aboard and strap themselves into their contoured chairs. With the shuttle vertical, they are lying on their backs looking straight up—the ideal position for a human body to withstand the launch acceleration.

After further check-outs, the countdown begins. The orbiter's three main engines are fired up first, drawing their propellants from the big aluminum tank. If "all systems are go," the two solid-propellant booster rockets are then ignited, and the awkward-looking contraption rises slowly off the launch pad, just like an old-style expendable rocket. At full sea-level thrust, with the orbiter's three main engines gulping hydrogen and oxygen at the rate of 3,100 pounds every second and the two big solid rockets blasting over 21,000 pounds per second of

The tank, orbiter, and booster rockets are assembled in the vehicle assembly building at Cape Canaveral, and are transported to the launch pad on an enormous tank-treaded "crawler." Here the shuttle has reached the pad, and is being readied for launch.

burned propellant out their nozzles, the shuttle's mass decreases rapidly, and it accelerates faster and faster.

After about two minutes, when the shuttle has reached twenty-seven miles altitude (about 140,000 feet), the solid rockets burn out. Instantly small explosive bolts separate the solid rockets from the big tank and clusters of small "retro-rockets" are fired to pull them quickly away from it, so that the orbiter won't have to waste precious propellants to accelerate their now dead weight. The empty rocket cases fall back to earth, pop out giant ribbon parachutes, and drop slowly into the ocean about 170 miles downrange (east) of the Cape. A recovery crew pumps out any water that may have entered the casings,

The launch. All engines fire simultaneously—the liquid-propellant orbiter rockets and the solid-propellant boosters.

The two solid-propellant booster rockets separate from the big tank at an altitude of twenty-seven nautical miles and a speed of 3,213 miles per hour. They drop back into the ocean (on parachutes) for recovery and rescue.

The orbiter continues on its own power, drawing its liquid-hydrogen and liquid-oxygen propellants from the big tank.

installs waterproof plugs in their nozzles, and tows them back to the launch site for refurbishment and reloading with solid propellant for their next flight. The "design life" for these big solid rockets is ten flights. If they happen to last longer, the cost of shuttle operations will decrease a little.

Meanwhile, the orbiter continues to climb out of the atmosphere, borne ever more rapidly by the increasing thrust of its three engnies and the decreasing mass of propellants in the tank. Just before it reaches its orbital speed of around 17,000 miles per hour toward the east (to take advantage of that extra 900 miles per hour or so of the earth's rotation), it sucks the last of the liquid propellants from

The 157-foot-long tank is jettisoned just before the shuttle reaches orbit. It tumbles, burns up in the atmosphere, and the few remaining bits and pieces fall into the Indian Ocean.

The orbiter "on its own" at last. Its on-board engines have given it the final nudge into orbit.

the big tank. The tank then separates from the orbiter and, obeying the physics of ballistic flight, follows an elliptical path back into the atmosphere. The thin-walled aluminum tank, tumbling slowly end-over-end, is designed to break apart readily when it reaches the atmosphere, and its pieces, like meteors, blaze into extinction. If any remaining chunks are too large to burn up completely, they will splash down in the Indian Ocean and sink to the bottom, where they will ultimately supplement the residence inventory of small sea creatures.

The coasting orbiter, alone in space at last, fires up its small Orbital Maneuvering System (OMS) rocket engines, which carry their own propellant supply on board, to provide the last gentle nudge into

The big cargo-bay doors open and the slender, jointed manipulator arm places a payload into orbit, one of the many jobs the shuttle is designed to perform.

The orbiter fires its on-board rockets to slow itself up for "deorbit."

orbit. Shuttle orbits are typically from about 175 to 250 miles up. Somewhat higher orbits can be achieved by the shuttle, as well as orbital inclinations to the equator different from the ideal 28.5 degrees offered by the latitude of Cape Canaveral, but only at the cost of reduced payloads in order to carry the extra propellants needed. The OMS allows the orbiter to make the small orbital adjustments that are needed to rendezvous and "dock" with payloads to be serviced, for example, but it doesn't carry enough propellant to make basic changes in the orbital path.

Once in orbit, the shuttle's crew of four to ten people can perform its assigned mission. Besides the OMS propulsion units, they have an even smaller Reaction Control System (RCS), a complex of many small rocket engines, to help turn the craft around its own center of gravity (that is, to change its pitch, yaw, and roll) as needed. In the absence of air the orbiter's aerodynamic control surfaces have no value; they're used only after reentry into the atmosphere.

Typical crew tasks might be to place a weather or communications satellite into orbit, turn it on, and check it out; to deploy (using a Canadian-built remote manipulator) a self-contained, unmanned, interplanetary space probe, prepare it for launch a safe distance from the shuttle, and then send it on its way; to set up and perform experiments in the gravity-free vacuum environment, using either the European-built Spacelab or a free-flying "pallet" outside the shuttle; to rendezvous and dock with an "ailing" satellite for repair and possible retrieval to earth, if necessary; to pick up a long-term space experiment package left by a previous crew; or any combination of these activities.

When their tasks are finished, which may be in a few hours or as long as a month, the crew will strap themselves in, calculate the proper place to start the reentry maneuver (for an eastward return to Cape Canaveral it would be somewhere over the Pacific), aim their craft in the proper direction using the RCS, and then initiate a short burst of the OMS to reduce orbital speed enough to allow the earth's gravity to begin bringing them home. As their instruments signal the outer fringes of the atmosphere, they check to make sure that the orbiter is aligned at the proper up-tilted angle (about forty degrees to the flight path), and blaze through reentry. The orbiter's thermal-protection system soaks up the heat without burning, although it glows white-hot in places like the nose and the wing's leading edges.

Finally the orbiter's wings, which up to now have been useless dead weight, are ready to do their job. Unfortunately, the orbiter flies much like the flatiron it resembles. Not only doesn't it have any engines, so that it has to be flown in "dead stick" like a glider, but its natural glide characteristics are much closer to those of a falling rock than a conventional airplane. All the pilot's skill is needed to bring it down safely on the three-mile Cape Canaveral runway.

When it finally rolls to a stop, a tractor hitches up to it and tows the orbiter to a large hangar. The ground crew repairs or replaces parts as needed, loads it back up with OMS and RCS propellants, replenishes the crew's food and water, charges the fuel cells that provide electric power, and generally readies the orbiter for relaunch.

Blazing its way through the thermal barrier of atmospheric reentry, the refractory tiles on the orbiter glow like the surface of a meteor—but they are carefully designed *not* to burn up.

Two weeks later, the orbiter is ready to be hauled up and mated to its tank and booster rockets for the next flight.

But many of the payloads to be carried by the shuttle need to be placed in orbits much higher than the few hundred miles it's capable of. Most communications and weather satellites and all interplanetary explorers have to go much, much higher. Providing the extra energy needed to get them there was to be the job of the space tug, as was so clearly spelled out in both the Mathematica study and the AIAA's assessment. But late in 1972, Dale Myers, who had taken over George Mueller's job as head of NASA's Office of Manned Space Flight,

After reentry, the orbiter plunges through the atmosphere enroute to its landing strip at Cape Canaveral. The shuttle orbiter pilot guides his "flying flatiron" to a steep, "hot" landing approach—dead stick. It's the heaviest, fastest "glider" in the world!

The orbiter prepares to touch down on its three-mile-long runway, just like its airplane cousins.

The orbiter is refurbished and prepared for its next flight.

confirmed that budget constrictions would prevent NASA from going ahead with development of the space tug. Instead, NASA would try to get the Air Force to develop a less capable "interim" tug using existing expendable rocket stages, such as the Centaur, Agena, or Transtage used with the current launch rockets Atlas, Delta, and Titan. "This means some delay of economic payoff for the shuttle," Myers said.

Such words were dear to the heart of the liberal Senate contingent. In 1972 Walter Mondale had turned to "better pickin's," since the shuttle program had so easily weathered the FY 1973 budget-approval process. William Proxmire, new chairman of the Senate appropriations subcommittee responsible for the NASA budget, promptly and gladly took over leadership of the anti-shuttle coalition in the Congress, and remained as the most powerful and dedicated space-program opponent throughout the 1970s.

Despite the battering the anti-shuttle senators sustained in 1972, Bill Proxmire was ready and loaded for bear in the spring of 1973 when the FY 1974 NASA budget came before his subcommittee. Ailing Clinton Anderson had finally resigned from his Senate seat, and leadership of Glen Wilson's Aeronautical and Space Sciences Committee had been taken over by Utah's Frank "Ted" Moss. Moss was a newcomer to space science, but, fortunately, a scrappy and highly visible politician who learned the ropes very quickly from his experienced and able staff. Besides, Thiokol, the supplier of the shuttle's solid-rocket boosters, was a Utah-based company. (It also didn't hurt that NASA administrator James Fletcher had come to his job from the University of Utah.) The staff was able to place both Moss and the Space Committee's minority leader, Barry Goldwater (an aviation buff and space hawk of the highest order), as *ex officio* members of Proxmire's appropriations subcommittee. So even though Proxmire personally chipped away mightily at NASA's budget, he could never muster enough votes even in his own subcommittee to do very much damage.

He did, however, put on one helluva show, and was highly successful in achieving what was probably his goal: national visibility for Bill Proxmire as the champion of social progress and guardian of the budget bastion against free-spending technologists. As a result, he continued to win his Wisconsin Senate seat by overwhelming majorities.

Aside from his much-publicized "Golden Fleece" awards* for "the biggest, most ridiculous, or most ironic example of government spending or waste" (of which NASA was an occasional recipient), Proxmire had an almost uncanny sense of the public's pulse, particularly in Wisconsin. Furthermore, he was a skillful tactician and debater, and did his homework carefully and thoroughly. He was an implacable foe, however, not at all averse to twisting words or distorting facts to achieve his ends. Proxmire's best-known anti-technology success was the cancellation of the U.S. supersonic transport prototype development program. His most telling ploy in that battle was his red herring about the "twenty thousand cases of skin cancer" that would result

* See Martin Tolchin, "The Perplexing Mr. Proxmire," *The New York Times Magazine,* May 28, 1978, p. 8.

from an SST fleet's depletion of stratospheric ozone by water vapor—a statement he made although a rather well-known scientific study had shown that water vapor tends to *increase* rather than decrease the stratosphere's ozone concentration. (It wasn't until later that nitric oxides and fluorocarbons were identified as the primary culprits in the chemistry of ozone depletion.)

The AIAA appeared before Proxmire's subcommittee for the first time in March 1973. As coeditors of the assessment, *New Space Transportation Systems*, Pres Layton and I testified with the AIAA's executive secretary, Jim Harford, to present the results of the assessment and to argue the case for the long-term beneficial impacts of the shuttle. We took little flak that first time (perhaps because our case was a good one, but more likely because the AIAA hadn't yet become an important enough adversary). But the senator (characteristically the only one who ever showed up for his subcommittee hearings) raked several other pro-shuttle witnesses over the coals. Oskar Morgenstern and Klaus Heiss gave as good as they got—their impeccable economic jargon was impregnable even to so skilled an antagonist. But Proxmire did get Air Force chief scientist Courtland Perkins to admit again, although his obvious intent was to support the shuttle, that the Air Force probably *could* get by with its current expendable launch-vehicle stable.

Despite Proxmire's virulent demeanor at the hearings, he just didn't have the votes to change the bottom line. The shuttle appropriation sailed through, and continued to do so for the next few years. It wasn't until the late 1970s, when the shuttle development neared completion and NASA was backed up against its closed-end 1972 commitment, that Proxmire was able to exert any real negative impact.

In contrast with the post-Apollo 1969-72 period, in which politics dominated the space scene, the 1972-77 period concentrated on hardware development. Del Tischler's "perspiration" phase became the central theme of space development.

Up to this point, technology efforts on reusable launchers had centered on developing conceptual preliminary designs to establish an overall configuration that made sense. Truax's Sea Dragon, Ehricke's Nexus, and other nonflyable but reusable concepts were dropped quite early in favor of the winged, flyback-booster designs. Some of these were to be launched vertically like expendable rockets, others horizon-

J. Preston Layton, chairman of the Space Transportation System Assessment Committee of the American Institute of Aeronautics and Astronautics (AIAA), releases his committee's assessment to the nation's press in Washington, D.C., on January 21, 1973. AIAA President Holt Ashley (center) and assessment co-editor Jerry Grey listen intently. The document supported the shuttle development, but called attention to several key shortcomings in the tightly budgeted program. Photograph courtesy of *Astronautics and Aeronautics.*

tally like an ordinary airplane; but all were to land like an airplane. Most of the arguments centered on the classic trade-off: investment cost versus operational costs, with reliability an important factor. If the Mathematica study did nothing else, though, it clearly demonstrated that the key element in any such trade-off analysis was the "payload" market, which was outside the control of the transportation-system designer.

Senator William Proxmire, chairman of the Senate Appropriations Subcommittee responsible for the NASA budget, gets a tip from a staff member during testimony by a pro-NASA witness. Despite his critical opposition, the shuttle budget was finally approved by Congress. Photograph courtesy of *Astronautics and Aeronautics.*

Many of the arguments also hinged on the old interservice rivalry. The Air Force obviously preferred the airplanelike shuttle, which ex-pilot generals could relate to. Early in the 1960s they had fostered ill-fated projects like Dyna-Soar and Aerospaceplane, which took off on air-breathing engines and transferred to rockets at high speeds and high altitudes. The Navy, on the other hand, not having the long land-based runways available to the Air Force, preferred nonflyable designs. Bob Truax was the main proponent of this view, citing in mid-1970 the sound argument that "unnecessary frills [land touch-down and flyback] will run up the cost . . . the mood of the country will not support another engineering *tour de force*." He called winged flyback boosters an "unparalleled money sponge . . . they make about as much sense as requiring airplanes to be able to land at rail-road stations." Pushing his Sea Dragon concept, he summed up his case with a comparison: "Water landing [has been termed] inelegant. I would agree, but how much are we willing to pay for elegance?"

But the system economics were such that Sea Dragon and its fellow "big rockets" were inexorably ground back into oblivion by the rapid growth of flyback-booster technology. The dominant personality in establishing this ascendancy was Maxime "Max" Faget, a Langley aerodynamicist since 1946, who used another man's revolutionary idea around which to fashion the shape of tomorrow's space-program centerpiece.

The shuttle-technology story actually began in 1952, when the Air Force was seeking a way to keep their ICBM nose cones from burning up in the 12,000° F inferno created when the "artificial meteor" reentered the atmosphere after its flight in space—the so-called "thermal barrier." A NACA (Ames laboratory) senior aero-nautical engineer named Harry Julian Allen came up with a truly radical idea in aerodynamics. Allen is known to the technical com-munity as H. Julian Allen, which is how he signs his papers, but his friends called him Harvey. Looking more like a football player than a scientist, Allen studied the "classical" reentry-body shapes, all of which were carefully streamlined needle-nose structures designed to reduce aerodynamic drag and, as aerodynamic boundary-layer theory clearly indicated, to minimize heat transfer to the structure. Scorning the computer used by Convair engineers to calculate the intricate aero-dynamic equations, he worked with a pad and a pencil to reach his revolutionary conclusion: "Half the heat generated by friction was going into the missile. I reasoned we had to deflect the heat into the air and let it dissipate. Therefore streamlined shapes were the worst possible; they had to be blunt."

Allen's idea became the touchstone for successful missile nose-cone development. To this day reentry nose cones are blunt. His idea was also picked up by Faget, who used it to design the Project Mercury capsule—the United States' first manned spacecraft.

But the Mercury-Gemini-Apollo capsules, successful as they were, were only single-purpose devices, extremely limited in their aerodynamics. Their cross-range capability was essentially zero. Further, they could dissipate the heat of reentry only by burning up part of themselves, an intentional process of harmlessly absorbing heat by ablating away a nonstructural "heat shield." Nevertheless, when the time came a decade later for designing the far more versatile reusable shuttle, Faget returned to the original Mercury concept in order to deal with what was still the dominant technical problem: the reentry thermal barrier.

Faget, a diminutive fountain of energy with some resemblance to singer Frank Sinatra (he was even partial to bow ties!), had cut his teeth on tough aerodynamic problems, and even prior to his brilliant Mercury design he had a string of significant accomplishments under his belt. Unlike most of his colleagues at Langley, he tended to mistrust wind tunnels, the experimental aerodynamicist's classical tool, preferring to derive his data from actual flight-tests. Without the need for extensive testing, though, he unerringly identified the same high-drag reentry principle used on Mercury and on ICBM nose cones as the proper mode for a manned airplane reentering the atmosphere. He gave three reasons for his decision, bulwarked to some extent by theories and wind-tunnel tests on aircraftlike shapes by several earlier investigators.

First, with the airplane traveling "flat," so that the air stream strikes it almost perpendicular to its lower surface, its resistance to the tenuous upper atmosphere is at its maximum. This starts its slowdown sooner, way up high, and the thinner the atmosphere, the less the heat transfer to the airplane's skin. Second, the high drag of the flat-flight attitude makes the total duration of the slowdown process shorter, reducing the total thermal energy the airplane has to absorb. Finally, and perhaps most important, only the *bottom* surface of the airplane gets hot, so many large areas—the tops of the wings, tail, and body—require no thermal protection at all, and even the sides of the body need only minimal protection.

But Faget didn't wholly trust his theories. Even in the conceptual design phase he had to fly "test vehicles"—in this case cheap, hand-launched models made of balsa wood and paper. The only real flaw in his early shuttle designs was the use of a straight wing, one of his pet aerodynamic foibles. The bigger payload bay, higher payload-mass requirement (Faget used 25,000 pounds in his 1968 designs; the final figure was 65,000), and cross-range performance later demanded by the Air Force required that Faget change to the much stronger, higher-lift (but also much bigger and heavier) delta (triangular) wing shape. But even without the Air Force requirement, the much lower average skin temperatures of the delta wing probably would have dictated its use anyway.

Once the basic orbiter concept had been set, the three main de-

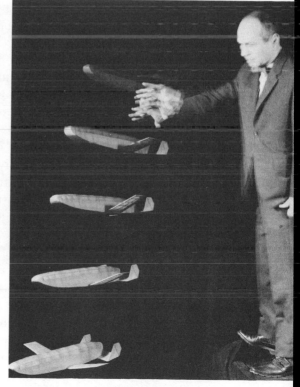

Shuttle designer Maxime "Max" Faget tests balsa-wood shuttle-orbiter models for aerodynamic stability during 1969 design study. Photographs courtesy of *Astronautics and Aeronautics.*

velopment problems were clearly evident: the thermal-protection system (the ablating heat-shield principle used by Mercury, Gemini, and Apollo was clearly inadequate for a *reusable* shuttle), the high-performance rocket engines, and the need for an on-board, self-contained flight-control system, since the use of Mission Center ground control, as in Apollo, was not suited to the complex and disparate missions the shuttle was expected to perform. Del Tischler's Shuttle Technologies Office swung into gear, attacking the massive technology advancements needed to solve these problems, and by the time Nixon decided to proceed with the shuttle, much of the necessary orbiter technology was reasonably well defined.

George Mueller had thought that the on-board, computer-operated flight-control system, which needed a "self-healing" computer to prevent any disastrous malfunction during key flight maneuvers, "might be a greater challenge than the first two." However, it eventually turned out to be the easiest of the three, due mainly to the enormous advances in microprocessor and other computer technologies that took place in the 1970s. The shuttle flight-control system benefited mightily from the same developments that converted the mid-1950s' IBM 1620 computer I used at Princeton—a roomful of air-conditioned electronic-equipment racks costing several hundred thousand dollars—into the mid-1970s' six-ounce pocket-sized programmable computer having the same capability and priced at only a few hundred dollars.

The thermal-protection system was considered by many of the shuttle's design engineers to be the toughest development nut to crack. First, of course, came the extensive aerodynamic studies and wind-tunnel testing to establish "the nature of the beast," that is, the temperature-time curves and heat-transfer behavior for all possible orbiter flight patterns. Then the candidate materials had to be found (or invented), developed, and tested—and then brought down in cost to acceptable levels. Three classes of materials were explored: metals, nonmetal refractory (high-temperature) materials, and ablative materials (the kind used on Apollo's heat shield).

At first, the only recourse for the shuttle's very highest temperature regions at the nose tip and the wing's leading edges, which would be exposed to temperatures as high as 3000° F, seemed to be ablatives; they were the only systems we *knew* would take the most severe heat-transfer loads. But they required replacement after every flight—scarcely a reusable feature—and hence would escalate already high operating costs. Finally, however, a refractory material known as "carbon-carbon" was developed: a composite made of graphite cloth layers embedded in "pyrolitic graphite" (a substance whose structure favors heat transfer in a direction parallel to its surface, but retards perpendicular heat transfer from the surface inside), coated with super-tough silicon carbide to prevent burning during reentry. For the other high-temperature regions (about 750° F to 2300° F), the orbiter uses 20,000 six-inch square tiles made of silica fibers coated with borosilicate glass. The tile structure (which gave the orbiter its nickname, "brick airplane," closely related to a "cement cloud") was needed because the ceramic-bonded silica fiber was far too brittle to be made in large sheets; the flexing of the shuttle's structure and thermal expansion would have cracked them into a thousand pieces. This material weighs between an eighth and a quarter as much as water (it feels like balsa wood when you heft it), but it can take the fiery orbiter reentry heat time after time.

The problems of not only developing and testing these exotic materials, but of integrating them into a high-performance aerospacecraft and meeting the rigid cost constraints, was a management-engineering accomplishment of the highest order. But at last the basic thermal-protection technology was available; the second of the orbiter's three key problems was solved.

The final development problem—the orbiter's main rocket engines —turned out to be the worst. This was no surprise to propulsion engineers; the engines had long since been identified as perhaps the pacing item in shuttle development. The competition had, in fact, started in 1969; Phase B preliminary-design studies by the three major competitors (Aerojet, North American Aviation's Rocketdyne division, and Pratt & Whitney) had been completed by the end of 1970. The three companies had submitted their proposals for development in April 1971, and in July the $500 million contract, to the surprise of many, was awarded to Rocketdyne.

The fact that a major shuttle *development* contract had been awarded six months before the President's announcement that the United States would proceed with a shuttle program slipped by almost unnoticed in the subsequent hullabaloo about the award itself. The rocket industry seethed for weeks, and ended up with a protest being filed by Pratt & Whitney against NASA for allegedly incorrect evaluation of the engine proposals.

The requirements of the space-shuttle main engine featured several unique demands for rocket engines. First, the engine assembly had to fit within the envelope of the shuttle orbiter's body, whose size and shape were fixed by its aerodynamics. Thus the large exhaust nozzles needed to extract every ounce of potential thrust from the engines had to fit within the "base area" of the shuttle. This requirement imposed a difficult design criterion: very high engine chamber pressures to get high thrust into as small a package as possible.

High pressure was also a must to meet the second requirement: the need for the highest possible performance to minimize the overall shuttle weight, probably the biggest single cost-increasing factor. Hydrogen-oxygen propellants were mandatory. But previous large hydrogen-oxygen engines, the J-2 developed by Rocketdyne for the upper stages of the Saturn V, and the M-1 developed by Aerojet (for a later aborted military requirement), had used much lower pressures than were required by the shuttle engines. These engines employed the well-known cycle first established by Goddard and perfected by von Braun—the so-called "gas-generator" cycle, in which the power needed to drive the propellant pumps was developed by a small, separate engine distinct from the main rocket chamber. But the gas-generator cycle was far too inefficient for the very high pressures and high performance demands of the space shuttle. Another smaller hydrogen-oxygen engine, the RL-10 developed by Pratt & Whitney for the Centaur (an upper stage for the Atlas booster), used a simple "expander" cycle, which could not provide the power needed for the high-pressure shuttle-engine pumps. So it was clear that a wholly new engine cycle would be needed.

The final "new" requirement was the long lifetime imposed by reusability. Rockets for expendable boosters had to last only a few minutes. The shuttle main engines had to fire for only about eight minutes on each flight, but they had to do it over and over again—at least fifty-five times. A seven-and-a-half-hour service life for a high-performance rocket was unheard of.

Each of the competing rocket companies had attacked the problem in its own way. Pratt & Whitney, with Air Force and some NASA support and with considerable input of its own company funds, had developed—and tested—essentially all the components for a high-pressure engine, the XLR-129. That engine had already met all the unique shuttle requirements, except that it was sized to deliver a

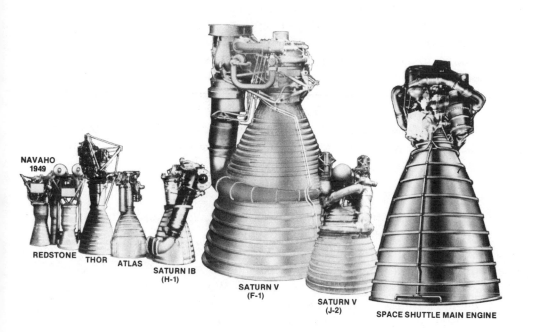

NAVAHO 1949

REDSTONE   THOR   ATLAS   SATURN IB (H-1)   SATURN V (F-1)   SATURN V (J-2)   SPACE SHUTTLE MAIN ENGINE

Liquid-propellant rocket engines used to launch U.S. space vehicles, from 1949 to the present space shuttle. Photograph courtesy of *Astronautics and Aeronautics.*

thrust of 250,000 pounds, practically within shouting distance of the shuttle engine's final sea-level thrust requirement of 375,000 pounds. It used what was called the "staged-combustion" cycle, in which all the rocket's fuel was first burned with only a fraction of the oxygen. The resulting low-temperature gas powered the turbines driving the high-pressure pumps, and then it was mixed with the rest of the oxygen in the main combustion chamber. By 1969 Pratt & Whitney had even developed and tested the turbopumps, the most difficult and complex part of the engine, up to the 350,000-pound thrust level.

Rocketdyne, meanwhile, had thrown much of its effort into a totally different engine design called the "aerospike." Although an interesting and potentially valuable concept, it was never used. Nevertheless, Rocketdyne's proposal specified the staged-combustion cycle, which Rocketdyne had explored only to the extent of a few limited component tests. When the contract award went to Rocketdyne, no wonder Pratt & Whitney erupted!

The basis for Pratt & Whitney's protest was that it had already *run* an engine that would meet most of the shuttle design requirements. They were satisfied that that engine worked, and they were willing to guarantee a slightly larger redesign. Rocketdyne, on the other hand, had never run a complete staged-combustion engine. They had conceived an engine in considerable detail, and they had run a combustion chamber a few times; it was a design that NASA's Marshall Space Center liked. But Rocketdyne had never built all their engine hardware and put it together, thereby demonstrating their mastery of its advanced technology.

Nevertheless, despite the protest, Rocketdyne got the job. NASA's real reasons for awarding the contract to them are hard to identify. They were used to working with Rocketdyne, and Rocketdyne had had great success with the big Apollo engines. The Pratt & Whitney people, although unquestionably highly competent, were aloof and much more difficult to get along with. They "played everything close to the chest" —perhaps a carry-over from Pratt & Whitney's principal aircraft-engine business, which is characterized by intense competition similar to that of the automobile industry. In any case, by late 1971 the engine development was well under way with great optimism expressed by all, except perhaps Pratt & Whitney and a few knowledgeable and worried engineers like Del Tischler and Pres Layton.

As the technology base for the shuttle grew, it became clear, late in 1972, that the hastily conceived compromise shuttle design would exceed NASA's stringent cost-per-flight commitment. A massive redesign of the whole system, eliminating all the "frills," reduced the overall design weight by 20 percent, with commensurate projected cost reductions. By then, the prime development contract for the overall system and the orbiter itself, the biggest single space plum of the decade, had been won (in July 1972) by North American Rockwell (which later changed its name to Rockwell International). The engine development contract had already gone, of course, to Rocketdyne (a division of Rockwell) in 1971; its specifications were later adjusted somewhat to meet the needs of the new shuttle configuration. The contract for the throwaway propellant tank went to Martin Marietta in August 1973. The final major subsystem development, the solid rocket boosters, was awarded to Thiokol Chemical Company in November.

Del Tischler's Shuttle Technologies Office, having established enough of the technology base that the development centers and contractors could now proceed, was disbanded—discarded like an old shoe. "The support for the Shuttle Technologies Office was abruptly withdrawn," Tischler told me. "Hell, I didn't even have my old propulsion job to go back to!" But Tischler had meanwhile observed that with the inordinate emphasis on the shuttle itself, everyone's attention was riveted on fixing the "bugs" in the initial budgeted configuration. Nobody was paying any heed to the shuttle's excuse for existence: its payloads. He wrote a memorandum saying that the next big problem was to get the payload costs down so that they would be commensurate with the low-cost launcher, but he (Tischler) didn't see that happening. NASA's new "Low-Cost System Office" was the result. As head of that office, Tischler was charged with developing the hard-nosed engineering approach needed to realize the payload cost reductions that the Mathematica study had touted as being one of the reasons for developing the shuttle in the first place.

He set up the same management practices he had used so successfully in his original Apollo propulsion research group and in the Shuttle Technologies Office. But the NASA center managers weren't about to give up control of their projects to a new headquarters office again, unless they had something to gain. Tischler estimated that he needed an annual budget of $30 million to "get the attention" of the NASA centers, each of which would otherwise work toward only its own pet programs. "I think George Low [NASA's deputy administrator] really agreed with this, but he wouldn't admit it. He said to me, 'You go fight for your money, like everybody else.' The most I was ever able to get out of him was eight million dollars," Tischler laughed ruefully. "We got a pretty good start, but whenever I got a hard-line argument about equipment selection or design approach, face-to-face with the project managers, they'd simply say, 'Go to hell!' And their center directors backed them up. After all, the centers thrive on their projects; hell, I couldn't blame them for trying to protect their own efforts. But I had never learned to swim without making waves," Tischler grimaced, "and I wasn't willing to tread water. We were at an impasse." The situation ultimately became so frustrating that Tischler gave up and retired from NASA. But, like Bob Truax in the generation before him, he keeps popping up.

Shortly after North American Rockwell won the shuttle contract, Dale Myers left NASA and was replaced as associate administrator for manned space flight by the leader of the unsuccessful McDonnell Douglas team, John Yardley. Yardley had been around for a long time; he'd converted Max Faget's first manned spacecraft design into the magnificently successful Mercury capsule. Yardley was probably the best possible choice for one of the toughest management jobs in the history of technology. He ran a tight program with consummate skill, balancing the tightrope between getting the shuttle development job done effectively and safely and never overrunning his budget by enough to draw OMB's or Congress's ire.

Yardley's shuttle program director was Dr. Myron Malkin, who originally had been brought in by Myers to head up the shuttle effort. In the physics department at Yale in the 1950s, "Mike" Malkin found academic life growing dull. He'd been working on heavy-ion accelerators—complex, elaborate, cantankerous machines. When space activities began to pick up, he did a brief career self-evaluation and decided he wanted to manage a space program. Not at all shy, he hied himself over to General Electric (G.E.) and told them he'd like to be a program manager. "What do you know about space or missiles?" he was asked. "Nothing!" was his blunt reply. "But I'm as smart as most of the guys you've got!"

At G.E. Mike worked on Titan nose cones and then on the multiple independently-targeted reentry vehicle (MIRV). Several subsequent moves brought him a broad base of management experience, and by April 1973, when he went to NASA, he was a natural for the shuttle-program director's job, fitting all the pieces of the complex project together. Malkin works well with people, and his skill as an arbitrator (as well as his control of the allocation of program resources) helped him smooth over a number of the controversies that could have resulted in serious program delays.

Nevertheless there *were* problems. Nothing ever goes exactly right in new high-technology endeavors; that's why development is needed before going ahead and building the "production" hardware. One example Malkin cited was in the exhaust nozzles of the solid-propellant booster rockets. These rockets are steered by deflecting their nozzles to produce sideways pressure forces on the rocket, meaning the nozzle joint to the main rocket motor casing has to be flexible. Multiple layers of heavy rubberized cloth are used to protect the flexible joint. Designing the "boot," as it's called, is a standard, well-known process, and Thiokol had bid it with absolute confidence. In fact, *they* thought they could do it with only two rubberized cloth layers, but NASA's Marshall Space Center, concerned about the need for reusability (the boosters had to last at least ten flights to make their projected operational cost estimates), had upped it to nine layers. To keep the rubberized joint away from the searing blast of hot gas through the nozzle, the nozzles are "submerged" so their inlets poke into the inside of the chamber; the flexible joint is then exposed only to the relatively stagnant gases around the *outside* of the nozzle duct. But on the first full-scale test, when the nozzle was deflected by the controls, the resulting asymmetry caused the hot gases in the chamber to "slosh" from side to side, considerably increasing the heat transfer to the joint. The result: *seven* of the nine cloth layers burned through on the first test. It took a while—and some unlooked-for expenditure of tightly budgeted funds—to fix that one.

Malkin ran into some strange situations as a result of the extreme technology demands of the shuttle project. One of the toughest fabrication problems Thiokol faced was in forming the big cylindrical steel sections for the solid boosters. The twelve-foot-diameter sections, each ten feet long, had to be cold-formed from solid forgings. The only outfit that could roll the sections so they came out as perfectly straight cylinders was a company in Milwaukee named Ladisch. But Ladisch's owner would work only under his own terms. He wouldn't touch federal development money; he took only fixed-price contracts: "You tell me what you want, I bid, I deliver, you inspect, you pay me. You *don't* bother me with government red tape."

Ladisch did its cold-forming of the massive steel sections behind a big green door. Nobody knew what went on behind that door, not even Ladisch's marketing manager, and certainly not NASA or the Thiokol people who paid the bills. Great, squat forgings went in, and perfect, straight, ten-foot-long cylinders, over twelve feet in diameter, came out. The Air Force, wanting another subcontractor just as a backup, went to one of the world's best-known steel-forming companies in Coatesville, Pennsylvania. All the sections came out crooked. Ladisch is still the free world's only supplier of shuttle rocket-booster sections.

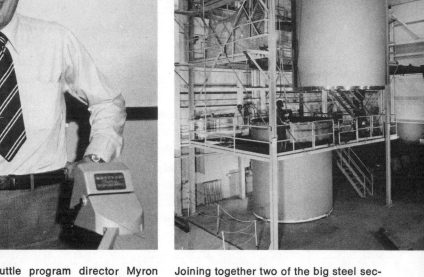

NASA shuttle program director Myron "Mike" Malkin in a characteristic pose. Photograph courtesy of *Astronautics and Aeronautics.*

Joining together two of the big steel sections of the shuttle's solid-propellant rocket booster.

Another oddity cropped up in building the big aluminum propellant tank made by the Martin Company. The twenty-seven-foot-diameter throwaway tank—looking like a good-sized blimp—has the thinnest possible walls, less than a quarter inch, to keep both costs and weight to a minimum. It would seem that the braces needed to hold its shape —thick ribs called "stringers," running the full length of each main tank section (the whole tank is 154 feet long)—should be built separately and welded into place on the thin tank skin. But no; the whole complex main-tank structure is machined—"hogged out" of a thick aluminum plate, stringers and all. Prohibitively expensive? Not at all —Alcoa and Kaiser aluminum companies were delighted to do the whole massive machining job *free*. All they wanted was to keep the chips!

I asked Malkin if he expected to change jobs again once his shuttle was routinely operational. Wouldn't life begin to get dull again, the way it did at Yale back in 1960? "Hell no," Malkin grinned. "I'm going to stay with this one. Once this bird is flying who knows *what* will come next? When the customers find out what a gentle ride we can give 'em, they'll be clamoring for more and bigger shuttles—and I plan to be here to develop son of shuttle!"

One of Malkin's main concerns in making sure that all NASA's contractors and subcontractors interacted smoothly and efficiently was with the shuttle's overseas contractors. Distance and language were not the primary problems; it was the complex relationships necessitated by "consortium" arrangements that gave him headaches. But the overseas contribution was essential, and was backed by decades of precedent in space cooperation. When NASA administrator Tom Paine had attempted in 1969 to strengthen his case for the shuttle in Congress

The first 157-foot-long, 27-foot-diameter orbiter propellant tank is "rolled out" of NASA's Michoud Assembly Facility near New Orleans on September 9, 1977.

by soliciting foreign participation in the program, he was drawing on a long history of international friendship. It was recognized very early in the space age (remember, it was the *International* Geophysical Year that spawned Sputnik) that "there shall be no national boundaries in space." United Nations General Assembly Resolution 1721, in December 1961, initiated the 1967 treaty governing space activities. Article II of that treaty states that outer space "is not subject to national appropriation by claim of sovereignty." But long before the U.N. Committee on Peaceful Uses of Outer Space was even conceived, the scientists and engineers of many nations had located each other, talked with each other about the crazy dream to which they had dedicated their lives, and formed the International Astronautical Federation (IAF)—a loose association of the interplanetary and rocket societies of all nations.

The IAF was the first viable international association wholly dedicated to the advancement of space technology. Actually founded in 1950, it was officially inaugurated in September 1951, when the first International Astronautical Congress was held in London. The federation's constitution is quite clear as to its purposes: the furthering of astronautics by (a) development for peaceful purposes, (b) widespread dissemination of technical and other information, (c) stimulating public interest, and (d) encouraging participation in research.

The congresses, held annually in one of the member societies' home countries, are often used for milestone space-development announcements. In 1953, for example, Fred Singer exposed for the first time in an international forum the practical concept of a scientific minimum orbital unmanned satellite (of) earth (MOUSE—a most appropriate acronym). The Sixth Congress, held in Copenhagen in 1955, featured the first public Soviet announcement of a formal satellite program. The first satellite clearly visible to the naked eye, the U.S. Echo satellite, made its debut over an outdoor reception at the Eleventh Congress in Stockholm (1960). I remember sitting at that same Stockholm Congress, a fascinated member of an audience of equally rapt engineers from all nations, as von Braun gave us all our first real look at NASA's thinking on manned flights to the moon. And the world was introduced to a flying space shuttle when Mike Malkin wowed the 1977 Prague Congress with hot-off-the-press films of just-completed atmospheric flight-tests. But perhaps the most famous IAF event was the opening day of the Eighth Congress in Barcelona:

October 4, 1957. Soviet delegation leader Leonid Sedov's Cheshire-cat smile, glowing complacently over the deflated egos of the United States delegates, confirmed their unaccustomed place in the backseat of the world's most advanced technology.

The real technical content of the early IAF congresses was somewhat spotty. The Soviets, for example, rarely exposed the details of their technology, dwelling instead on broad philosophical matters and elegant mathematical treatises. The U.S. presentations were usually rehashes of papers given at prior U.S. meetings, and substantial European, Japanese, and other contributions didn't begin to roll in until well into the 1960s. The IAF, in fact, picked up a reputation as a "chowder and marching society," compared with some of the later but more serious scientific organizations such as the Committee on Space Research (COSPAR) of the International Council of the Scientific Unions. But the informal associations and corridor button-holings that featured the IAF meetings should not be underestimated; they were a vital element in establishing and maintaining close relationships between the international partners in the new realm. The scientists went to COSPAR and other highbrow scientific meetings; the engineers and technologists who were responsible for getting things done in space tended to favor the less prestigious but far more flamboyant IAF congresses.

Early spark plugs of the federation were such public figures as Arthur C. Clarke (who collaborated with Singer, for example, in conceiving the MOUSE acronym) and Theodore von Karman; later congresses featured astronauts and cosmonauts, heads of state, administrators of national space agencies, and United Nations officials. The real nature of the IAF, though, was shaped by less well known but far more fascinating characters. Of all those I remember from these early days, Andy Haley was unquestionably the most unique.

Senior partner in the prestigious Washington law firm of Haley, Doty, and Wollenberg, perhaps the most influential nongovernment shaper of present U.S. and world telecommunications legal and regulatory policy, Andy Haley (nobody *ever* called him Andrew) nevertheless was a space "nut."

My early encounters with Andy left me totally perplexed. I already knew him by reputation as one of the very first persons shrewd enough to turn his space enthusiasm into sizable profits. He had befriended Theodore von Karman, himself a barroom character of no mean repute, although one of the world's most renowned scientists. When von Karman's Cal Tech group was developing its solid-propellant rockets for JATO units during World War II, Andy Haley persuaded von Karman, two of his brightest students, Frank Malina and Martin Summerfield, and a few others, that they ought to set up a company to manufacture and sell these as yet highly unpredictable new rockets. Haley kicked in the bulk of the capital and took the controlling majority share of Aerojet—the United States' second rocket company (after Reaction Motors), and for years the dominant force in United States rocket development. When General Tire later bought out Aerojet's owners, Haley's cut was well into the millions.

But until one worked closely with Andy Haley, it seemed incomprehensible that such a crack lawyer and a shrewd businessman could also be such a buffoon. Always impeccably dressed (vest and all, even in those days), he sported a sharp hooked English nose, but there his lawyer-businessman image ended. He was fat and pompous; when he spoke his words tumbled over themselves. I have listened to long, detailed Haley speeches in which I understood all the words but had no idea of what he had said! Moreover, he was probably the heaviest drinker I've ever met. As president of the American Rocket Society in the 1950s and the IAF in 1963-64, he never stood on a platform sober. In fact, I hardly remember *ever* seeing him without at least a few under his belt. The highest (or perhaps the lowest) point in his alcoholism was reached at an annual meeting of the American Rocket Society, when Andy Haley stood up at the center of the head table before an audience of a thousand or so black-tied engineers to introduce the distinguished banquet speaker—and promptly fell backward off the podium. Undaunted, he clambered back up, grabbed the table to haul himself to his feet, and continued right on with the introduction. After the startled gasps, the audience gave him a deafening round of applause for his stunning performance.

And that, perhaps, was Andy's most outstanding characteristic. Through all the years of public faux pas, no one in the industry ever laughed at him or ridiculed him. We recognized and respected his great contributions to the advancement of space flight. But we also recognized his great sorrow: he knew he would never achieve his greatest desire of flying in space himself. Andy Haley was the real-life counterpart of Robert Heinlein's protagonist Delos D. Harriman in the classic *The Man Who Sold the Moon*. Harriman, like Haley, made space flight possible through his business activities, but became so indispensable on earth that he could never get into space—the *real* reason for all his efforts. Unlike Harriman, who finally made it to die on the moon in Heinlein's sensitive final chapter, "Requiem," Haley never did get beyond the atmosphere. He died in 1966, leaving a legacy of accomplishments and a gap in international space-law leadership that has yet to be filled.

One interesting vignette to Haley's story: when he sold Aerojet to General Tire, General wanted not just control, but 100 percent of the stock. But during Senator Joe McCarthy's campaign to ferret out Communist sympathizers, he had fingered two stockholders in Aerojet—von Karman's two former students, who along with many others in the entertainment world and elsewhere, had "joined up" after Russia, then our ally, had helped so significantly to end World War II. Summerfield was a professor at Princeton at the time of McCarthy (it was, in fact, Summerfield who hired me when I finished my doctorate studies at Cal Tech), and he elected to stay and fight. He lost his security clearance, and as a result was hampered for years in his rocket-combustion research. His clearance was eventually reinstated after he doggedly fought out, with strong university support, an exhaustive series of government investigations. The money he got from General Tire for his one-sixth share of Aerojet helped him survive that difficult period. He is currently chairman of New York University's Department of Applied Science.

Von Karman's other student, Frank Malina, had been much more active in Communist activities than Summerfield, and when McCarthy got on his back he had no choice but to leave the work he loved and start over elsewhere. He took up residence in Paris with his wife Marjorie, and because he was unable to find employment in his professional field he had tough going. He undertook a former avocation—art—and by skillfully applying his superb technical background, he invented a new medium, best described as "illuminated mobiles." He worked as hard in his new field as he ever had in rocketry, and eventually became recognized in the avant-garde Paris art world as one of its most distinguished members. His mobile electro-paintings have been hung in the world's major museums, including New York's Museum of Modern Art.

But when Malina left the United States, of course, he'd taken with

"Andy" Haley, founder of Aerojet Engineering Corporation, president of the American Rocket Society, and a guiding light (and president) of the International Astronautical Federation. A prominent space lawyer, he was instrumental in having space recognized as an area for international cooperation. Photograph courtesy of *Astronautics and Aeronautics.*

him his Aerojet stock: a sixth share in the company. When General Tire bought out everyone else, they couldn't locate Malina. As Aerojet-General Corporation, the company's fortunes skyrocketed, and along with them the value of the original Aerojet stock. When Malina surfaced again, he found himself the richest "struggling artist" in Paris. Later he returned to the space program as president (after von Karman) of the Paris-based International Academy of Astronautics; he currently serves as the academy's executive director.

As the IAF matured, it became more and more the central forum for the world's astronautical engineers to discuss their mutual technological program interests. When NASA administrator Tom Paine made his 1969 circuit seeking the foreign cooperation he needed, the IAF was building its reputation. In the 1970s it became *the* international forum for space technology, in no small part because of the international prestige it could generate for its member-societies' nations. The Soviets used the IAF to "leak" important new information they did not want to release formally; the United States and Europe used its platform to cement their technical cooperation in space; the U.N. admitted the IAF, like COSPAR (for space science), as a formal observer to the Committee on the Peaceful Uses of Outer Space; and the smaller space-faring nations came to see the IAF as their principal contact with the technical world of astronautics.

There's a reason for my emphasis of the IAF here. The next dec-

Frank Malina was one of Aerojet's co-founders and a dominant figure in the science of rocketry and space flight in the late 1930s and early 1940s. A world-renowned artist, he is currently executive director of the International Academy of Astronautics, and, like Haley, has dedicated much of his life to the cause of international cooperation in space. Photograph courtesy of *Astronautics and Aeronautics.*

ades of space activity must, almost by necessity, become more and more internationally oriented. Space has no national boundaries, and as its utilization develops, the world's nations must, willy-nilly, work together. The IAF, clumsy as it is, has demonstrated that cooperation is not restricted solely to the political and legal arena of the United Nations. Technical information *can* be interchanged. I was elected U.S. vice-president of the IAF at the Twenty-ninth Congress in Dubrovnik, Yugoslavia, in 1978, and I see the IAF's three decades of cooperative growth as the harbinger of the world's space future. It will be one of my primary goals in the coming years to help "make it happen."

In 1970, though, international cooperation was traveling a rocky road. The *idea* of international cooperation was firmly entrenched; President Nixon, in a 1969 address to the United Nations, had stated it well. Man's epic venture into space should be, he said, "an adventure that belongs not to one nation but to all mankind, and one that should be marked not by rivalry, but by a spirit of fraternal cooperation." But the practical implementation of that idea was fraught with an impenetrable tangle of political protocols and economic concerns.

Of the six nations Paine had solicited in 1969 for specific post-Apollo cooperative efforts (England, Germany, France, Canada, Australia, and Japan), none seemed willing to make any commitment, although the Europeans had evinced considerable interest. A

Canadian company, with the encouragement of its government, later proposed to develop and build a major shuttle subsystem, the remote manipulator for placing and retrieving payloads, and eventually built it successfully.

The European nations had very early recognized the need to maintain at least some degree of parity with the U.S. and U.S.S.R. efforts. Val Cleaver, head of Rolls Royce's rocket-engine division and the acknowledged elder statesman of England's space program, bluntly portrayed (in 1962) Europe's common concern: "The absence of a European space programme [*sic*] would probably be the beginning of a downhill slide for our science, technology, and industry—maybe a very long and gradual slide, but fatal for all that." But a crippling dichotomy immediately surfaced: some Europeans believed an independent European launch capability was essential to prevent Cleaver's "downhill slide"; others, principally scientists, wanted to throw all European resources into spacecraft payloads, and were willing to utilize the obviously superior U.S. (or U.S.S.R.) launchers. This schism dominated European space cooperation for over a decade. Its first consequence was the formation of *two* European consortia: the European Space Research Organization (ESRO), dedicated solely to space research, and the European Launcher Development Organization (ELDO), whose function was to evolve a heavy launch rocket.

This already unwieldy organizational structure wasn't bad enough; it was further complicated by three other separate bodies set up to promote European space "cooperation." The European Conference on Satellite Telecommunications (CETS, in French) was to coordinate a European position for Intelsat, the global telecommunications satellite network; the European Space Conference (ESC) was to set policy for ESRO, ELDO, and CETS; and, of course, the North Atlantic Treaty Organization (NATO) had its own strategic space-system network.

It was no wonder that the European space effort, with a few exceptions, floundered miserably for the decade of the sixties. As Charles Sheldon of the U.S. Congressional Research Service put it, "It almost seems incredible that agreement was reached and sustained for some years to build flyable hardware." Innumerable abortive attempts, especially of the failure-ridden Europa series of rocket launchers, finally convinced the British to drop out of ELDO and fall back on the United States for whatever launchers they needed. The British withdrawal cooled the Germans on Europa, and they tried to get a guarantee from the United States that NASA would provide launchers to Germany. The French were also ready to drop out of the dying ELDO, but, always independent, intended to develop their own launcher.

The crux of the problem, though, was that, because of its legal commitments to Intelsat, the United States would not launch any communications satellite that encroached on Intelsat's global network. The Europeans, however, planned their own regional communications satellite network, and NASA had refused to launch the French/German Symphonie satellite, the harbinger of the European system. Without a European launcher, and as long as the United States stuck to its Intelsat commitment, there was little chance of setting up the new system.

The fluctuations in United States space-shuttle plans in 1969-72 had also disenchanted the Europeans. They had done extensive Phase A studies of a reusable space tug whose development could serve as their "price of admission" for shuttle launches in the 1980s. NASA had originally told the Europeans that they could pick and choose their favorite program: a tug, a "sortie" module for manned experiments in space, or building various shuttle-orbiter components. But then, in June 1972, NASA withdrew the tug option, narrowed the component possibilities, and imposed stringent management practices on any European shuttle-related project.

NASA's reasons were evident: the agency had committed itself to developing a highly complex machine on a shoestring budget. Delays or shoddy work on major shuttle subsystems would spell disaster, and the Europeans had certainly not distinguished themselves by their ability to organize and operate a successful long-term space program. Both ESRO and ELDO were in a shambles, ESC had no power to make a commitment, and the Europa launcher had nothing but a string of zeros to its credit. Joseph Karth's concern about ever getting significant European participation in the shuttle program appeared to have been well founded.

Nevertheless, the European reaction to the "hard-line" NASA position was not surprising; a typical comment (from England) blasted the NASA edict as having "an absolutely disastrous effect on future confidence by Europeans in collaborating with the United States on large space programs." The Europeans had favored the tug project, because even though its development cost was twice that of the sortie module (then estimated as $500 million versus the sortie lab's $250 million), the market for production units of the tug was much better. The Europeans thought they could produce and sell twenty to thirty tugs over the next decade to recoup their investment, but only two or three sortie labs.

This was probably the low point in international cooperation in space. The upswing began only six months later, at an ESC meeting in Brussels. Europe decided to abolish its decrepit organizational structure and form a single European Space Agency (ESA). ESA's two principal programs were to be the shuttle-compatible "space laboratory" (Spacelab), as the Europeans preferred to call the sortie lab, and a new large launcher called Ariane, derived from the ill-fated Europa but with a number of major new elements. These two projects finally joined the decade-old European space-program dichotomy by both ensuring European access to U.S. launches (one of the price tags for the Spacelab development) and guaranteeing the Europeans the independence to launch their own communications satellite system even if it did run afoul of the U.S. commitment to Intelsat.

It actually took over two years of both intra-European and European-American haggling to crystallize the Brussels decision into an operating European Space Agency, but there is no question that the Brussels meeting marked the beginning of the end of the difficult period. The Spacelab contract with NASA was undertaken in August 1973, as a complicated intergovernment agreement ultimately signed individually by nine nations: Belgium, Denmark, France, Germany, Italy, the Netherlands, Spain, Switzerland, and the United Kingdom. These nations made funding commitments, selected a prime contractor (ERNO), and finally got going. The organizational takeover by ESA, when it was eventually formed in May 1975, was smooth; the Spacelab program has run efficiently and on schedule ever since.

Back in the United States, development of the shuttle orbiter, the boosters, the big tank, and their various subsystems was proceeding with remarkably few apparent glitches. But Proxmire was still on the warpath. His eagle-eyed staff continued to ferret out disturbing but apparently insignificant irregularities, but they were unable to shake the obviously solid NASA shuttle program foundations. True, there

A cutaway view of the Spacelab, designed and built by the European Space Agency (ESA) for conducting in-orbit manned experiments aboard the U.S. space shuttle. It could be the key to future space industry.

were sporadic overruns in various development efforts, but NASA said these were inevitable in high-technology programs. To stay within their overall budget limits, they transferred funds from unexpectedly successful developments, reshuffled test programs, accelerated some development steps, and eliminated others as "unnecessarily conservative"; all in all, they seemed able to compensate handily for the few programmatic "bad spots."

Proxmire smelled smoke, but he couldn't find the fire to help him win any significant budget battles, even in his own subcommittee. He did, however, insist on and secure an annual shuttle-program review by the congressional budget watchdog, the General Accounting Office (GAO). The GAO ran up warning flags a few times in the mid-1970s, but NASA was able to counter them successfully. Then, on September 17, 1976, Orbiter 101, space-shuttle orbiter *Enterprise*, was rolled out of Rockwell International's Palmdale, California, hangar and the next summer underwent what some old hands thought was the most successful series of initial atmospheric flight-tests on record. They verified beyond any doubt the unpowered orbiter's ability to maneuver in the atmosphere after reentry and to make that tough, high-speed dead-stick landing; furthermore, it was done ahead of schedule and at considerably below budgeted cost.

But these heady events couldn't completely hide the subterranean specter of cost overruns. In April 1976 the GAO's annual shuttle status report had warned,

> NASA's revised development plan is introducing risks that could result in increased costs, schedule delays, and performance degradations. . . . Also [there] is the recurring question of whether the system will fulfill the space transportation needs of the Nation.

The GAO's concerns usually focused on budget-shuffling, scheduling, effects of inflation, projected operations costs and marketing, and to some extent on development progress. Each year it picked one main subject to bulldog. In 1977 it was the need for five orbiters: the GAO thought it would make better sense to wait until the first two orbiters were flying before proceeding with the other three. Whatever it did, the GAO's motive seemed to be to draw as many red herrings as possible across the shuttle's path, regardless of their real pertinence. Proxmire was pleased, but the GAO became a perennial headache to NASA. Every time a draft report came out, the entire NASA organization, including Mike Malkin, heaved a deep collective

NASA administrator James Fletcher demonstrates a shuttle model to President Gerald Ford on September 8, 1976. It was at this meeting that the President announced the name of the first space-shuttle orbiter: *Enterprise.*

Space-shuttle orbiter *Enterprise* is rolled out of its hangar on September 17, 1976.

sigh and got to work refuting, for the record, all the inanities of the necessarily superficial analyses, an almost preordained consequence for a "bean-counter" agency having only limited expertise in the frontier technologies of the shuttle program. The GAO, in fact, was often accused of using its prestige and influence as implements of politics rather than for its true function as watchdog of the federal books for Congress.*

Proxmire went to the GAO well for anti-NASA ammunition so often that he practically had his own captive GAO analyst: Richard

Enterprise was tested in the atmosphere to verify its dead-stick landing ability. It was carried aloft for these tests "piggyback" on a specially modified 747 airliner, in a manner quite remin- iscent of the *Maia-Mercury* seaplane back in 1938. This picture shows the first separation of *Enterprise* from its carrier plane, which took place on September 12, 1977.

* See Karen de Witt, "GAO Has Much More Than Ledger Domain," *The New York Times,* June 25, 1978, p. E-3.

Enterprise making its fifth successful free-flight dead-stick landing, on October 26, 1977.

Gutmann, director of GAO's Procurement and Systems Acquisition Division. In 1978, for example, Gutmann dusted off his previous year's views on shuttle-fleet limitations (this time he thought three orbiters would be enough, instead of the original five), but he came up with the startling recommendation that to save money, the military shuttle launch station at Vandenberg Air Force Base in California should be eliminated.

Now, many of the Defense Department's payloads require "sun-synchronous" orbits; that is, orbits that pass almost over both the earth's poles. This requires either a north-south launch or an unacceptable sacrifice in payload weight because of the enormous amount of energy—and therefore extra propellant weight—needed to make major orbit changes. A north-south launch from Cape Canaveral would require flying shuttles over the densely populated U.S. Northeast and Canada, and, perhaps even more important, over the heartland of the Soviet Union. The military implications were staggering. Imagine the U.S. President calling the Soviet Premier every week or two, casually mentioning that a U.S. military reconnaissance satellite would be passing over Moscow in an hour or so on its way into orbit. "No missiles on board, of course . . . and, oh yes, we're pretty sure the throwaway propellant tank you'll see sailing over your cities will come down in the ocean. Don't worry about it!"

Undersecretary of Defense for Research and Engineering William Perry stated flatly that the Cape Canaveral polar launch would be totally unacceptable to Defense Department requirements in the mid-

1980s; NASA administrator Robert Frosch was even blunter: "I'm afraid I must characterize the suggestion as irresponsible."

Congress gave Proxmire and Gutmann short shrift. Even though the Office of Management and Budget had cut NASA's request to Congress from five to four orbiters (not quite as far as Gutmann wanted to go), both houses of Congress reinstated the fifth and included full Vandenberg funding in the defense budget.

Ironically, it was one of the concerns Gutmann had flagged perfunctorily years earlier and which Proxmire had never used extensively in his diatribes that almost proved NASA's undoing. It wasn't even Proxmire who raised it when it finally became evident in early 1978, but NASA's conservative supporter Adlai Stevenson III, chairman of the Senate Subcommittee on Science, Technology, and Space, which had taken over NASA's budget supervision when the Aeronautical and Space Sciences Committee had been eliminated by the 1976-77 Senate committee reorganization. The problem? Our old nemesis: the orbiter's main rocket engine.

The fact that the engine development was not going well had been evident to knowledgeable propulsion engineers long before 1978. In December 1974, during NASA's customary annual review of its program by outside experts (the NASA Research and Technology Advisory Council—RTAC), Pres Layton had been asked to chair a special *ad hoc* Working Group on Space Power and Propulsion. Although the group's function was to advise on research and technology rather than ongoing programs, Layton's final report, issued in May 1975, cited specific cautions in the high-pressure staged-combustion engine technology so important to shuttle-engine development. His statements were specifically directed toward an advanced, reusable space-tug engine design slated for use in the mid-eighties rather than the shuttle, but they read easily and well between the lines. For example, ". . . the ASE [advanced space engine] is a scaled-down version of the space-shuttle main engine. It represents a maximum extension of the state of the art in cooling, pump, and turbine technology, bearings and seals, and controls."

The working group's report was received and digested assiduously by NASA, but tight budgets, as usual, precluded any real action. By September 1975 only 13 of the 964 engine tests required for final flight certification had been completed. NASA kept saying it was O.K., that the engine test program was "padded," and that the first orbital test-flight would still go on schedule in March 1979.

But by mid-1977 it was getting harder and harder for NASA to "sweep under the rug" their engine development problems. The FY 1978 budget had taken considerable "reprogramming" (a euphemism for fast shuffling) of funds to meet the unforeseen higher costs for development. There was, in fact, a rumor rampant in Washington, totally unsubstantiated but nevertheless disquieting in its implications, that a letter from Rockwell International had been placed on the NASA administrator's desk recommending a full redesign of the engine, which would delay the shuttle program a full year. Whatever the reason, NASA administrator Robert Frosch began to remind everyone that NASA had, in 1974, identified *two* first-flight dates: an "internal" NASA target of March 1979 (the original one) and a "public" target of June 1979. He gave March less than a fifty-fifty chance; June was only two to one. "And that's probably a little optimistic," he acknowledged.

Truly concerned about NASA's most important program, Senators Stevenson and Harrison Schmitt, former NASA astronaut-scientist who had won a New Mexico Senate seat and had become the minority (Republican) leader of the Senate Space Subcommittee, wrote on December 14, 1977, to Frosch: "Recognizing . . . that the engine development continues to experience difficulties . . . we ask that an independent review [be conducted] . . . so that it can be considered during the FY 1979 authorization hearings."

The National Research Council organized an *ad hoc* Committee for the Review of the Space Shuttle Main Engine Development Program, chaired by MIT Professor Eugene Covert. As special adviser to his committee, Covert drafted Dick Mulready, project manager of the Pratt & Whitney XLR-129 engine that had lost the shuttle competition to Rocketdyne.

Considering that he had only three months to assemble his data and write his report, Covert did a commendable job. The report's formal conclusions, though, were couched in the most cautious of terms:

• "The development of the engine is not as far along as the timetable may suggest. . . . The committee finds that problems now being encountered are not alarming, but rather typify the early stage of any similar new technological development."

- "While many elements of the engine development point to the ultimate success of the program, incorporation of changes and the tests to assure their effectiveness could result in delays. The ambitious timetable may have to be extended."
- "The committee sees no reason to suggest that a safe and reliable main engine cannot be developed ultimately."
- "Some of the problems [are] unresolved. Solutions have been proposed but are yet to be proved correct through testing."
- "NASA and Rocketdyne have laid out an ambitious time-table . . . the committee considers such an optimistic schedule not likely to be realized."

The committee made a number of excellent detailed recommendations to NASA as to how best to proceed, but cautioned against taking the "quick-fix" approach that is so prevalent when costly and politically sensitive programs approach their "drop-dead" dates. The bottom-line recommendation was insipid, but probably the best possible under the circumstances: Wait until fall 1978, after the key engine tests have been made, and then take another look at the situation.

Views of the Covert report ranged widely. Del Tischler felt that much of the hot committee debate had not reached the public report. Mike Malkin suspected that "the range of delays predicted by the committee ran from zero to nineteen months" (Mulready's estimate). "But," Malkin continued, "we've seen this kind of thing before. The technology base is there. Every Monday I expect to get the word that *this* is the week we've turned the corner." Tischler, on the other hand, saw the NASA attitude in a wholly different light: "That's what I call an Evel Knievel kind of optimism. You know, you jump out of an airplane at forty thousand feet without a parachute but with the intention of hitting one of those seven haystacks. You just have to get lucky!"

For a while, it appeared that NASA and Rocketdyne *did* get lucky. During the summer and early fall of 1978 they were able to pile up enough test time in full-duration, full-power engine runs to put them almost back on schedule. President Carter, in a speech to Kennedy Space Center employees on October 1, 1978, even announced that the first shuttle would fly in time for his birthday, on September 28, 1978.

But the wave of optimism was short-lived. Tischler's forebodings turned out to be deadly accurate. A series of engine test failures in the late fall and winter of 1978 postponed the earliest possible launch to November 1979, with most knowledgeable engineers convinced that the shuttle couldn't possibly be ready until well into 1980.

A shamefaced NASA had to go back to Congress for a $185 million supplement to the FY 1979 budget. A far more serious concern on the part of enthusiasts, however, was that the critical engine pump section might require a major redesign in order to meet the orbiter's performance, safety, and reusability specifications—a project that could delay shuttle operations even further.

But despite these problems, plans for the future had to continue. A year's delay (or even two, as some were darkly predicting) would be serious, but it could not deter preparations for the *real* business ahead—the business of making space pay off.

CHAPTER

5

THE TRANSITION

"When there are young generations of Americans chomping at
the bit to move our civilization of freedom back to the frontier of
space we say to them, 'Wait! One percent of our budget, or one-
fifth of one percent of our gross national product, is too much for
such childish dreams.' Hogwash! . . . Civilization is moving in-
extricably into space."

—Senator Harrison H. Schmitt (former scientist-astronaut)
Address to the Institute of Electrical and Electronic Engineers
September 1978

SPACE IS NOT ONLY THE FUTURE HOME OF CIVILIZATION, IT IS THE
seat of the world's new industry. Making that industry more productive is the job for which the shuttle was created. But getting payloads
into space—out of the deep "gravity well" of the earth—is only the
first of many complex operations. Those payloads need to perform
wondrously and well to create a viable industry out of Tsiolkovsky's
and Goddard's dreams.

My story of space enterprise up to this point has centered almost
totally on government support, both in the United States and overseas.
The reason is obvious: the need, in space activities, for enormous
up-front capital investments. In the case of such preceding enterprises
as the automotive, aircraft/airline, and computer industries, individual entrepreneurs were able to start up companies with initial
investments as small as a few thousand dollars. But even the cheapest
spacecraft costs millions, and to reach the point at which a space
"business" could become useful and profitable takes hundreds of
millions of dollars or more. Private industry is just not willing—in

fact, not able—to make that kind of investment in a high-risk, long-payback enterprise.

In the early days, of course, there was little thought of real economic payoff. The first artificial satellite was conceived in the guise of scientific research; the race to the moon was a barefaced push for national prestige; and military defense needs dominated all else. But Andy Haley, Arthur Clarke, and other space stalwarts were convinced that space offered two totally unique features that someday would turn an honest profit, in the true hard-nosed businessman's sense. These features were a location high above the earth and her atmosphere, and an environment characterized by essentially zero gravity and a near-perfect vacuum.

The high vantage point of an orbiting satellite has so far been the only one of these features to be exploited for economic profit. The stage had been set by Project SCORE (Signal Communications by Orbiting Relay Equipment)—the first rudimentary satellite communications experiment. A tape recorder, a receiver, and a transmitter, all powered by a battery, were launched into orbit by an Atlas missile. On Christmas 1958, President Eisenhower's peace message was transmitted to the entire world as SCORE rose and set every ninety minutes.

Like Apollo, SCORE was designed as a political-prestige "stunt"; it worked for only twelve days, and then its batteries went dead. Two years later, Echo—a huge hundred-foot-diameter metal-foil balloon inflated after it reached orbit—was the United States' next communications experiment in space. As the first artificial satellite big and bright enough to be visible to the naked eye, it caused quite a stir. Echo was nothing but a simple reflector: a signal beamed to it from earth just bounced off and was reflected to a receiver, much as shortwave radio signals bounce off the earth's own ionosphere (a layer of electrically charged molecules above the stratosphere).

But Echo wasn't really practical; by the time radio signals made the round trip, they were too weak to be of much value. Besides, Echo offered no directional control, so point-to-point transmission possibilities were limited. From 1960 to 1962, *active* communications satellites were developed and tested. The first real milestone of space "business" was Telstar 1, launched in July 1962. Not only could it transmit television pictures as well as radio and utilize solar energy to power its circuits, but it was paid for, owned, and operated by private enterprise: the American Telephone & Telegraph Co. (AT&T). Telstar created the first live "via satellite" pictures flashed on television screens. It heralded live news-event transmissions between Europe and the United States.

But even Telstar was only a primitive step in achieving the ultimate use of the space vantage point for terrestrial communications. Back in 1945, British engineer Arthur Clarke, whom we now know as the dean of science-fiction writers, had written a startling article in the trade journal *Wireless World*. Twelve years *before* Sputnik, he pointed out that an artificial satellite could be placed in an earth orbit high enough so that the speed needed to balance the pull of the earth's gravity would take it around the earth in just twenty-four hours. Thus if that orbit were directly above the earth's equator, and the direction of the satellite's motion were the same as that of the earth's rotation, the satellite would appear to hover perpetually over a single point on the equator. And, if three such satellites were spaced equally around the equator in that so-called "geostationary" orbit, they could cover the entire earth with radio (or other signal) transmissions. That is, a signal from New York, for example, flashed up to a geostationary satellite placed over the Atlantic Ocean, could be retransmitted to North America, Europe, West Africa, and South America, and simultaneously transmitted to the two sister satellites (located over the Pacific and Indian oceans) for retransmission to Asia, Australia, Polynesia, and East Africa.

This concept of a geostationary-orbit communications satellite network reveals an interesting dichotomy about Clarke—his rare ability to balance hard science and engineering vis-à-vis imaginative and gripping fiction like *2001: A Space Odyssey*, the first modern science-fiction movie. This bifurcation carried through his personal life, too. His "home away from home" in the United States was the Hotel Chelsea, on New York's Twenty-third Street; his real home is in Colombo, Sri Lanka. The Chelsea, a seedy, run-down, part-residential, part-transient, past-its-prime hotel, has long been a home for notorious writers like Thomas Wolfe, Brendan Behan, Dylan Thomas, and Clifford Irving. More recently it has become a mecca for way-out British rock-and-roll groups "on the road" in the United States. But although Clarke loved the free and easy atmosphere of the Chelsea, he couldn't quite go along with it all the way. He continued to rise at 7 A.M., don his customary English suit, vest, and tie, and, with attaché

The geostationary communications satellite system now in use worldwide was conceived and described in 1945 by Arthur C. Clarke, the famed science and fiction writer. Photograph courtesy of *Astronautics and Aeronautics.*

Clarke's system of three communications satellites, in orbit 22,300 miles over the equator, can provide coverage to 90 percent of the earth's surface.

case in hand, venture into the totally deserted corridors and elevators still pervaded with the stale marijuana smoke of the up-till-dawn Chelsea clientele. I lived in the Chelsea for a few months, and, also dressed in suit and tie and carrying my briefcase, was usually on my way to Princeton at the same hour he was off for a lecture or a meeting with his publisher. We must truly have been a strange sight to the rare musician returning home late from his gig!

Arthur Clarke thought his idea for a global world communications network might be realizable by the end of the century, or fifty-five years after he conceived it. But even Clarke—renowned for his soaring imagination—would never have dreamed that in less than twenty-five years, by 1969, his flamboyant theory of global communications "via satellite" would be in routine operation. In that year, three geostationary communications satellites, one over the Atlantic, one over the Pacific, and one over the Indian Ocean, went into service to make the globe, for the first time, truly "one world."

How was it that this incredible feat was brought about by private industry? The business prospects for satellite communications had become apparent as early as 1961, when President Kennedy announced that U.S. policy would be to have private industry develop the civilian satellite communications system. The Communications Satellite Act of 1962 set up the private (but closely regulated) Communications Satellite Corporation (COMSAT), which opened its doors in February 1963. In April 1965 COMSAT's first offering, nicknamed "Early Bird," was in its geostationary orbit 22,300 miles over the Atlantic Ocean, transmitting, among its other services, live commercial television between Europe and the United States. Early Bird demonstrated very clearly its potential: this single, relatively primitive satellite could transmit as many messages as three transatlantic cables at less than a quarter the cost.

"Global" is the correct word for satellite communications. Early Bird's proper name was Intelsat 1—the first satellite servicing the International Telecommunications Satellite Organization (Intelsat). Since then there have been five series of Intelsats, each more advanced than the one before. By 1978, scarcely nine years after Arthur Clarke's "wild idea" became a reality, there were 102 member nations of Intelsat, using eleven operational satellites carrying over 10,000 full-time two-way telephone circuits connecting 200 earth stations along 550 different communications pathways. And despite inflation, the cost to place one satellite circuit-year in orbit dropped from Early Bird's initial $30,000 (in 1965) to Intelsat IVA's $1,000 (in 1975).

The Eastern European bloc has its own international network—Intersputnik—and by 1978 a dozen nations had their own domestic satellite communications networks. As soon as a profit can be made—even in so seemingly esoteric a field as space—there is hard cash available for investment. In 1977 worldwide revenues from satellite communications reached $500 million, and the surface has barely been scratched. Satellite Business Systems (SBS), for example, a new consortium of COMSAT, Aetna (insurance), and IBM, was formed in 1976 to service private industry with a host of different and unique

AT&T's Telstar communications satellite, the first embodiment of commercial space enterprise, is checked out prior to its successful launch on July 10, 1962. Photograph courtesy of Bell Laboratories.

The first Intelsat IV-A communications satellite, now the mainstay of current global communications, undergoes prelaunch preparation. Photograph courtesy of Hughes Aircraft Company.

communications services. SBS expects to invest over $1.5 billion in new capital before it completes its global network of seven satellites and 2,500 ground stations.

By far the majority of the people involved in satellite communications today wouldn't have been caught dead in the space business twenty years ago, before COMSAT came into existence. But, there are a few exceptions. John R. Pierce is perhaps the most notable. If we attach familial designations, I suppose he would be the father of satellite communications, with Arthur Clarke unquestionably cast in the grandfather role. Pierce, who was director of research at Bell Telephone Laboratories in the early sixties, bullied and badgered the conservative AT&T management until they finally agreed to finance Telstar. As today's largest single industrial user of satellites (their Comstar, operated by COMSAT, is the biggest of the world's domestic satellite systems), AT&T has reaped the profits of Pierce's insistence many times over. Pierce is now retired from active participation in the industry, but continues to inspire students from his position as professor at Cal Tech.

One of the few people "in at the beginning" who still plays a dominant role in satellite communications is Dr. Burt I. Edelson, currently director of the COMSAT Laboratories, which inherited from Bell Labs the mantle of senior laboratory in satellite communications. Edelson started his career in the Navy. Like Bob Truax he was an Annapolis graduate, but unlike Truax he had absolutely no interest in space until twelve years after he graduated. A Navy engineering officer involved in the design of navigation equipment for the Bureau of Ships, he volunteered to attend a meeting in November 1959 on the subject of ship navigation using satellites. Bob Freitag, an old Truax associate who had become the Navy's top communications satellite expert, was there.

"That meeting changed my whole life!" Edelson said. "I'd never seen anything like it before. Those people were so enthusiastic that the excitement and glamour of what they were talking about converted me, then and there." Edelson recognized right away that communications would clearly be the first practical space application; that, mixed with the glamour of fiery and (then) unpredictable rocket launches, was an irresistible bait.

He joined the team—a three-service (Army, Air Force, Navy) communications experiment called "Advent." His job was to set up a shipboard terminal. Advent turned out to be a failure, but Edelson's thirty-foot shipboard antenna system worked beautifully. It was later used as the "ground terminal" for the very first geostationary communications satellite experiment—Syncom, in 1964—and later provided the only reliable communication link to the Indian Ocean area for Gemini and Apollo tracking ships.

Edelson continued to be fascinated by the possibilities of satellite navigation and communications systems. During the Advent project, he, Freitag, and other Navy officers met in each other's homes in the evenings—almost like a clandestine club—plotting to keep the Navy in space. They worked up a ship-based satellite launcher called "Sea

Scout," which could use the "ideal" equatorial launch location (to get maximum benefit from the earth's rotation), but the Air Force found out about it and the project was canceled. One of their most prescient projects was a ship-launched anti-satellite—the ship could maneuver right under the target satellite's orbit. The project's code name was "Early Spring," to hide it from the Air Force. As Edelson put it, "In those days the saying was, 'Nobody can be against motherhood or Early Spring!' " But that project was canceled (there are many today who wish that it hadn't been) and Defense Secretary McNamara finally lowered the boom on the Navy (and the Army, too) by assigning all long-range missile and defense satellite activity to the Air Force.

Edelson, meanwhile, had become well known through his successful ship-terminal design for Advent, and was able to engineer its use for Syncom through his associations with senior NASA communications staff members. He had taught himself all there was to know about satellite communications (his Naval Academy degree in metallurgy was of little help), and had become the Navy's most knowledgeable engineer in that subject. When the National Aeronautics and Space Council began to prepare the Communications Satellite Act, he called Ed Welsh, the executive director of the NASC, and got himself assigned to the council, much against the will of Navy brass who wanted a high-level captain in that key White House position instead of an upstart lieutenant-commander engineer.

Edelson soon became the council's expert on satellite communications, and helped steer the Communications Satellite Act through the congressional maze. During his three years on the Space Council, he established the basic tenets that shaped the satellite communications business. When COMSAT was formed, for example, it was suggested that it should be responsible for all military as well as civil satellite communications. Edelson and an Aerospace Corporation engineer named Wilbur Pritchard strongly opposed that idea: civil and military communications had almost diametrically opposite missions, and they felt that *both* roles would suffer if assigned to a single organization. Between them, they were able to kill the joint military/civil concept. COMSAT became a civil-market operator, and the Defense Department developed its own system.

Bored with Washington after six years, Edelson went to London in 1965 and, working for the Office of Naval Research, helped set up

NATO's defense satellite communications program and also the British defense system "Skynet." Pritchard, meanwhile, had been offered the directorship of COMSAT Laboratories, and asked Edelson to be his associate director. Edelson accepted, left the Navy in 1967 to join COMSAT, and when Pritchard left in 1973, Edelson took over the directorship.

Edelson's genius was his ability to see immediate, practical applications of what at first appeared to be way-out ideas. When he was still on the Space Council, for example, he had noted that NASA used television to cover only the *launch* of the early Project Mercury missions; the balance of the missions were reported to the public by radio. He studied the situation and concluded that it would be relatively easy to cover the landings by TV, too. NASA demurred; it was too difficult, they said, and besides, suppose an astronaut were injured or killed on landing? Edelson finally convinced them, and sure enough, not only did it turn out to be remarkably easy to do (and wholly successful), but it set up the invaluable precedent for full public coverage of all U.S. space activities, a sharp contrast to Soviet secrecy.

Although deeply involved in satellite communications almost from the beginning, Edelson's main influence was to come much later. Everyone else seemed to see satellites simply as a substitute for cables, but Edelson recognized very early the enormous new capabilities offered by systems located in space. In the late 1970s, with commercial global and domestic systems operating routinely and successfully, the field began to experience its "second coming," with Burt Edelson as its prophet. In Chapter Six we'll see where he's leading us.

The second early use of the perspective offered by a satellite location in space was for meteorology and weather forecasting. Although never developing into a commercial enterprise the way communications satellites did, weather analysis and forecasting by satellite are so closely interwoven with daily life on earth that they rank a very close second (to communications) in economic implications. As with communications, early weather satellites were placed in low orbits, scanning the earth's atmosphere as they skimmed over it at about 17,000 miles per hour. But the geostationary orbit offered advantages nearly as obvious for weather observations as for communications. From a "fixed" vantage point, a satellite can watch storms develop and grow, track cloud masses and fronts, monitor the temperature and humidity changes that herald the inception of hurricanes, typhoons,

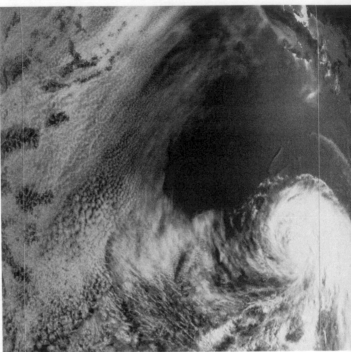

Dr. Burton I. Edelson, director of COM-SAT Laboratories. His concept of putting the complex and expensive communications hardware into space and thereby allowing use of cheap, inexpensive stations on earth is the guiding principle for advanced communications satellite systems. Photograph courtesy of *Astronautics and Aeronautics.*

A geostationary weather satellite snapshot of Hurricane Hyacinth in the eastern Pacific (August 11, 1976). Baja California is at the upper right-hand corner. Photograph courtesy of National Oceanic and Atmospheric Administration.

and even small-scale weather systems like tornadoes and line squalls. Ultimately, geostationary weather satellites will provide the data needed to predict long-term changes in weather and maybe even the climatic impacts of mankind's industrialization of the earth.

But although "today's satellite weather pictures" have become as familiar now to television viewers as talk-show hosts, and despite the enormous economic value of accurate weather and storm predictions to hundreds of commercial operations (farming, resorts, airlines, fisheries, building, shipping, and such), weather forecasting is considered a government service, and is not itself a commercial activity.

In some respects, therefore, space-based meteorology falls just outside my space enterprise story, like the equally important and far more fascinating realm of space science and exploration.

But what *should* be considered a government service and what really *is* a commercial activity for private enterprise? This question has plagued the rational development of a technology that might eventually turn out to be the most valuable use ever made of the space perspective. It is called "remote sensing"—a term first defined in 1960 by the Office of Naval Research to distinguish potential civil applications from the wholly military-oriented designation, "surveillance and reconnaissance."

"Remote sensing" may be a relatively new word, but it's an age-old mechanism: it simply means gathering information from a source far away from the "sensor." People have always used their eyes to perform this function. More recently telescopes and movie and television cameras have added new and important dimensions to our capability for remote sensing.

Our eyes respond only to visible light. Special films can pick up other wavelengths—X-rays, for example. But every object or material on the surface of the earth and its oceans reflects or absorbs other wavelengths of the "electromagnetic spectrum," of which visible light constitutes only a very small portion. The reflected radiation, if we could "see" it, is a unique "spectral signature" of the object or material, just like a fingerprint. To our eyes, for example, the spectral signature of vegetation is its green color; various shades of blue denote sky, certain flowers, or gas flames. Our eyes are therefore multi-spectral remote sensors able to analyze complex differences in the visible-light part of the electromagnetic spectrum.

There are instruments that can "see" substantial ranges of the spectrum above and below the visible-light portion. "Black-light" detectors see ultraviolet; heat sensors see infrared; X-ray detectors pick up the very short wavelengths. The most useful spectral signatures for looking at important features of the earth and the oceans from space are mainly in the infrared and microwave (radar) regions; that is, wavelengths slightly longer than those of visible light.

The possibilities turn out to be almost limitless, depending on the number of different wavelengths used and the ability of the instruments to distinguish small objects or features on the earth's surface from a few hundred miles up. It is this ability, called "resolution," that has generated most of the hang-ups in applying remote sensing to those limitless possibilities. In agriculture, remote sensing (and proper analysis of data) can tell wheat from corn; it can distinguish healthy crops from diseased crops; it can tell whether soil is too wet or too dry; and it can identify the nature and the scope of pest infestation. It can even tell how many sheep or cows can be supported by a given piece of land and when they should be moved. When used for inventory, remote-sensing data can guide crop production and, if coordinated globally, it can be used—*in advance*—to direct crop surpluses to food-shortage areas. Remote sensing can find scarce minerals (even oil!); it can guide forestry planning; it can detect and predict river flooding and monitor irrigation; it can detect and monitor air and water pollution; it can map heat losses to improve energy-use efficiency; it can guide urban land-use planning; it can detect wetlands encroachment and the littoral drift that destroys or damages beach areas; it can track Arctic ice growth and guide ship movements; it can even locate schools of fish for fishermen. The list is literally endless. Microwaves can "look" below the surface of the ocean, and even a few feet down into the earth's crust.

Weather satellites, of course, also use remote sensing to gather their meteorological data. But to realize the myriad potential opportunities offered by "looking" at the earth and its oceans, the United States developed special series of satellites called "Landsat" and "Seasat." Landsat 1 was launched in 1972, Landsat 2 in 1975, Seasat 1 and Landsat 3 in 1978. In practically no time, everybody was clamoring for data—states, cities, environmental protection agencies, forestry services, wildlife organizations, fisheries, agricultural agencies, mining and oil companies, and many foreign nations.

"If I had to pick one spacecraft, one space development to save the world," said NASA administrator James Fletcher a few years ago, "I would pick Landsat and the satellites which I believe will be evolved from it." By 1978 eight nations had bought or built Landsat receiving stations—Argentina, Brazil, Canada, Chile, India, Iran, Italy, and Zaire—and were each paying the United States $200,000 per year for access to the satellites' data. On January 2, 1978, President Carter told the Indian parliament, "The intricate electronics of a space satellite can be as useful to earthbound farmers as a new plow." By July 1978, forty-eight of the fifty American states had used natural-resource pictures and other data from Landsat for water-quality assessment and planning, wildlife-habitat inventories, geological mapping, surface water inventories, flood control, crop inventories, and forest inventories, among others.

It would seem that here was another made-to-order "space business" with even greater potential than the already booming satellite communications industry. But again, politics reared its ubiquitous head; this time complicated much more seriously by strident military concerns. The Landsat debate started almost with the first launch in 1972 and continues to rage to this day—in the halls of Congress, in the amphitheaters of the United Nations, and in the dim recesses of the Pentagon and the Kremlin.

First of all, NASA's charter, the National Space Act of 1958, specifically precludes the agency from engaging in *operational* space programs. This mandate was no problem in satellite communications— a lucrative commercial market was ready and waiting for private industry to take over—or in meteorological satellites—the weather service (actually the National Oceanic and Atmospheric Administration—NOAA—in the Department of Commerce) was an obvious operator. The first three Landsats (and the first Seasat) were properly designated as "experiments," and were thus unquestionably in NASA's bailiwick, just like Echo and the other early communications satellite experiments. But, fortunately or unfortunately, Landsat 1 (then called ERTS, for Earth Resources Technology Satellite) was an instant success. Everyone wanted ERTS data; it was easy to use and invaluable in saving money and time when compared to airborne or ground-

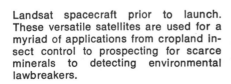

Landsat spacecraft prior to launch. These versatile satellites are used for a myriad of applications from cropland insect control to prospecting for scarce minerals to detecting environmental lawbreakers.

A Landsat image of the New York metropolitan area. Such images are used for land-use planning, tracking sewage sludge dumped into the New York Bight, and checking littoral drift along the beaches.

based surveying methods. So NASA almost unwillingly had to become a pseudo-operator of Landsat, because first, there was no single agency whose jurisdiction embraced all of Landsat's capabilities (Department of Agriculture? Department of the Interior? Environmental Protection Agency? Army Corps of Engineers (flood control)? Department of Energy?), and second, the market was too fragmented and too diverse for private industry to move in on its own (the investment would be large and, despite the myriad benefits, the *economic* risks high). And third, there was no strong advocate in the government to set up a semipublic corporation like COMSAT, mainly because of military concerns.

So Landsat bumbled along, a beautiful orphan. In 1977 Congress authorized a fourth "experiment," Landsat D, to employ much more sophisticated scanning and data reduction methods. (NASA satellites are designated by letters until they are launched, when they change over to numbers. Hence Landsat D will become Landsat 4 after it is launched in 1982.) NASA also put together an interim "Regional Applications Program" to "sell" the states and local agencies on the use of the Landsats, while bill after bill to set up an operational system foundered in Congress.

President Carter's space policy message of October 11, 1978, again relegated Landsat to a further round of studies by an "interagency task force" to "examine the options." Adlai Stevenson III, chairman of the Senate's Space Subcommittee, promptly submitted a bill *mandating* the creation of an operational remote-sensing system, starting another cycle of often acrimonious debate.

Meanwhile the military thunder rumbled around the world. Landsat's military implications are obvious: Country A's satellite takes pictures of Country B (as Landsat does), and releases that information publicly (as a civil program should). It has almost certainly taken pictures of things that Country B considers to be military secrets. Now, if that information is freely available to the public, Country C, which may be considering military operations against Country B, suddenly has access to information that Country B may be trying desperately to hide from Country C. So Country B stands up in the United Nations and demands that no Landsat data be released—a condition which, if approved, would wipe out much of Landsat's economic and social benefit.

Now, the space-faring nations obviously take pictures of each other's military installations from space; that's the purpose of the bulk of the military missions NASA wants the Air Force to use the shuttle for. But *military* data are kept secret—the United States knows the Soviets have detailed photos of the United States, and the Soviets know the United States has detailed photos of the Soviet Union. But the Soviet Union, for example, clearly does *not* want China to see these pictures. And Israel, for example, might be severely compromised if Syria, Jordan, and Saudi Arabia secured detailed military data from a U.S. satellite. So the release of Landsat data could have truly serious military implications *if*—and here's the crux of the matter—*if* the Landsat data were capable of distinguishing militarily important features. The key to that is "resolution." A remote-sensing device with good resolution can distinguish ("see") small objects; the poorer the resolution, the bigger the smallest object the device can recognize. Resolution is stated in feet or meters: a resolution of ten feet (about three meters) can readily distinguish a car from a truck, for example, but not one kind of car from another.

The resolution of military satellite sensors is of course secret, but is obviously incredibly good. One official said recently, "They used to talk about reading license plates from orbit. Now we're able to see the bolts that hold the license plate on." Our military people joke about giving nicknames to certain Soviet truck drivers; they are recognizable from the satellite images.

The course that has been selected to prevent military use of Landsat images, therefore, is to forbid the use of high-resolution remote sensors on civil spacecraft. Landsat 3, for example, can resolve objects with dimensions of about one hundred feet (thirty meters)—a far cry from a license-plate bolt, but adequate to tell whether vegetation is healthy or diseased or to detect the telltale river-pollution plume being discharged illegally from a chemical plant. Nevertheless, there is continued pressure to allow Landsat resolution to improve, since the quality and usefulness—and therefore marketability—of its data would be considerably enhanced. Present images, for example, do not allow such useful potential applications as counting individual homes for land-use planning, measuring highway traffic for efficient traffic control, or, perhaps even more important, detecting the rather small-scale geological features that often indicate the presence of oil and other valuable minerals.

There is of course much controversy over these military shackles on Landsat resolution. Some experts believe NASA's limit, because it is formally imposed by the U.S. Office of Management and Budget, is strictly a cost consideration. High-resolution systems *do* cost considerably more, not only to develop and build but to extract useful data from. However, others feel that OMB is simply acting on behalf of the military in its mandated role of overseeing national-security matters for the President.

Some experts believe that military restrictions on resolution are totally unnecessary, simply because military needs are very different from civil needs. The military, for example, needs a temperature-difference detector only to tell whether or not a soldier, or a tank, is in a given area; it doesn't need to *measure* that temperature difference accurately over a broad area, as would be needed for crop information. As one expert put it, "If [the military scanner] hits something even slightly warmer than the background, the screen goes white. But that kind of scanner would be horrible for thermal plume modeling— you'd lose all your information!"

But whatever the rationale, the impasse remains, and as long as it does, this enormously promising potential "space business" will remain just that: a promising potential. There has been much pressure to convert Landsat D into an operational system, and that option still exists, but it will be at least six or eight years before even that could be realized. Meanwhile, no entity—city, state, nation, or corporation—is as yet willing to commit itself to dependence on what still remains an "experimental system." So, until the civil-military questions are resolved, remote sensing via satellite cannot become an economically viable operation. But the enormous promise is there, and it eventually will be realized. The only question is, when.

The commercial use of the space *environment*, unlike the well-defined and expanding use of the space *location* I've detailed up to now, has been an elusive but enormously attractive prospect. With all our inventiveness, it certainly would seem that the sudden availability of an enormous volume of nearly empty space, unfettered by the bonds of gravity, would offer a literally infinite scope of opportunity for new processes and products. All sorts of grandiose plans have been formulated, studies pursued, and experiments performed to explore the potential of "space-processing" opportunities that might eventually be developed into real "space-industry" operations.

So far no luck. The promise is still a chimera.

But the prospects! For some reason the first space-industry opportunity everyone wanted to publicize was the manufacture of ball bearings in space. In space, they reasoned, one can make perfect spheres simply by allowing a mass of molten metal to cool—the lack of gravity means that natural surface tension will draw any glob of liquid into a perfect spherical shape.

But why would anyone want to make ball bearings in space, no matter how perfect they might be? We make quite suitable ball bearings by the millions here on earth right now, at perhaps a thousandth (or maybe a millionth!) of what it would take to amortize and operate a space-based ball-bearing factory. *That* "opportunity" gave space processing a bad name, one that NASA is still trying to live down. "Hey! We can make perfect ball bearings in space!" now causes as much cringing at 600 Independence Avenue as, "If we can go to the moon, why can't we . . . ?" used to.

Another early prospect was the manufacture of vaccines and other biologicals in space. Certain biological materials are manufactured by separating them out of a solution by a process called "electrophoresis," in which a weak electric field does the separating. But gravity complicates the process: heavy particles tend to fall (sedimentation) and the liquid solution develops tiny temperature differences that cause it to move and swirl (convection). In space, without gravity, there is little or no sedimentation *or* convection. An early space experiment on Skylab found that cells capable of producing urokinase, an enzyme used to dissolve blood clots, could produce six or seven times more urokinase after being separated in space than the unseparated cell mixtures that have to be used here on earth.

The bandwagon almost broke down from the crowd that jumped on it. Major drug companies were forecasting multi-billion-dollar businesses in a few years. Vaccines, unlike ball bearings, are admirably suited to space-based manufacture: small amounts draw huge prices, and the equipment needed to manufacture them is also small and not heavy.

But the bloom faded fast. Even in zero gravity, electrophoresis was not all that efficient, and when the extra costs of basing factories in space and carting materials up and down from orbit were factored in, the commercial prospects weren't that great.

Many other potential avenues for using the zero gravity and the high vacuum of space were explored, both in the manned U.S. Skylab and Soviet Salyut space stations and in a number of unmanned satellites. Space-processing tests were even done in sounding rockets (Space Processing Applications Rockets—SPAR), which offer five or six minutes of zero gravity near the tops of their trajectories after the engine shuts down and before the drag starts when they fall back to earth. Possibilities included containerless processing of high-temperature materials, which normally were contaminated by the crucibles needed to hold them on earth; growing unique (or very large) crystals for specialized electronic applications such as computer microcircuitry or solar cells; making special glasses and composites having unique properties that are normally not obtainable because of gravity-induced sedimentation or convection; joining critical assemblies by vacuum welding; making wholly new materials such as foamed metals, and so on.

But despite the great promise of all these ideas, none seemed to be able to project real commercial success. A special study by the National Research Council in 1978 failed to identify "any examples of economically justifiable processes for producing materials in space, and recommend[ed] that this area of materials technology not be emphasized in the NASA program." Nevertheless, there are many who believe that space processing *will* prove to be commercially successful. They liken negative studies such as that by the National Research Council to a fictitious Spanish government review panel that probably would have turned down Columbus' voyage—we just don't yet know what the possibilities are. For example, John Carruthers,

NASA's director for materials processing, said the council studied only past programs and didn't even consider the possibilities for future work offered by Spacelab and the shuttle.

One of the faithful believers in a massive future business enterprise in space-based manufacturing is Dr. Philomena Grodzka, a staff scientist in the space-processing group at Lockheed's Huntsville, Alabama, laboratory. A chemist by training (Ph.D. in analytic chemistry from the University of Michigan in 1961), she was "turned on" to space research when she was assigned by AVCO Corporation to help design analytic chemistry experiments that would be used in a rendezvous with a comet, a mission that was of some interest. One of AVCO's consultants at that time, incidentally, was Carl Sagan, the popular Cornell astronomer.

Grodzka moved to Lockheed in 1965, where one of her first studies involved setting up a theoretical explanation of the mysterious "red spots" on the moon—flares that had been observed from the earth near the craters Copernicus and Aristarchus, and in which one observer had detected carbon, the chemical which life on earth is based. "And then they canceled *Apollo 18*," she laughed, "which was supposed to explore either Copernicus or Aristarchus. I'm still waiting for them to explore the moon more fully to see whether my hypothesis was right!"

Space processing as a science was born in 1968, when NASA got interested in the effect of gravity on the formation of crystals. Grodzka had been working on phase-changing fluids to insulate spacecraft from the sudden heat and cold surges experienced when satellites plunged into and out of the earth's shadow. Since the manner in which these fluids froze into crystals was a key factor in her research, she got involved immediately in studying the whole gamut of zero-gravity phenomena, and thereby became one of the nucleus of scientists who began to define the products that might be manufactured in space. She flew experiments on *Apollos 14* and *17* (demonstrating surface-tension convection and identifying a new source of convection in zero-gravity fluids caused by spaceship vibration—she called it the "g-jitter"). She also supplied experiments on Skylab (to observe the effect of convection on crystal formation and growth) and on the joint U.S.-U.S.S.R. Apollo-Soyuz flight in 1975 (to observe the effect of convection on chemical reactions in foams).

As one of the space-processing pioneers, Grodzka was instrumental in forming a new Technical Committee on Space Processing for the American Institute of Aeronautics and Astronautics, and in 1975 became its first chairman. It was, incidentally, the first time any of the institute's thirty-nine technical committees had been led by a woman.

One of my first memories of Philomena Grodzka was of her sitting quietly toward the back of the auditorium at the 1975 Princeton Conference on Space Manufacturing Facilities. Anyone seeing her listening to the first day's speakers—Gerard O'Neill, Del Tischler, Arthur Kantrowitz, and other well-known space luminaries—might have wondered why this small, blond, almost mousy woman was there at all. The wonder lasted only until she stood and walked to the podium to deliver the invited lead paper in the production session.

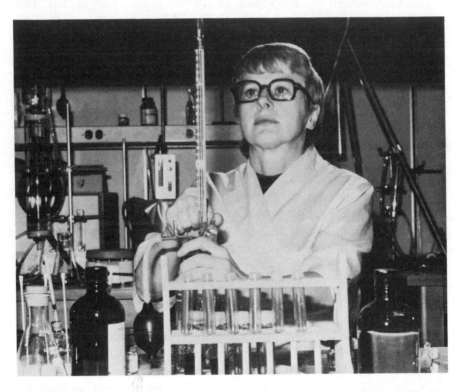

Dr. Philomena Grodzka, space processing scientist, working out details of an experiment that was performed on the U.S.-U.S.S.R. Apollo-Soyuz test project in July 1975. The enormous potential of unlimited vacuum and zero gravity has yet to be realized in practical returns, but Dr. Grodzka is absolutely certain that it will be. Photograph courtesy of Lockheed Missiles and Space Company.

But Grodzka was not only a competent scientist. Beneath her quiet demeanor and self-effacing manner lay a steely belief in her science and her vision of its role in the development of space. In June 1976, she and I testified as space-processing experts before the Subcommittee on Aerospace Technology and National Needs of the Senate's Aeronautical and Space Sciences Committee. In her clipped, precise, but small voice, which one had to strain to hear, she carefully and meticulously criticized NASA's "go slow" approach to space-processing research via the long-established "principal investigator" method, characterized in the main by academic people staffing the advisory and proposal review committees that selected the experiments and the investigators. She suggested a more streamlined approach which would make it easier to respond quickly to new ideas and which would encourage much broader participation by industry.

Her frank statements won the plaudits of the senators and their staffs, but generated some displeasure among the top brass at NASA's Marshall Space Center. It is to Lockheed's credit that although NASA is their principal customer in Huntsville, the company never censured Philomena and, in fact, it continued to support her extravocational activities in promoting the science of space industrialization.

After her Senate appearance, she became concerned about the way the planning for space-processing research was progressing. The few experiments she saw coming up were complex and expensive. "If you don't come up with a universal cure for cancer, the experiment is considered a failure," she said. "We need more 'quick and dirty' experiments in the basic materials sciences. If nobody's expecting great things to come out of them, we'll pick up a lot of interesting and useful knowledge—and history tells us something useful is *bound* to come out of that."

Her concerns about space processing extended into the entire field of space technology. She worried about the institutionalization of space by vested interests—a "priesthood of technology: keepers of the sacred flame of knowledge"—who excluded newcomers to the "club" in order to preserve their own established (and often decaying) supremacy, whether corporate or individual. "So what happens," she said, "is that you get a lot of tired old ideas. But if they didn't work before, why should they work now?"

Her studies of the Tennessee Valley Authority (Huntsville, Alabama, is in TVA territory) revealed a charter which in its early days provided convenient access of all concerned parties to TVA projects. She therefore proposed (in a paper to the American Astronautical Society in October 1977) a "Space Utilization Authority (SUA)" conceived along lines parallel to those of the TVA. Her SUA may never come about, but the principles on which it is based are cited often as a potential methodology for bringing in much wider (and stronger) popular support for space development, long regarded as the exclusive province of an elite group.

Grodzka's main problem in achieving her goals is not unique: she can't get enough people, particularly those in high places, to listen to her. But rather than sit back and complain, as many of us do when confronted by the typical "don't make waves" syndrome, she quietly but doggedly works to combat it. She delightedly accepts invitations to present her views to audiences all over the country, fortunately with the continuing support of her employer—an essential for a no-nonsense working scientist. And in the long run, she believes implicitly that she and others like her will succeed. Space *will* become a major commercial success as did the automotive, aircraft, and computer industries that preceded it.

But "selling" space is not just a problem for people like Philomena Grodzka with new and grandiose ideas. The basic rationale for the space shuttle when its development was finally accepted by Congress and the administration in the early 1970s was that it would pay its way—in hard economic terms as well as in opening new frontiers. So although NASA had finally learned how to sell its programs to OMB and to Congress during the tough Proxmire-dominated 1970s, the agency found itself in the wholly unaccustomed role of "space salesman" (in every sense of that phrase) to other federal agencies, to states and cities, to the military, to foreign nations and *their* agencies, and, surprisingly enough, to the general public. Shuttle marketing became a major undertaking, and NASA assigned a competent and experienced pro, former Skylab program director Chet Lee, to be its huckster. As program director for space transportation system operations, Lee hired a young fireball, Jon "Mike" Smith, to mastermind the marketing push.

Smith was unorthodox in his approach, but he got results. The original shuttle development had finally been sold on the basis of a projected 560 shuttle flights during the twelve-year shuttle "write-off" period from 1980 to 1992. But that was only a "best guess" on

NASA's part (and, as noted earlier, one much criticized by Pres Layton and many other NASA-watchers); in fact, there was not much more than crystal-ball gazing behind the projections for 1985-92, which averaged out at sixty flights per year, or a flight every *six days*. Comparisons of that schedule with a 1976-79 NASA launch rate averaging only about twenty flights per year, all with much smaller payload capability than the shuttle, made the critics' concerns seem all too accurate.

Now, everyone knew that once the shuttle was operational and people began to realize what could be done with it, the demand for launches into space would skyrocket. This point had been well made in the AIAA's original assessment in 1972-73. But one doesn't convince OMB or the Congress, fighting to control inexorable inflation in the face of mushrooming federal budgets, with statements like, "Everyone knows that . . ." They wanted much harder evidence that the shuttle would pay its way. So Chet Lee and Mike Smith had to get out and hustle *real* payload commitments, preferably accompanied by up-front deposits of cash.

They went first, of course, to the big users—those who needed all or at least half of the big shuttle payload bay to handle their equipment. Commitments were readily secured from the booming communications industry: Western Union, Satellite Business Systems, RCA, COMSAT, and Telesat/Canada all signed up for early launches. Big industrial users like Rockwell International and the German giant Messerschmitt-Bölkow-Blohm were also on board early, and, of course, a few NASA space-science and military payloads were already scheduled.

But NASA needed much, much more, particularly to begin filling those voluminous sixty-foot payload bays which were supposed to be going better than once a week in the later flights. They conceived the idea of the "Getaway Special"—formally the Small Self-Contained Payload Program—for payloads weighing less than 200 pounds and measuring smaller than five cubic feet. The price? A mere $10,000 for a full-sized package; as low as $3,000 for a 60-pound, one-and-a-half-cubic-foot space. And, anyone who met NASA's safety and other operational launch requirements could buy in—without having to disclose the exact nature of their payloads.

It turned out far better than anyone had expected. Getaway Specials sold like lottery tickets. The first buyer to put up the required

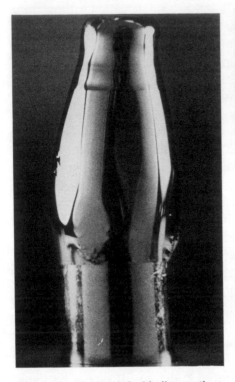

A space-grown crystal of indium antimonide. Large, perfect crystals are considered one of the promising prospective space products.

The shuttle retrieves an orbiting satellite for repair or replacement. This is a key feature in reducing costs of space operations.

$500 "earnest money" was, surprisingly enough, an individual: R. Gilbert Moore. Gil Moore is currently general manager of Thiokol's Astro-Met Division in Ogden, Utah, but I often wonder when he finds time to run his business (which, incidentally, he seems to do very well —it continues to prosper). A fountain of energy and an irrepressible space enthusiast ever since I've known him, perhaps twenty years now, Gil's main purpose in life seems to be the promotion of space as the best thing for the world that's come down the pike since Adam's rib got animated.

Sporting a Dayan-like black eyepatch, Gil Moore has that unique capability of charging up everyone with whom he comes in contact to his own fever pitch of enthusiasm. He got three presidents in a row (Nixon, Ford, and Carter) to commemorate the July 1969 moon landing with a National Space Week, and he is forever stumping the country to infuse high-school audiences with his own fireball attitude. But perhaps the best example of his take-the-bit-in-the-teeth-and-run approach to promoting space is his "Project Enterprise" (a name I am particularly fond of) to promote the use of shuttle payloads for student experiments.

Gil's Project Enterprise was born the day John Yardley announced the availability of the Getaway Special at the 1976 International Astronautical Congress in Anaheim, California. Gil promptly whipped out his checkbook and presented Yardley with NASA's first $500 down payment. But once Moore and his wife and kids worked out what they wanted to fly (he won't tell me what it is—"You'll find out soon enough," he said), he realized he'd need only half of the five cubic feet he'd bought, so he donated the other half to Utah State University for use by some of its graduate students. Utah State officials were delighted by Gil's gift, and promptly set up an extensive program for implementing and expanding shuttle space experiments. Gil's 1980 shuttle "ticket" was followed up immediately by Rex Megill, a physics professor at Utah State, and then by thirty other faculty members, reserving Getaway Special space in 1981 and 1982 respectively. Moore then went to his local AIAA section, and in typical Moore style, he made the pitch to them at 8 P.M. one evening and had raised the whole $500 by 8:30 the next morning.

The program mushroomed under Gil's energetic prodding. By July 1978, less than two years after he'd plumped down his first check, forty-seven payloads had been purchased for universities (and even some high schools and junior highs) all over the nation. The list continues to grow daily. And these educational payloads are only a small fraction of the landslide Moore started. Also by July 1978, NASA had over 250 deposits of "earnest money," from industry, foreign interests, and individuals. The names on the list raise some interesting conjectures; they include people like Steven Spielberg and Michael Phillips (of *Close Encounters of the Third Kind* fame), who, like Gil Moore, won't disclose what they plan to do with their shuttle payload. But the list also boasts some outfits that don't spend money unless they expect to see some return: Johnson & Johnson, Dow Chemical, General Electric, Ford Motor Company, McDonnell Douglas, General Dynamics, Coor's Beer, International Harvester, GTE Sylvania, and Bethlehem Steel.

And Gil Moore thinks the surface has barely been scratched. He is quick to point out (in classic Moore language), "the absolutely gold-plated, diamond-studded opportunity the shuttle programs hand to you and me to revitalize science and engineering education in this country." He never forgot the time when, as an engineering student at New Mexico A&M College in 1947, he was assigned by the Naval Research Laboratory to prepare and install X-ray densitometers on the tail fins of a V-2.

"Wow! The thrill of seeing 'my' bird go roaring into space has never faded," he said. "I can still see in my mind's eye those faint images on my film cassette that came from the rocket's brief flight above the atmosphere!"

"Now," he continued, "we old hands in the rocket business spend a lot of our time moaning to each other that the public doesn't care about space anymore, and that no bright, fresh, sparkly kids are coming up through the educational system to pick up our heavy burdens as we totter off into the sunset. Well, here's our chance. We can turn it around right now!"

And turn it around is just what NASA is doing. The agency was flooded with over 350 proposals for life-sciences experiments on the first two Spacelabs dedicated to that purpose. OMB in 1977 had virtually killed all biology research funds; now NASA found itself able to waggle its sheaf of proposals under OMB's haughty nose to demonstrate the high level of national interest in this field alone. Courses were offered all over the United States; typical was UCLA's one-week "Space Experiments Workshop," coordinated by someone named Hap Hazard—hopefully not an indication of the workshop's content!

Meanwhile, Mike Smith went out and hired a consumer-product consultant organization (a euphemism for an industrial public-relations firm) to help beef up his "space sales" efforts. George J. Abrams and Company had impressive credentials for identifying new business prospects, as recited in Abrams' book, *How I Made a Million with Ideas.* Abrams had developed Richard Hudnut's suntan lotion from an industrial soap used to remove grease stains from Texas oil drillers' hands. When the soap combined with the oil, it left nearly permanent stains. Ergo, a suntan lotion! Abrams was adept at turning problems like that into solutions. He invented Toll House cookies when the Snickers candy line at Nabisco was experiencing excessive drippings

Success of the U.S. space shuttle will depend on the demand for payloads to be launched. R. Gilbert Moore purchased the first space on a shuttle for a Getaway Special—a small self-contained payload. Hundreds of others have followed suit—including science-fiction movie producer Steven Spielberg. Photograph courtesy of *Astronautics and Aeronautics.*

and droppings. Instead of collecting and reboiling them, Abrams told Nabisco to throw them into the nearby cookie line.

Smith and Abrams came up with a number of new approaches previously abhorrent to the conservative federal hierarchy. As long as the prospective payload customers satisfied NASA's stringent safety and "acceptability" criteria, Smith took their money. "Suppose this famous glassblower comes to me and says he would like to go up there in orbit and blow a piece of glass that will be of high value. Six months ago I'd have said, 'No way!' But now I say, 'Wait a minute. That's a community I don't know anything about—the art community.' If what he does would impact the public, in the sense that a

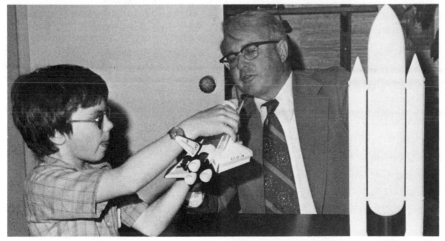

All potential space customers are important. Here NASA deputy administrator Alan Lovelace explains some shuttle fine points to one of those future customers, Joe Hall, Jr., from Plumtree, North Carolina (April 22, 1977).

museum does, maybe it's all right. You sure can blow different kinds of glass in orbit than you can on the ground."

Lee organized the shuttle operations like an airline. In fact, he used American Airlines' organizational chart as a model for a businesslike operation, including, for example, opportunities for reduced rates via charter flights. NASA was, of course, immediately criticized for exceeding its legislated bounds—the National Space Act of 1958 specifically defined NASA's role as being limited to research and development. But for once the agency was at least one jump ahead of its critics: it had already evaluated the prospects for turning shuttle operations over to private contractors as soon as they became routine. Yardley was able to trot out an extensive study by Booz, Allen and Hamilton (performed with the help of knowledgeable space subcontractors Rockwell International, McDonnell Douglas, and General Electric), recommending a private-industry take-over of shuttle operations in 1982. And Boeing is at this time examining very actively the prospects for actually owning and operating the shuttle system as a profit-making enterprise.

But in the middle of all this euphoria one old dragon kept rearing its ugly head. Way back in 1971, the "deal" James Fletcher had made with OMB and Congress on the shuttle compromise had excluded the development of a high-performance reusable space tug to cart payloads between the shuttle's low earth orbit and the higher-energy orbits, particularly the geostationary orbit, required by many customers' payloads. NASA had had its back rammed right up against the wall by OMB, and there'd been no way to include both the shuttle (even the compromise design evolved by Mathematica) *and* the tug. Following its now-classic pattern of leaving the consequences to the future—to be resolved in some as yet undetermined manner— NASA had given up the tug.

Space-wise engineers like Pres Layton and Burt Edelson had railed at so obviously shortsighted a decision, but to no avail. According to applications-oriented Edelson, "The guys who made the shuttle decisions were rocket enthusiasts—they just *assumed* they'd find plenty of use for the shuttle once it was developed. I kept screaming that by far the major need in the future would be to put payloads into the geostationary orbit, but nobody paid any attention."

And sure enough, when Chet Lee and Mike Smith were selling their shuttle space, their biggest stumbling block was the lack of a

good tug. Their best customers—the communications industry—
wanted to go up to geostationary orbit, just as Edelson had foreseen.
Further, the vaunted capability of the shuttle to repair and retrieve
payloads didn't make any sense at all without a tug that could either
go to geosynchronous orbit and *bring back* a satellite or take a man
up there to do the repairs. No such tug was available, or even under
development. True, NASA had finally prevailed upon the Air Force
to develop a halfhearted substitute—an expendable and not very cost-
effective device first (and properly) called the "interim upper stage"
(IUS). Then, when NASA clearly was not developing the high-performance tug as originally intended, the by then well-known acronym
IUS was lamely changed to "inertial upper stage."

But the IUS was developed by and for the Air Force, to be used
both with the shuttle and with the Air Force's standard Titan-III
expendable launcher. As such, it was overly expensive and not at all
optimized for most civil payload missions that had to go beyond low
earth orbit. For example, one future NASA scientific mission to Mars
(unmanned, of course), requires *four* IUS's, or two shuttle launches
and an extremely complex (and therefore not too reliable) series-
parallel automatic deployment to obtain the necessary launch performance. As one potentially big industrial shuttle customer put it,
"Everybody in the business has been desperately trying to get any
kind of information [on the IUS]. What does it look like? What will
it do? What are the stages? The Air Force is very careful about what
it says, but we get nothing. . . . The Air Force people have a wall
in front of them. The IUS is an essential part of [NASA's] system,
but how do you expect me to use the system when I don't have any
idea what it is?"

Recognizing the limitations of the IUS and that the Air Force, despite its protestations of support for the shuttle program, really didn't
care too much about civilian applications for its substitute tug, NASA
sought a viable alternative. Without any budget flexibility available,
and with the lid on development clamped down on them by the
original shuttle legislation, it was like trying to play in the big leagues
without a bat. By dint of much pushing, shoving, cajoling, and possible threatening, NASA finally convinced an aerospace company to
use its own funds to develop and manufacture small, simple, expendable upper stages that could be used to deliver *most* of the civil
payloads to geostationary orbit. The company hoped to recoup its

A space tug is needed to shift satellites from the shuttle's low earth orbit (around 200 miles) up to the geostationary orbit 22,300 miles up. Here is the first interim tug, called the Inertial Upper Stage (the ribbed structure marked U.S.A. with its black nozzle attached). Two tugs are shown with their payloads attached; one has already been released, the second is about to be ejected from the shuttle orbiter. Illustration courtesy of Boeing Aerospace Company.

investment by selling the stages to NASA customers who needed the extra boost. But these solid-propellant rocket stages, so simple they were spin-stabilized like the United States's very first primitive 1958 Explorer 1 satellite, had no excess capability at all, and certainly no retrieval, repair, or even orbit-adjustment capability. They were, in fact, called SSUS-A and SSUS-D—spinning solid upper stage–Atlas and spinning solid upper stage–Delta—because even with the shuttle to boost them into low orbit, they could just about match the geostationary orbit delivery performance of the old expendable Atlas and Delta launch vehicles! It was like using a nuclear aircraft carrier to launch a Piper cub airplane. According to Edelson (who represented one of NASA's principal present *and* future customers), "NASA took a terrible risk by placing all its geostationary orbit business in the hands of so poorly thought out orbit-transfer vehicles as IUS, SSUS-A, and SSUS-D. If anything keeps the shuttle from being a commercial success, it will be the lack of a good tug."

The Europeans, who had gone ahead with the development of their new (but still expendable) Ariane launcher, were delighted. The vaunted U.S. shuttle, whose low-earth-orbit capabilities overshadowed Ariane's like an elephant does a mouse, was so limited by its lack of a good upper-stage complement that it was scarcely better than Ariane for the all-important geostationary-orbit emplacements. That lack, in effect, put the U.S. Mack truck in the same performance and price range as the Ariane Volkswagen for delivering payloads to geostationary orbit—opening up a serious (and wholly unnecessary, with a good tug) competition for many non-U.S. payloads.

Pres Layton, of course, had predicted this unfortunate outcome many years earlier, as had Edelson and the entire committee that produced the 1972-73 AIAA assessment. Del Tischler had suggested, in an extensive article in 1975 in the AIAA's *Astronautics and Aeronautics* magazine, a sound, phased approach to tug development, starting with a simple but well-designed solid-propellant rocket stage and then proceeding to an advanced hydrogen-oxygen stage in the early 1980s, when retrieval from geostationary orbit would be needed. NASA was finally persuaded—although still without OMB or congressional approval—to undertake at the very least a "requirements and definition study of advanced (including manned) orbit transfer vehicles." Such a study was started in 1978, but there was very little chance of getting an advanced tug into operation much before 1985, even assuming the necessary budget approvals were obtained. By then NASA was expected to be flying at least sixty shuttles per year. But, shackled by the shuttle's limited upper-stage capability, Chet Lee's and Mike Smith's hard-sell efforts for the mid-1980s and beyond seemed doomed to failure.

That view, however, was founded on the shortsighted precept that shuttle business could come only from space missions already conceived and designed. In the late 1970s Edelson, Layton, Heiss, and two visionary engineers from Aerospace Corporation named Ivan Bekey and Harris Mayer, were all busy analyzing potential systems that went much, much further in utilizing the enormous potential offered by the environment of space.

The bud was finally starting to bloom.

CHAPTER

6

THE PROJECTION

"We can fix anything!"

—Charles "Pete" Conrad, Jr., Skylab 1 Commander
May 25, 1973
(Just after being launched to
rendezvous with disabled Skylab)

"Fastening things together in space is easy—but they'll have to invent a more comfortable suit to wear."

—Charles "Pete" Conrad, Jr.
January 1976

PETE CONRAD EXPRESSED RATHER SUCCINCTLY THE SENSE OF THE United States space program as it changed in the decade of the 1970s. The unbridled optimism following the shuttle go-ahead and the sparkling success of Skylab (an embryo space station) gradually slowed to a cautious, "Sure it's good for the nation, but let's be *very* careful and not spend too much money." The result was veritable doldrums of indecision, most notably after President Jimmy Carter took over the reins of government in 1977. "Visible applications" became the theme: "What's good for the man and woman in the street right now is what we're going to do." In other words, near-term patching, instead of forging a solid basic structure for long-term benefit. The same philosophy that led that United States to the brink of international bankruptcy as a result of President Carter's energy policy also brought the budding, effervescent, space enterprise down to a plodding walk.

There was certainly no lack of ideas. As in the past, new communications concepts led the pack, but following close behind were vastly promising applications of remote sensing and a host of new prospects for the elusive "pot o' gold" offered by the space environment, of which perhaps the most fascinating was the idea of enormous satellite solar power plants collecting solar energy in space and beaming it down to the earth for terrestrial use. Many of these seemingly far-out ideas were soundly based on current technological knowledge, and although they needed considerable engineering effort to "work out the kinks," they could realistically be projected for first operational use within a decade or two—provided the necessary advocacy and financing could be generated. So again, there were two facets to the near-term projection of U.S. space endeavors: technical (and to a large degree, economic) realism on the one hand and, on the other, the ever-shifting sands of the political arena, with its infighting and its often obscure (but powerful) motivations.

Before adversary positions can be taken, though, it's necessary to establish what the fighting is all about. NASA's Advanced Programs directorate was charged with the responsibility for formulating possible space futures for the nation; unfortunately, its placement within the Office of Manned Space Flight tended to make its suggestions rather suspect to those people (like Proxmire) who kept seeing manned-Mars-flight conspiracies in every program NASA dreamed up. The subsequent name changes to Office of Space Flight and then to Office of Space Transportation Systems did little to whitewash Advanced Programs planning documents, and their budget became a perennial football in the yearly Congress-NASA-OMB approval exercise.

But there were ardent (and erudite) proponents of rational advancements in space technology *outside* NASA, and their influence began to grow rapidly in the late 1970s as Congress became more and more disenchanted with the President's lackluster space program. Despite the shackles placed on NASA by an overcautious administration, the proper directions for advanced space planning slowly began to take shape.

The key piece in the jigsaw puzzle of what to do next in space was identified by Burt Edelson. He tied it to his own field, communications, but the general principle applied to all space applications. As a self-characterized practical engineer, Edelson had recognized very early that satellite communictaions were very different from either cable or overland microwave communications. The satellite was in effect a nerve center, which could be utilized to service an almost limitless array of customers spread over the entire planet—provided the satellite could be made large enough, sophisticated enough, and powerful enough to do the job asked of it. This reasoning allowed Edelson to zero right in on the correct approach: to put the bulk of new technology and financial investment into the satellite—and make the earth stations (receivers and transmitters) as small, cheap, and simple as possible.

Because satellites in the 1970s were limited by expendable-launcher capabilities (and also because the new space-communications industry was still flexing its muscles and wasn't quite ready to plunge into any major expansion in satellite costs), Edelson first turned his attention to earth stations. The first Intelsat stations needed hundred-foot antennas; COMSAT was able to reduce them to fifteen feet. Twenty people had been needed to run them; Edelson's lab developed stations that could operate automatically—unmanned. The early stations needed to be out in the boondocks, away from potential sources of interference; by 1977 earth stations were being mounted on customers' roofs or in their parking lots. And, most important, the new stations cost less than fifty thousand dollars, compared with over five million dollars for the early ones.

All this was accomplished with little or no improvement in satellite capability at all. And that's where the *real* progress will be made in the 1980s. The improvements made in earth stations so far have been a mere drop in the bucket compared to what can be accomplished with *really* advanced satellite systems (but still with no brand-new technology—just what we already know will work).

Edelson's approach to in-space satellite development led him and his lab colleague, Walter Morgan, to the concept of the orbital antenna farm, which is just what it sounds like: a "farm" of many different antennas, each designed for a different task. Located in the geostationary orbit and with enough on-board power (either solar or nuclear) to handle the necessary communications loads, Edelson envisions these complex satellites as operating totally by digital electronics, which has made possible the current explosion in ground-based data processing and computerized operations. "True switchboards in the sky," he calls them.

Up to this writing satellite communications have been used for

One of the large expensive communications ground stations that can be replaced by smaller, less-complex terminals using Edelson's approach. Photograph courtesy of Philco-Ford Corporation.

Applications Technology Satellite (ATS)-6. The experimental forerunner of the "complex space terminal, simple earth terminal" principle.

point-to-point voice transmission (telephone and radio), image transmission (facsimile and television), and, of course, data transmission of various kinds. Edelson sees orbital antenna farms as able to augment these services mightily, but also to expand to service ships, airplanes, and automotive vehicles (for both navigation and communications), broadcast systems, data collection, disaster warnings, space tracking, business networks, educational TV, citizens'-band transmissions, and on and on—*all* able to be handled by a single satellite having multiple antennas.

Edelson's orbital antenna farm is likely to be the first of the new breed of advanced satellites to be spawned during the shuttle era of

The ATS-6 satellite provided educational television coverage to five thousand towns and villages throughout India in a massive one-year experiment in 1976. This photo shows a typical simple antenna installation in Rajasthan.

the 1980s. But perhaps even more important is his basic premise: putting the sophisticated hardware into space instead of on the ground. This premise was picked up and run with, perhaps even more spectacularly than practical, conservative communications engineer Burt Edelson would have liked, by the imaginative engineer/scientist team of Ivan Bekey and Harris Mayer.

Bekey and Mayer's ideas were anticipated by a broad but intensive NASA exercise termed the "Outlook for Space," commissioned in 1975 "to identify and examine the various possibilities for the civil space program over the next twenty-five years." The final report of the study presented "no *new* ideas about what might be done in space. . . . What we have done is to identify some of those possibilities which are within reach over the next twenty-five years."

The Aerospace Corporation was asked by NASA's Advanced Programs directorate to take its "shopping list" of possibilities and at-

Walter Morgan (left) and Burt Edelson discuss their orbital antenna farm—a direct consequence of Edelson's basic concept of putting sophisticated equipment into space to reduce the costs of earth terminals. Photograph courtesy of *Astronautics and Aeronautics.*

tempt to synthesize space-system concepts that might realize some of the opportunities (within the twenty-five-year time frame) and also to define their common needs for transportation and other space facilities.

The response was truly spectacular. I could devote an entire book to describing the concepts Bekey and Mayer came up with. All were based on the Edelson/Morgan principle of putting the bulk of the sophisticated equipment at the "nerve center"—in orbit—and making the earth-station equipment as small and cheap as possible. And, according to Bekey and Mayer, "The concepts represent reasonable extrapolations of today's technology and operate on known principles —they are not science fiction or mere wishes."

Perhaps the most impressive of the Bekey/Mayer concepts was the modern counterpart of the Dick Tracy wrist radio used so effectively

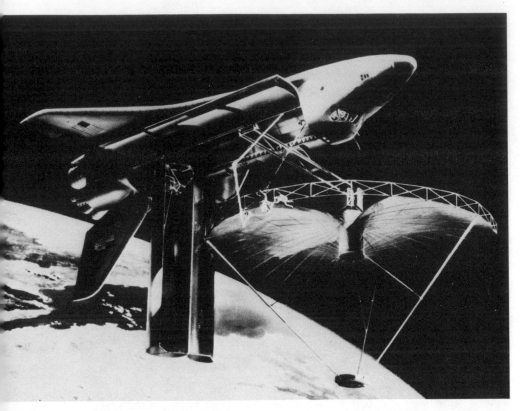

The first step in expanding space capabilities: an experimental large antenna being assembled in space by astronauts working out of the space shuttle.

by the comic-strip hero several decades ago. But the "Personal Communication System," as Bekey and Mayer called it, would not be just for elite crime fighters and the like. A thousand focused transmitting beams from the satellite could cover the entire United States; with roughly 100,000 wrist-radiophone wearers in each beam area, the system could service 100 million customers. As Martin Newman of the AIAA put it:

> It's 1992. You're sunning yourself at Jones Beach in New York, when you suddenly remember that it's your mother's birthday— and she's back home in San Francisco. Since you're never without your trusty ten-dollar wrist radiophone, you sit up, raise your arm, and speak her number into the transmitter. Mother, in turn —who never leaves home without *her* wrist radiophone—happens to be in a shop at Fisherman's Wharf when she hears your beep. She's delighted that you remembered, and the two of you chat

Ivan Bekey (right) and Harris Mayer developed a whole gamut of almost incredible but technically feasible space application concepts using the basic Edelson principle of putting the complex hardware in space instead of on the ground. Photograph courtesy of *Astronautics and Aeronautics*.

happily for five or six minutes on your own private line. Later on, at the end of the month when your telephone bill arrives, among the items listed is sixty cents for that particular call. Plus tax.

And that's just the tip of the iceberg. The same wristwratch-sized "earth terminal" could provide its wearer with not only his own personal portable-telephone system, but also a voting and polling booth, a search-and-rescue beacon (should he become lost in the dark woods, in his small sailboat, or in a big city), a personal emergency "panic button," a self-locator (for use when traveling in unfamiliar territory), a compass, a speedometer, a medical monitor (to detect extreme changes in blood pressure, pulse rate, etc.), a civil-defense alarm— and, of course, a very, very accurate wristwatch.

The wrist radio capable of all this magic doesn't have to be at all expensive. Using current microcircuit "chip" technology, Bekey and Mayer believe that it should cost no more than today's simple walkie-

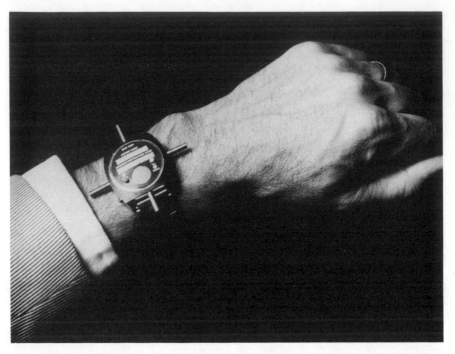

Dick Tracy's wrist radio—a direct (and realizable) application of the sophisticated multi-spot-beam communications satellite. This single inexpensive device can serve as a personal communicator (to anyone in the world!), a personal locator beacon, a universal "instant voting" machine, and even a very, very accurate wristwatch!

talkies, which, although not miniaturized to the degree possible, sold for $8.95 when Bekey and Mayer completed their study in 1976.

But the satellites! The combination of functions listed above would require at least two of them. One would be an advanced communications satellite having a single large (200-foot) antenna capable of generating hundreds of signal beams, one for each city or toll center. The other would be an enormous cross, each leg of which might be a mile long and perhaps ten feet wide. One leg would scan the earth beneath it from north to south; the other from east to west, pinpointing any earth terminal location to within 300 feet.

Bekey and Mayer are somewhat optimistic on the cost and power requirements of their satellites—$300 million for one and only $100 million for the other, with electrical power needs of only twenty-one and two kilowatts respectively. Both could be shuttle-launched, although they would need advanced tugs to get them to the geostationary orbit and to service them. Their inventors, after a rather elaborate preliminary design calling out specific subsystem and component details, considered such prospects as "low- to medium-risk" enterprises.

A quick calculation shows that the wrist-radio communication function alone (that is, just the personal telephone), at ten cents per minute, could generate about $600 million per year in revenues, and virtually the entire operating cost is a write-off of the initial investment. So, one is immediately tempted to ask, why aren't wrist radios on the market yet?

Burt Edelson and other knowledgeable communications-system engineers are quick to draw a fine line between what Bekey and Mayer propose and what we now have operating in the sky. According to Edelson, "Bekey and Mayer tell us what's *possible*; I work only on what's *practical*. Eliminating cross talk and noise from a hundred million cheap twenty-five-milliwatt terminals all talking through the same satellite switchboard may be possible, but I don't believe it's anywhere near practical." Edelson is also concerned that enormously attractive but possibly impractical ideas like Bekey and Mayer's might tend to detract from the expeditious development of such wholly practical new concepts as the orbital antenna farm. Pres Layton, although he strongly supports the kind of innovative "conceptualizing" advanced by Bekey and Mayer, just doesn't believe they gave anywhere near enough thought to the multitude of engineering considerations in such prosaic but essential elements as transportation to geosynchronous orbit or on-board electric power systems.

But regardless of its shortcomings, the Bekey/Mayer "wish list," even if only potentially realizable, served to open up to public view the myriad of opportunities made possible by the "routine" and convenient access to space which is symbolized by the new shuttle. The entire list, as I've pointed out, is far too extensive to recount here, but a few examples can illustrate the almost incredible potential. And remember, these mind-searing concepts may require extensive attention to engineering details (which could make them economically nonviable), but they involve only well-known technology and, in nearly every case, utilize existing or at least already-developed components. No *Star Wars* gobbledygook here!

The wrist radiophone itself has many special-purpose features besides that of a "personal communicator." The use of short digital messages would permit polling of millions of people on major government issues, which in turn could provide the capability for instant public decisions for the first time in history. Bekey and Mayer's system can garner (and record) the opinions of a hundred *million* people in an hour. Relatively small groups of key people (for example, the world's two hundred or so heads of state) can have their own "hot-line" network for closed-circuit jam-resistant communiqués. The value to police departments and military commanders is obvious. The same wrist radiophone can also serve as the "earth station" for a personal navigator, health monitor, and the other functions I've already noted.

The personal navigation system capability also implies other valuable applications. Once the big crossed-antenna satellite is in orbit, cheap wristwatch-sized earth stations can be attached to important packages, luggage, or vehicles in order to track their locations continuously. No more lost parcels or suitcases—you may not have them, but you'll always know exactly where they are! Auto rental companies and railroad dispatchers will always know where their cars are. Bekey and Mayer say their preliminary design could locate a billion packages per hour within 200 feet in all kinds of weather twenty-four hours a day.

An expanded application of this idea could conceivably eliminate one of the main public concerns with the widespread use of nuclear power: misuse or pirating of nuclear fuels by terrorists or political extremists. Fuel-rod assemblies could be tagged with a small transmitter on manufacture and tracked from space throughout their lifetimes. Problems of signal penetration through shipping-cask shields and nuclear fuel-storage containers will be troublesome, but appear tractable. The transmitters can easily be designed to self-destruct upon being tampered with or removed from their fuel-assembly "mother," instantaneously revealing any hijacker's attempt to fool the system.

Similar systems having the same basic technology can be used to prevent maritime collisions, not just between large ships equipped with elaborate navigation equipment, but between small pleasure boats (even rowboats) and between boats and reefs or other large objects. A universal international air-traffic control system "falls out" of the same kind of technology.

Effective border surveillance could also become economically practical. Millions of tiny "intrusion-detection" sensors—microphones with self-contained transmitters—could be scattered in rows along borders.

Easily disguised as small stones, these sensors would signal their satellite monitor when activated by footsteps or tire sounds. The same idea is readily adaptable to undetectable citywide burglar-alarm systems.

Perhaps the most fascinating of the possibilities offered by Bekey and Mayer is three-dimensional image transmission. "Holography" is a well-known technology that uses laser light to project three-dimensional images into a room just as ordinary light projects two-dimensional images (movies) onto a screen. You can walk all around a hologram—it *looks* real—but you can also walk right through it—because it isn't.

Bekey and Mayer came up with a satellite-system concept that transmits holograms. Why not? Holographic sculptures and mobiles arc fairly common in many art museums and galleries today. But long-distance holography can be much more than a new and exciting art form; it could, in fact, literally change the way we live. I quote Martin Newman again:

> Picture a world of commerce in 1990 where teleholography, to coin a clumsy word, is commonplace. The head of a large Chicago-based marketing organization is about to call a routine meeting. He is considering adding a new piece of equipment to the line, and it's now time to sit down with his five regional sales managers, look at the sample, discuss its possibilities, and make a decision. No more bucking the traffic to the airport. No more flights from New York/Atlanta/Phoenix/Seattle to Chicago. Nor hotel rooms, nor expense accounts. Instead, each sales manager goes into the holography-equipped conference room at the office, turns on the equipment, and suddenly, via satellite, the room is filled—or seems filled. They're all together, in five cities at the same time—one flesh-and-blood person and the rest holograph people, talking, walking, looking over each other's shoulders, and examining the new sample. And occasionally, in a shortcut across the room, walking through each other.

But don't run out and buy stock in the company yet. Not only are Edelson's concerns about practicality still to be satisfied, but what about the economic disruptions to airlines, hotels, restaurants? Nevertheless, it's extremely significant to know that such prospects exist and, moreover, are technologically feasible. Bekey and Mayer (and many communications systems engineers) continue to refine their ideas and test them wherever possible, because the advent of the shuttle in the

1980s could transform many such "blue-sky" opportunities into practical, useful, and *marketable* service systems.

Although Bekey and Mayer point the way to what will almost certainly happen in space in one form or another during the next quarter century, there are other opportunities that can be realized in the 1980s —opportunities perhaps just as far-reaching in their sociological implications (although not in their technology) as teleholography. These prospects involve combining the two most successful space-technology applications: communications and remote sensing. The most interesting of these is what is often called a "global resource information system," and its champion is, of all unlikely professionals, the economist Klaus Heiss.

From his earliest association with space activities, Heiss held the conviction that the gathering and efficient dissemination of information was the second most valuable utilization of space after communications. When he left Mathematica in 1973 after completing the shuttle economic study, a long talk with NASA administrator James Fletcher had convinced him that the rational economic projection of benefit/cost trade-offs in space activities was sorely needed in the new "hard-look" environment of federal "budgeteering." Instead of taking a high-paying job with the Morgan bank (which Morgenstern had set him up for), he decided to go out on his own, and formed the econometric analysis firm ECON, Inc. Among ECON's first jobs were NASA contracts to project the costs and benefits associated with Landsat and Seasat and their potential descendants.

The matching of the wholly new field of "space economics" to the hoary economic profession was truly a golden marriage. Although he had been initiated into the unique characteristics of space operations through the shuttle study, Heiss had been skillfully guided by Oskar Morgenstern, one of the best and most forward-thinking of the "old pros" in the business. Compared to classical economists Klaus Heiss was still very wet behind the ears. One of his favorite stories in that regard was the time he and Morgenstern were traveling by train from Princeton to Washington to present their first formal report to NASA. Morgenstern looked at Heiss, who was still wearing the same suit he had come from Vienna in five years earlier, and said, "You can't make a presentation to NASA in that suit. I will buy you a new one." And, sure enough, on their way from Washington's Union Station to NASA, they stopped off and outfitted Heiss in a manner commensurate with his status as a learned economist advising NASA on how to spend some billions of dollars.

As soon as he and his ECON colleagues began to dig into the details of the Landsat system and its capabilities, they realized its enormous potential. In 1974 the United States had contracted to sell a large portion of its wheat crop to the Soviet Union at what first appeared to be a favorable price, based in good part on projections of both Soviet and U.S. crop yields later in the year. Those crop projections turned out to be way off—it was an extremely bad year for wheat —so the United States ended up delivering millions of tons of wheat to the U.S.S.R. at a price considerably below the world market. Nobody has yet admitted how much that infamous deal cost us; it was certainly well into the billions of dollars. But the important point is that Landsat data could have provided an accurate forecast of that wheat crop, not only in the United States, but also in the U.S.S.R. and the rest of the world. That knowledge was not available at the time, even though Landsat was in the sky, because nobody was analyzing Landsat images for those data; we didn't yet know the true value of large-area crop inventorying. If we had, though, the United States could have set a proper price, based on sound and incontrovertible crop information, and saved those billions of dollars. The savings on that one transaction alone would have paid the total cost of the entire Landsat and Seasat programs, with a billion or so left over.

ECON's analyses pointed to many similiar economic benefits, not just in wheat crop forecasting, but in other agricultural products, mineral and ocean resources, and all the myriad Landsat and Seasat capabilities detailed in Chapter Five. One experiment performed to evaluate such resource-predicting capabilities was the large-area crop inventory experiment (LACIE), which was restricted solely to wheat (too late to help the United States in the Soviet grain deal, though). It turned out to be marginally successful, mainly because of limitations of the experimental Landsat data-analysis capabilities.

So Klaus Heiss began campaigning for a global information system, based on the deployment of an *operational* earth-observation network in combination with dedicated global communications, all using satellites. The technology (and, in fact, even the hardware) was "old hat"; all that was needed was to set up the system, finance it, and operate it —not as a government "charity," but as a good old-fashioned economic profit-making enterprise like Intelsat.

Heiss was still a young man at this time (he had received his doctorate in Vienna at the tender age of twenty-two, but he was incredibly energetic and dedicated. One time during the shuttle economic analysis, when he was zeroing in on what later turned out to be the final shuttle compromise, he *had* to discuss its details with John Yardley (then shuttle study project director for McDonnell Douglas in St. Louis), who had done a rough preliminary design on that very configuration. But Yardley could give him only one day out of an unusually crowded schedule. Heiss left Princeton in time, but misjudged the traffic on the New Jersey Turnpike and missed his evening flight from Philadelphia. The next flight for St. Louis didn't leave until midmorning, so Heiss jumped back into his car and headed west. By 4 A.M. he had only reached Cleveland. Realizing he couldn't make it to St. Louis in time, he stopped at Cleveland's Hopkins Airport and was fortunate in being able to book himself on a 6 A.M. flight to St. Louis. He grabbed an hour's sleep at a nearby motel (the proprietor was startled by his 5:30 A.M. wake-up call, left at 4:30 A.M.!), left his car in Cleveland, and made the meeting with Yardley—which later turned out to be the focal point of the entire shuttle-program decision.

So when Klaus Heiss got his teeth into an idea he really dug in. He testified before congressional committees; he met with sacrosanct OMB staffers; he made statements to the Republican and Democratic national committees when they were drawing up their platforms for the 1976 election; and he made as much noise as possible in international forums like the U.N., the IAF, and the various international financial institutions. One of his most effective arguments for the global-information-system concept appeared in a joint paper he and I prepared on behalf of the AIAA for the 1979 U.N. Conference on Science and Technology for Development.

His main suggestions were that full access to all information be made available to any nation that wanted it (a point hotly debated in the U.N. and elsewhere), and that developing nations be granted access to the system for incremental cost only; that is, the cost of setting up only their own data-processing system (including whatever satellite modifications were required). They would not have to kick in a share of the original investment needed to set up the system in the first place.

All Heiss's arguments, of course, were predicated on the institutionalization of an *operational* rather than an experimental system. The

United States debate on this subject continued to rage into 1979, and despite its obvious benefits, President Carter's ineffectual and indecisive space policy, like his overseas nuclear-proliferation policy, never came to grips with this crucially important application of space technology. This indecisiveness on the part of the administration, and its unwillingness to move boldly to take full advantage of the developing space technologies, were epitomized by President Carter's bland space policy message of October 11, 1978. Reminiscent of the administration's vacillations just after Sputnik 1 was launched in 1957, it finally prompted Chairman Adlai Stevenson of the Senate's Subcommittee on Science, Space, and Technology to submit the Space Policy Act of 1978, a bill aimed specifically at developing the enormous potential of space enterprise launched twenty years earlier by the National Space Act of 1958. Quoting liberally from Klaus Heiss's economic projections for global information systems, Stevenson prodded the limp Carter administration: "Efforts to plan the Nation's future in space lack . . . foresight and imagination. . . . In recent years, the planning process has been little more than annual encounters between Congress and the OMB. . . . As a consequence, U.S. leadership in space has begun to erode. Morale in the space program has declined. And the public is understandably confused over the reasons to sustain a U.S. presence in space."

Stevenson's bill listed a host of specific but ambitious goals for the next decade. But perhaps even more important, he later submitted, with Senator Wendell Ford, another bill to create an operational remote-sensing satellite system. With the momentum that Klaus Heiss had helped to build up, the military/political/economic impasse that had been in place since 1972 appeared susceptible to breaching, and there finally seemed to be a fair chance of realizing the incredible potential of that vantage point in space.

Similar views on the use of space were held by former astronaut Russell "Rusty" Schweickart, who directed NASA's Office of User Affairs in the mid-1970s. His job there was to serve as the conduit between NASA and the outside world to accelerate the use of space technology, principally the remote-sensing opportunities. But after two years of all-too-slow progress, he was chomping at the bit. Rusty was totally dedicated to space, and was impatient with the snaillike pace at which things were happening.

Although by nature a thinker, he was also a doer. He had left the astronaut corps because he thought he could be more effective in promoting space utilization from NASA headquarters. I remember my first meeting with him, at the 1974 International Astronautical Congress in Amsterdam. Florence and I had just arrived in town and found ourselves in a hotel way out in the boondocks. It was late, we were hungry, and the only open restaurants were in the center of the city. Another U.S. delegate to the Congress was in similar straits— a tall, gangling, reddish-haired young man with a beautiful flowing moustache to match. We introduced ourselves—it was Rusty.

We tried to call a taxi, but none was available. The concierge gave us directions to the nearest city bus, a few blocks away. It was raining hard, but we *were* hungry, so we buttoned up our raincoats and began walking. About a block from the bus stop, we saw the bus approaching, but we still had a long way to go. "Not a chance," I groaned. "And it's a half hour till the next one!" Rusty was, though, a doer. He was off like a shot, his long legs eating up the distance, racing the bus to the corner. When Florence and I finally puffed up, he was cheerfully holding the door and asking the driver for pointers on restaurants. "I wasn't *about* to get a half hour hungrier and wetter," he said.

The same impatience drove him from the slow-moving NASA headquarters to the heady job as space adviser to California Governor Jerry Brown. Brown was at that time (1977) promoting a satellite-communications system for the state, and had set aside $5 million toward that end. Rusty saw in this program a real opportunity to demonstrate the value of space to state- and local-government users; Brown's political and personal charisma provided an ideal vehicle for national visibility. With Rusty's help, Brown turned the occasion of the 1977 space-shuttle flight-testing into a major political statement, and there was much talk of his riding the "space horse" into the White House in 1980. But then came Proposition 13, and the California communications satellite was one of its victims. Rusty is still at it, though, and, like Klaus Heiss, he knows where the future is.

But there was one technical element in all these wonderful projections for utilizing the nation's new shuttle-based capabilities that, like the weather, everybody talked about but few people tried to do anything about. All space missions require on-board electric power, and the most interesting of the missions projected for the future needed lots of it—far more than the satellite power systems available in 1980 could provide.

Some of us had forecasted that need many years ago; for example, in the mid-1960s, I had written a number of articles in *Astronautics and Aeronautics*, decrying the lack of a consistent national effort in good-sized space power systems. Meanwhile, of course, the use of photovoltaic (solar-cell) power had become routine for virtually all spacecraft. But their maximum long-term electric-power demand through the 1960s and 1970s was rarely more than a kilowatt, and usually considerably less. The only missions not well served by solar cells were scientific flights to the planets far from the sun (the Pioneer and Voyager flights to Jupiter, Saturn, and beyond), where the solar energy was inadequate; lunar or planetary exploration (the experiments left by the Apollo astronauts on the moon and the Viking spacecraft that landed on Mars in 1975 to search for extraterrestrial life), where the spacecraft was out of the sunlight for long periods; and short-term manned flights such as Apollo and the space shuttle, where the spacecraft's relatively fast maneuvering would have played havoc with the very large solar-cell arrays needed to supply the required high power levels. Chemical fuel cells were used for Apollo and the shuttle; they were compact and could provide the high power levels necessary (up to fifteen kilowatts), but because they consumed hydrogen and oxygen fairly rapidly, they were good for only a few weeks. For the Pioneer, Voyager, and Viking spacecraft, as well as for the Apollo Lunar Science Experiment Packages (ALSEP) left on the moon, power was provided by radioisotopes, whose radioactive decay generated enough heat to drive "thermoelectric converters" for a century or so. Thermoelectric converters are just high-power versions of the ordinary thermocouples used to control refrigerator and oven temperatures; they are based on the principle that when certain types of dissimilar materials in contact with each other are heated, they generate an electric voltage. In an oven that voltage is used to switch off the heating element when the temperature reaches the preset value; in the radioisotope thermoelectric generator (RTG) used in spacecraft, the voltage is used to drive communications transmitters and other on-board electrical devices. Because of the low power available from the radioisotopes, even if used with efficient gas-turbine converters, they are limited to only a few kilowatts.

But for Bekey and Mayer's wondrous gadgets, for space processing operations such as welding and melting metals, or for assembling and operating large multipurpose satellites like Edelson's and Morgan's orbital antenna farm, much higher power levels are required. NASA recognized this need, but because of budget constraints was able to pursue only what amounted to a "quick fix" to supplement the space shuttle's and Spacelab's minimal power available to customers' payloads (three kilowatts for twelve days). They were able to adapt a twenty-five-kilowatt solar array (originally designed for a different program) to be carried aloft by the shuttle, unfolded in space, and left in orbit as an "energy depot" to be tapped whenever Spacelab, for example, needed some extra power for a particular experiment.

But this twenty-five-kilowatt power module, parked as it was in orbit, would not be accessible to any spacecraft not in that particular orbit, so its usefulness was relatively limited. And although NASA projected expanding the twenty-five-kilowatt module simply by hooking a string of them together end-to-end to provide up to two hundred fifty kilowatts, the enormous size of the solar-cell arrays needed to generate that kind of power made them prohibitively unwieldy. The twenty-five-kilowatt array measures 13 feet by 230 feet (two "wings," each 13 feet by 115 feet); larger-size units would need to be continuously controlled to prevent distortion by such normally tiny forces as the pressure of *sunlight* or the difference in gravity between one end of the array and the other. Such enormous panels certainly couldn't be easily moved around in space, as would be necessary for many spacecraft missions.

So, long before NASA began preliminary design of its twenty-five-kilowatt solar space power module, farsighted engineers had been considering the use of small, compact nuclear reactors for space power. One such reactor was actually developed by the United States; called "Space Nuclear Auxiliary Power System No. 10A" (SNAP 10A), it made a successful test flight in 1964, and still remains safely shut down in a distant orbit high above the earth. The Soviets developed two nuclear-electric power systems for space, called Romaschka and Topaz. Romaschka used thermoelectric converters, as did SNAP 10A; Topaz used much more advanced, higher-efficiency thermionic converters to generate electric power. The Soviets used these reactors to power a number of their military satellites; it was, in fact, one of these that tumbled out of orbit over Canada and stirred up a major international ruckus in January 1978.

But when the United States was working on nuclear space reactors most intensively, in the 1960s, the only "market" for the high power levels that justified their use (some designs called for as much as 50 *megawatts*—50,000 kilowatts—of electric power) was in "electric propulsion," a high-performance method for propelling spacecraft on difficult interplanetary and orbit-transfer missions. So-called "electric rockets" utilize electric or electromagnetic forces to blast out electrically charged gas molecules called "ions" at extremely high speeds, thereby getting much higher thrust out of each pound of propellant (the gas molecules) than is possible with an ordinary "chemical" rocket engine. To get appreciable thrust from these electric rockets takes a lot of power; hence the interest in compact, powerful nuclear-electric generators.

But it takes literally thousands of pounds of power-plant mass to produce each pound of thrust this way, so although electric rockets can generally carry larger payloads on many types of deep-space missions than ordinary chemical rockets, it takes a long, long time for their tiny thrust to build up speed. This trade-off, thrust level versus propulsion efficiency, is typical of all space propulsion devices; it's a general rule that high thrust levels must be sacrificed for most efficient use of each pound of propellant that has to be carried.

There was a compromise, though, between the chemical rocket and the electric rocket—the "nuclear rocket"; it had been carried to the verge of development prior to the shuttle era. In the nuclear rocket a nuclear fission reactor similar in principle to that of a commercial nuclear power plant (but *very* different in detail) heats a propellant fluid to very high temperatures (around 4,000° F) to produce thrust just the way a chemical rocket's combustion gases do. The benefit is not so much the high temperature (combustion-generated gases are even hotter), but the fact that the propellant can be selected not for its combustion properties but solely for its thrust-producing properties. Nuclear rockets thus use the lightest chemical element—hydrogen, all by itself—to develop the greatest volume of gases per pound. As a result, they can deliver about twice the performance (thrust per pound of propellant consumed each second) of the best chemical rockets.

Almost as soon as the practical use of nuclear energy was demonstrated in the early 1940s, one of the most imaginative engineers I've ever met, Robert W. Bussard, began thinking of ways to use this enormously powerful new energy source for space exploration. (He was, of course, predated by science-fiction pioneer Hugo Gernsback, who published a picture of his uranium-fueled "atomic rocket" in 1921—almost twenty years before nuclear fission was even discovered!) In 1945 Bob Bussard was able to sell his idea to the U.S. Army Air Corps, which later became the U.S. Air Force, and by the mid-1960s, after several metamorphoses, the NERVA (Nuclear Engine for Rocket Vehicle Applications) had successfully demonstrated its ability to run repeatedly and well (at the Nuclear Rocket Test Station in Jackass Flats, Nevada—*not* in space). Jointly sponsored by NASA and the old Atomic Energy Commission (AEC), NERVA was considered by most future space planners as the logical "next step" for deep-space propulsion after the hydrogen-oxygen chemical rocket.

But once again NASA's planning went awry. NERVA had been sized big (75,000 pounds of thrust), based on its projected primary use as a lunar "ferry" to run between earth and moon orbits, a demand that never materialized. NERVA was also the obvious propulsion choice for the manned flight to Mars. Further, all the big nuclear-powered electric rocket research and technology projects, which had been running concurrently with NERVA, were aimed at ambitious planetary flights, many of them manned, to such exotic and difficult-to-reach places as the moons of Jupiter and Saturn. When the NASA "big space" post-Apollo balloon got punctured in 1969, there suddenly wasn't any real use for NERVA and its nuclear-electric side-kicks. So after spending over a billion dollars, NASA and the AEC abruptly canceled NERVA, along with most of the nuclear-electric propulsion projects, and relegated all nuclear-propulsion activity to low-level technology efforts. The final vestige of Bussard's once-vaunted idea was a one-fifth-scale advanced version of NERVA, the Small Nuclear Rocket Engine project (NASA finally seemed to have learned how to name projects not to draw budget cutters' ire). It continued halfheartedly for a few years at Los Alamos, but then in January 1973, under both budgetary and anti-nuclear pressure and with no possible use for a nuclear rocket in any of its projected shuttle missions, NASA closed out all space programs involving nuclear reactors. The nuclear rocket was, for all practical purposes, dead.

But during its heyday, the nuclear space program developed some fascinating concepts. One of the most active centers for nuclear- and nuclear-electric-propulsion research was at Princeton's Guggenheim Jet Propulsion Center, whose chief engineer was Pres Layton, and its Nuclear Propulsion Research Laboratory, of which I was director. Between us, Layton and I had been involved in every aspect of nuclear space activities and, in fact, all advanced space power and propulsion research, almost from its inception. I had taught myself nuclear reactor theory by the best method imaginable: teaching a course at Princeton called "Nuclear Power Plants" (which was, incidentally, the first such formal university course ever offered). Meanwhile, Layton, whose old Navy buddies from the early rocket days were running Aerojet, had become their consultant on the original nuclear-rocket engine contract they'd received from the Air Force; he later also worked with the Lawrence Radiation Laboratory at Livermore, California, on advanced space power reactors. By 1956 my early work in chemical-rocket combustion instability had moved into its "routine phase," so I had turned it over to a former graduate student, Dave Harrje, and moved full time into the fascinating fields of space power and nuclear propulsion. Layton and I formed an effective consulting team, and my university research effort provided excellent professional visibility in advanced space nuclear systems.

Unfortunately, we were well ahead of our time. I still hold a (useless) patent on the liquid-core nuclear reactor and a high-density heat exchanger developed from it. As recently as 1976 Layton and I cochaired a NASA-sponsored Princeton Conference on Partially Ionized and Uranium Plasmas, another "advanced concept" that didn't quite die in the 1973 purge; it still piddles along on a pittance of NASA research funding. However, the line of instruments I developed for my experimental research turned out to be a valuable asset long after the demise of nuclear-rocket research: a gadget that could measure temperatures up to 25,000° F was quite useful in such unfriendly environments as rocket exhausts, arc-heated wind tunnels, steel-furnace interiors, and the like.

We worked on the NERVA—as consultants to Aerojet and to NASA—and also on the Small Nuclear Rocket Engine, the SNAP 8, SNAP 50, and a multitude of other now-defunct space power programs, as well as similarly doomed air-breathing nuclear systems for ramjet propulsion of missiles and jet aircraft propulsion. As one nuclear propulsion or power program after another was canceled, I occasionally began to wonder whether there *was* any future in advanced space power. But Pres Layton kept me beating my head against the brick wall all those years.

Layton has an odd way of approaching and carrying out his research and development activities. Most people find him totally impossible to work with. His finicky attention to detail drove co-workers mad; he would interminably revise and redraft and rewrite and redesign and recalculate and retest every aspect of a problem. "I'd like to fuss with it a little more," he'd say to a chorus of groans from people with deadlines to meet. When he traveled, he jammed appointments in at the last minute. "We've got a whole hour before flight time," he'd say. "Let's drop in to see whatsisname at NASA." We made more airplanes that already had one engine running as we dashed frantically up the ramp! Layton also loved to work in difficult fields where there were few guideposts to follow and little way of knowing whether or not he was on the right track, thereby picking up his "Don Quixote" reputation.

But I learned very early that no matter how odd or strange a Layton decision seemed to be (and he really pulled some of them out of the blue), it paid to listen carefully and never, never ignore or brush him off. I found that out the hard way, shortly after I came to Princeton to run the experimental part of the rocket combustion instability program.

In 1952 we were breaking totally new ground in instrumentation. To measure the high-pressure, high-temperature, high-frequency (and often destructive) rocket combustion oscillations, we needed the ultimate in fast-response instrumentation. The head of the instrument lab at the Guggenheim Jet Propulsion Center was a brilliant Chinese theoretician named Frederick F. Liu. He was largely self-taught; his Ph.D. was in political science, not electronics. Whenever I had a problem with my totally unpredictable data-recording system he would shout, "I fix! I fix," disappear into a back room for a few hours, and dash back with a hand-soldered jumbled maze of tangled wires, capacitors, switches, and variable resistors jammed into a rack-mounted cabinet. "My new multiple-phase, delay-line-modulated, super-heterodyned signal processor and integrator!" he would announce triumphantly. "I just invented it!" After some frenetic dial turning and resoldering, and every now and then a "Humum!" and an "Aha," sure enough, there would be my signal—but it never lasted beyond the next test. After a few months my beautiful new lab (I had, for example, one of the very first tape recorders Ampex built for data gathering) looked like an electronics junkyard.

Then there was our instrumentation consultant, Howland B. Jones, Jr., exactly the opposite of Fred Liu. He was a totally practical electronics engineer. "Jonesy's got electrons in his fingertips," the technicians used to marvel. When an obscure ghost would flutter across our oscilloscope signal during a test, Jonesy would pick up a piece of wire and a few resistors, study for a moment the complex multichannel system that led from the rocket to the recorder, and jump the precise two terminals (out of perhaps five hundred possibilities) that were picking up the "noise." "Jones circuits," we used to call them. I was dying to get Jonesy to come and run the lab for me, but he refused. He was too rich. He'd inherited a few million dollars several years earlier, and liked to work only on his own terms. He spent a day a week with us at Princeton for years, but he much preferred to divide his time between the house he'd built with his own hands in Short Hills, New Jersey, and his very own lighthouse at Norwichport on Cape Cod.

So there I was, desperately looking for a competent rocket-instrumentation engineer, when out of the blue a top program director at one of the few good rocket labs in the country told me he wanted to leave industry and get back to *real* university research. Where better than Princeton? His reputation in rocket testing was impeccable; I jumped at the chance. Layton, as chief engineer of the center, had to pass on my appointment. I was bouncing excitedly around his office, describing in gleeful detail the qualifications of the man I was about to hire. "I think you're making a mistake," Layton said. I was aghast. "You know how badly we need him!" I remonstrated. "Look what he's done in the field! He's just right. We'll never get a better man!" Layton was imperturbable. "I'll go along if you insist," he said. "But I think you'll be sorry." He couldn't (or wouldn't) tell me why. "Just a hunch," he shrugged.

Everyone congratulated me on my good luck. I was on top of the world. What progress we'd make!

A year later, by mutual consent, my "find" departed for less scientifically demanding employment elsewhere. Layton had been dead right. My man had turned out to be a total loss.

I never forgot that lesson. Sometimes it took years before it became evident, but it was a rare Layton decision that backfired. And in space power, he was also dead right. He'd only been a little early. Once the shuttle era approached, with its implied potential for new payloads demanding high power, people tumbled over each other to resurrect some of the old skeletons in our closets. In 1977 Los Alamos trotted out a new family of advanced, compact, fast reactor designs for power ranges up to a few megawatts—we'd been promoting them for a decade or two. The Department of Energy added $10 million to its FY 1979 budget for space reactor-technology development in the multi-hundred-kilowatt range. Layton (who'd since retired from Princeton) was hired by several companies eager to get in on the ground floor of the upcoming space-power-system manufacturing business. People began designing the advanced space radiators needed to reject large amounts of power-plant waste heat in orbit, just as we'd tried to get them to do years earlier. A hybrid we'd invented—the dual-mode nuclear propulsion/power system to provide high-thrust nuclear rocket propulsion when needed near earth and other planets, and low-thrust, high-efficiency electric propulsion when needed in deep space—was dusted off and reconsidered for some of the difficult planetary exploration missions projected for the 1990s.

Right in the middle of this new flurry of activity, though, the Soviet Cosmos 954, a military reconnaissance satellite powered by a nuclear reactor, tumbled back into the atmosphere and spewed slightly radioactive debris over a large portion of northern Canada. The resulting international bedlam, with its hysterical cries to ban forever the use of nuclear power in space, totally ignored the fact that the Soviets had been unbelievably careless in their methods for ensuring the safety of their nuclear systems. U.S. practice, for example, even for the single reactor we had flown, was to not even start up a reactor in space until it had achieved its proper orbit. The debate still rages in the U.N. Committee on the Peaceful Uses of Outer Space, and elsewhere.

But despite this hitch, the unquestionable demand for compact sources of electric power in large amounts has reactivated the nuclear treadmill again. Unfortunately, such systems take a long time to develop, so it will be ten to fifteen years before the fruits of that resurrection begin to show up in orbit. But during the decade-long "dry period" in space nuclear-power activities, the growing capabilities of solar cells had become more and more evident. For several scientific space missions (such as a rendezvous with Halley's comet in 1984), NASA desperately wanted to use electric propulsion, which seemed the only way to achieve the necessary instrument payload mass for such a difficult mission. Without any nuclear power available, it had no choice but to develop a "solar electric propulsion stage" (SEPS) to do the job. Twenty-five kilowatts were needed—more power than had ever been put into space in one package before. So they developed the SEPS, and then the Halley's comet rendezvous (literally a once-in-a-life-time opportunity, since the comet comes around only once in eighty years) was canceled.

But in 1978, when the need for more on-board power for the shuttle and Spacelab and some of the newer projected programs became evident, here was this almost-developed twenty-five-kilowatt solar-power system! True, it was makeshift and unwieldy, but in 1978 it was the only game in town. And then, with NASA's usual luck (or is it really very, very careful planning?), large solar arrays in space (which everyone in the know agreed should be displaced for on-board power needs by nuclear power plants as soon as power demand climbed to the twenty- to fifty-electric-kilowatt range) turned out to be one of the most promising future prospects for servicing the *earth* with electric power. So NASA promptly proclaimed that twenty-five-kilowatt last-minute fill-in as the prototype "test unit" for future multimegawatt solar-power systems for *earth*, as well as a backup system for Spacelab and the shuttle, which was its original purpose.

The pieces were finally beginning to fit together: Edelson and Morgan's orbital antenna farm; Bekey and Mayer's advanced communications ideas; Spacelab and Getaway Special experiments to explore space-processing potential; Heiss's global-resource information system; NASA's advanced reusable-space-tug study; and finally the electric power needed to make everything work—with the possible future goal of solving the earth's energy crisis. Add the NASA program for space science and exploration, the growing military demand to monitor Strategic Arms Limitation Talk (SALT) agreements and to keep close observations on foreign military activities; and the rapidly developing market in navigation and communications (commercial) and meteorology (government)—and the first decade of space-shuttle operations was beginning to look very rosy indeed.

The only trouble with this rosy picture was that nobody was picking up the ball.

The Carter administration had taken a down-to-earth applications-oriented position, which fell right into line with Bill Proxmire's vendetta against space expenditures and precluded all the exciting prospects that might be opened up by the advent of the shuttle in the 1980s. The pro-space Senate Committee on the Aeronautical and Space Sciences had been dissolved in the 1976-77 Senate reorganization, and its "space-hawk" former chairman, Frank Moss, had lost his 1976 reelection bid. It was left to the old guard, the powerful House Committee on Science and Astronautics headed by staunch space-defender "Tiger" Teague from Texas, to assume the space-advocate's mantle.

And Teague did just that. In January 1978 he scheduled an unprecedented full-committee hearing on future space programs, usurping (with the only-too-willing agreement of its chairman, Florida's Don Fuqua) the normal dominion of the Subcommittee on Space Science and Applications. Fuqua's acquiescence wasn't all that altruistic: Teague had announced his retirement, effective in 1979, and Fuqua was next in line to assume the full committee chairmanship.

The hearing was reminiscent of the post-Sputnik era. Teague and virtually every member of his committee raked NASA administrator Robert Frosch and presidential science adviser Frank Press over the coals as no previous administration witnesses had been since 1958, when Lyndon Johnson had rammed a national space program down Eisenhower's throat. Here are some of their comments, straight out of the *Congressional Record*, upon hearing Frosch's and Press's testimony:

Mr. Winn (Larry Winn, Jr., Republican, Kansas): I don't know how to say this without sounding rude . . . but most of us on this committee are really excited about the space program and about our accomplishments. After listening to the testimony of you two gentlemen, you leave us very bored. . . . You are not bringing us any new challenges. . . . I have been sitting here for one hour, and I haven't learned a thing that's new.

Mr. Fuqua (Don Fuqua, Democrat, Florida; Chairman, Subcommittee on Space Science and Applications): What are you talking about for the future? The [Carter] administration was able to get along for a while saying, "We are new and we're trying to formulate our policy." We are . . . almost at the two-minute warning, and we need to be getting on with the program of what we are going to be doing down the road.

Mr. Lloyd (Jim Lloyd, Democrat, California): We *know* what all the limitations are. I *know* where the money stands. I *know* what the attitudes of the public are, but I need a vision, and I don't have the capability of creating that myself. I think that is where we are frustrated. We want the vision from you.

Mr. Scheuer (James H. Scheuer, Democrat, New York): Sometimes when you *don't* go ahead you make policy too. I get the feeling that Dr. Frosch didn't want to do *anything* until all the feasibility analyses were in and the "i's" were dotted and the "t's" were crossed and we could identify on a cost-effectiveness basis the results of an investment there [in space]. . . . You know we all have to answer to the taxpayers. . . . This admittedly is risk taking. . . . We do not have the fine-tuned cost-benefit analyses . . . but if we sit around and fiddle and faddle, we incur enormous costs. I think this committee is very excited about the prospects, and I think we are all frustrated by getting a very diffident reading, frankly, from Dr. Frosch.

The "go-slow" space policy of the Carter administration, which spurned the considerable potential returns offered by capabilities developed during the 1970s, frequently exasperated forward-looking congressmen like Don Fuqua, chairman of the powerful House Committee on Science and Technology. Photograph courtesy of *Astronautics and Aeronautics.*

To give NASA administrator Robert Frosch due credit, the tone of his testimony appeared to have been set "on orders" from his boss, Jimmy Carter. In a previous speech (to an AIAA workshop conference on aerospace technology transfer in November 1977) he had sung an entirely different tune, much more in keeping with the bullishness of Teague's committee:

> There is no sense in trying to look at future situations involving technology in terms of . . . the current system, because technological change does not simply modulate the system; it changes it into a new system. Certainly there was no market waiting for the automobile. In fact, if we used current technology assessment techniques, we would have concluded it was a silly investment . . . we would have been appalled at the amount of capital required to be spent over the ensuing fifty years to build an otherwise totally useless road network. It must have cost this country five hundred billion dollars to build the road network, the gasoline station network, and the whole processing system that led to it. Clearly, anybody making that prediction in today's climate for assessing new technologies would have simply said that the country cannot produce the capital to do that. Of course, *that* country, that ran on horses, could *not* have produced such capital. The country that produced the capital for the automobile was also the product of the automobile. The system that produced the capital was a different system. This is exactly the modeling problem that most economists not only have not coped with, but they have not even discovered it to be a problem!

Frosch was dead right. The system *was* changing in the late 1970s, but it wasn't easy to overcome a decade's inertia. People were still thinking that space programs would bring nothing home but a few hundred pounds of moon rocks. And even farsighted space engineers like Burt Edelson, Philomena Grodzka, Ivan Bekey, Klaus Heiss, and Pres Layton weren't looking far enough ahead. *Their* capital investment concepts were scaled in the billions, or maybe tens of billions. But there were ideas out there that made even these lofty concepts seem niggling. The shuttle era was just beginning to open up some *real* vistas for mankind in space.

And there were thousands of people ready to bet their very lives on it.

CHAPTER

7

THE POTENTIAL

"Railroad carriages are pulled at the enormous speed of fifteen miles per hour by 'engines' which, in addition to endangering life and limb of passengers, roar and snort their way through the countryside, setting fire to the crops, scaring the livestock, and frightening women and children. The Almighty certainly never intended that people should travel at such breakneck speed."

—*Martin Van Buren*
Governor of New York (later President of the United States)
1829

"Aerial flight is one of that class of problems with which man will never be able to cope."

—*Simon Newcomb*
1903

"The popular mind often pictures gigantic flying machines speeding across the Atlantic carrying innumerable passengers in a way analogous to our modern steamships. It seems safe to say that such ideas are wholly visionary."

—*William H. Pickering*
Astronomer
1910

"We hope the Professor from Clark College [Robert H. Goddard] is only *pretending* to be ignorant of elementary physics if he thinks that a rocket can work in a vacuum."

—*Editorial,* The New York Times
1920

"There has been a great deal said about a three-thousand-mile rocket. In my opinion such a thing is impossible for many years. I think we can leave that out of our thinking."

—Vannevar Bush
1945

"As chairman of the Senate subcommittee responsible for NASA appropriations, I say not a penny for this nutty fantasy [the colonization of space]."

—William Proxmire
October 1977

SUCH IDEAS AS THE ROUTINE EMPLOYMENT OF MEN AND WOMEN in the deep vastnesses of space do indeed instill a "future shock" reaction, not only in Senator Proxmire and the lay public, but also in many aerospace engineers and scientists as well. Perhaps it is a result of the modern heritage of science *fiction*—nobody really ever expects those events to happen—or perhaps the sense of mankind's bondage to the earth and its gravity is one of the deep-seated driving forces of our psychology.

Whatever the reason, it certainly is not rational analysis that makes space seem remote, hostile, and unachievable to all but a chosen few. Given our newly developed ability to overcome the powerful force of gravity that had heretofore bound us inexorably to the earth, the space environment is not all that difficult to live and work in. True, there is no air to breathe, but neither is there air beneath our oceans —and millions of men and women, boys and girls, enjoy scuba diving regularly. Submarines with complements of hundreds cruise the Arctic for months at a time without surfacing. And contrary to popular opinion, failure of a space suit or space capsule won't cause a human body to explode from internal pressure. People can live for several minutes upon being exposed suddenly to a vacuum, provided routine precautions are utilized to prevent the "bends" and other easily avoidable problems.

Besides, space has many advantages—no rain, hail, sleet, or snow; no earthquakes, tidal waves, hurricanes, or tornadoes; no corrosion, poisonous air pollution, smoke and haze, or dust; and, most important, no gravity to drag at our feet and make building such simple things as houses so complicated. Practically the entire mass of every building on earth is devoted to holding itself and its contents up against the force of gravity! Remove that restriction, and truly functional architecture becomes possible for the first time in history, along with many other totally new facets of the arts, sciences, and human endeavors.

Concepts of human habitation in space have long been the province of storytellers and dreamers. But although Tsiolkovsky himself was the first serious proponent of deep-space habitats for people, most early space scientists and engineers thought of manned space flight solely as a means for exploration and scientific investigation rather than as a source for economic expansion. It was a remarkable confluence of three factors that opened the first serious consideration of massive industrialization and habitation in space, although as in all enterprises, the necessary seeds had been in place for years before germination occurred.

First, a rash of "doomsday" predictions began to appear, best characterized by Dennis Meadows' study, *The Limits to Growth*, sponsored by the Club of Rome and touted as signaling the death knell of mankind due to accelerating pollution and profligate consumption of the earth's resources. Then, public realization of the "energy crisis," of which the oil war of 1973 was probably the principal bellwether, pointed toward either a harsh future or a sudden increase in the rate at which we approached the "limits to growth."

Now, thoughtful social scientists recognized that neither of these two factors *necessarily* meant disaster for the human race. Herman Kahn, for example, projected a leveling off of population and postulated a stable civilization with more than enough resources, provided we utilized our technological capabilities, to give us "the good life" for the indefinite future. Many pointed to the classic example of Malthus, who had failed to take into account the enormous impact of food-production technology in his gloomy, century-old prediction of worldwide starvation. Nevertheless, there was a great deal of public uneasiness, and much national soul-searching.

So when a Princeton physics professor named Gerard K. O'Neill came up with the apparently sound suggestion that space offered a limitless opportunity for human expansion, which he suggested initially in 1974 articles in *Nature* and *Physics Today*, he received almost instantaneous popular acclaim and much publicity.

The energy crisis also turned out to be approachable from space. Back in 1968 Peter Glaser, a solar engineer at the Arthur D. Little Company, had proposed using enormous solar collectors in space to convert solar energy to electricity and beam it down to earth—a novel and extremely interesting (and possibly even practical) idea. So maybe space could not only solve the limits-to-growth problem, but perhaps also the energy crisis.

But these ideas had been around for years. It was a third factor that finally became the catalyst for serious consideration of schemes that a science-fiction writer might have turned down a few years before as being visionary. That third factor was our growing capability —indeed, our familiarity—with working and living in space. Fixing the damaged Skylab, as well as the safe recovery of the *Apollo 13* astronauts after an explosion that aborted their mission, demonstrated that people in space could deal effectively with the unexpected as well as perform flawlessly when all went well. The advent of "routine" access to space offered by the space shuttle in the 1980s began to lend solid technical credence to such grandiose, futuristic concepts as O'Neill's and Glaser's.

The best evidence of the gradual change in attitude by the engineering community (remember Arthur Clarke's three stages of development that introduced Chapter Four!) was public recognition by the American Institute of Aeronautics and Astronautics: "Satellite Solar Power" showed up as a chapter in the AIAA's April 1975 assessment, *Solar Energy for Earth*, and the institute cosponsored and helped O'Neill organize a Princeton Conference on Space Manufacturing Facilities (Space Colonies) in May 1975. That meeting, incidentally, marked the first public marriage of Glaser's solar-power satellites (SPS) and O'Neill's space colonies.

Although O'Neill's concept was the first of the two to catch the public's attention, principally as the result of Walter Sullivan's front-page *New York Times* coverage of O'Neill's first Princeton Conference (held prior to AIAA's involvement, in May 1974), the solar-power satellite idea has progressed much further toward demonstrating "proof of concept."

Perhaps the most fascinating aspect of satellite solar power is that it requires no technological "breakthroughs" to achieve its projected performance, as attested to by U.S. Patent No. 3,781,647, describing a "Method and Apparatus for Converting Solar Radiation to Electrical Power," issued to Dr. Peter Glaser on December 25, 1973 (a Christmas present for the world?). Here's how it works:

An array of photovoltaic converters (solar cells, just like the ones in current use on nearly all spacecraft, except thinner, more efficient, and *much*, much cheaper) is placed (or built) in the geostationary orbit—the same orbit used for Arthur Clarke's communications satellites—so that as the earth rotates the array remains "fixed" over a single point on the earth's equator. The direct-current electricity generated by the solar cells is converted to microwaves (by devices called "amplitrons," similar to those used in TV transmitters and other well-known microwave systems here on earth, or by "klystrons," also relatively standard electronic components) and beamed through the 22,300 miles of space to the earth below. The earth receiver can be located anywhere along the meridian of longitude that passes through

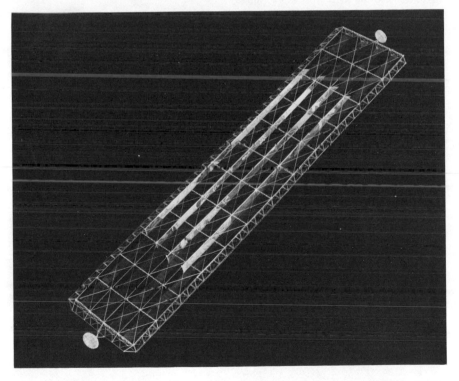

Early concept of a completed geostationary-orbit, photovoltaic solar-power satellite, eighteen miles long by four miles wide. The two circular antennas at the ends deliver a net electrical power of 10,000 megawatts to terrestrial utility networks. Illustration courtesy of the Boeing Aerospace Company.

The earth receiver of solar-power satellite electricity, transmitted from space 22,300 miles away by radarlike (shortwave) radio waves called microwaves. This receiver, which would deliver 10,000 megawatts to the local grid, is five miles by seven and a half miles, but its open structure permits the use of the land under it for farming or livestock grazing. Illustration courtesy of Boeing Aerospace Company.

the point on the equator over which the satellite hovers (or even some distance east or west of that meridian) up to perhaps fifty degrees north or south, where the curvature of the earth tends to make the receiver area unacceptably large in the north-south direction. The receiver itself is constructed of millions of simple, familiar devices called "dipole rectifiers," which convert the microwave beam from the satellite back into electric current, ready for delivery to the local electric utility grid (possibly after another well-known electrical pro-

Should land space be at a premium, even for double use as farm or grazing land, solar-power-satellite receiving antennas could be built offshore, or possibly even as a floating structure out at sea.

cess called "inversion"), in much the same form as the electricity generated by a conventional oil, coal, or nuclear power plant.

Several alternatives to Glaser's original concept have been suggested and are under active consideration by NASA and the Department of Energy. Instead of using solar cells, for example, Boeing engineer Gordon Woodcock detailed the use of enormous parabolic mirrors, formed of extremely thin mylar films, which focus the sun's rays on a central absorber either to generate steam or to heat an inert gas. The steam or gas then powers a turbo-generator just as is done in conventional earth-based power plants. This "solar-thermal" power plant concept has been used on the ground in the United States' first good-sized (ten megawatt) central-station solar-electric power plant, being built in Barstow, California, to supply electricity to Southern California Edison's customers.

One variation on Glaser's initial concept uses lasers instead of microwaves to deliver power to earth. Another employs a long waveguide (tube that guides electromagnetic waves) with thousands of solid-state converters instead of amplitrons or klystrons to convert electricity to microwaves. That variation, because of its length, uses the difference in gravity between its top and its bottom to stabilize it in orbit. Still another concept shuns the use of the geostationary orbit. Here, several satellites are placed in elliptical orbits, each tracked as it "rises" and "sets" by a number of earth receivers in the same manner as the Soviet Molniya communications satellite system.

The preferred configuration that always seems to bubble up out of the dozens of analyses and preliminary design studies that have been performed, however, is pretty close to Glaser's original concept. There is still some question as to the best kind of solar array to use—some say silicon, which is plentiful, cheap, and has received the bulk of development attention by the Department of Energy and NASA; others like gallium arsenide, which is more expensive but can be used at much higher temperatures, so that most of the intercepted sunlight can be reflected by inexpensive mirrors onto the solar cells, considerably increasing the power output of each cell.

But nearly everyone agrees on what the big *problems* are, no matter what configuration is used: the cost of the satellite power system and its possible impacts on the environment. Behind these are stacked a host of lesser but nonetheless difficult engineering problems. One such problem is to design and build a rotary joint between the collectors

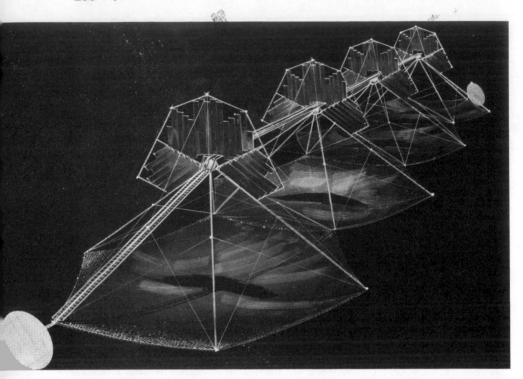

Another type of solar-power satellite. This one uses the thermal energy of sunlight: giant but diaphanous mirrors focus the sun's rays on the central spherical absorbers, heating steam or gas to drive the turbogenerators. The whole structure is over fourteen miles long; its two circular antennas deliver a net power of 10,000 megawatts to the earth-based electric utility grid. Illustration courtesy of the Boeing Aerospace Company.

(which must always face the sun) and the microwave transmitter (which must always face the earth). That joint has to carry anywhere from 1,000 to 15,000 megawatts of electric power. (A typical large earth-based nuclear power plant generates around 1,000 megawatts; New York City's peak summer use in 1978 was about 8,000 megawatts.) Another problem is how to handle the sudden change in temperature called "thermal shock," which hits the miles-wide satellite as it comes in and out of the earth's shadow. This situation, fortunately, occurs only twice per year for a few weeks around the spring and fall equinoxes and obscures the satellite's sunlight for a maximum of seventy-two minutes around local midnight. A third engineering problem is stabilization of the miles-wide, tissue-thin structure against the pressure of sunlight and the difference in gravity between one end of the satellite and the other—a job that will be performed by small electric rockets controlled by a central computer and drawing their power from the satellite itself. Other "details" involve the reliability of the solar cells and their electrical connections, the amplitrons or klystrons, and the other massive electrical components. There are innumerable, but solvable, problems associated with the construction, transportation, assembly, operation, and maintenance of so large and massive a structure: some designs range up to fourteen miles long and weigh over 100,000 tons—not much compared to the average 250,000-ton oceangoing supertanker, but *40,000 times* what the shuttle and its interim upper stage can carry on one trip to the geostationary orbit!

And therein lies the crux of the solar-power-satellite problem: its cost, which may turn out to be the real nemesis. Clearly one would *not* use today's shuttle to carry so massive a payload into orbit—it would be like ferrying 300 people across the ocean in 300 Piper Cubs instead of using a single 747. So if a decision is ultimately made to go ahead with a full-scale solar-power satellite in the 5,000- to 10,000-megawatt class (which was the range most experts were bandying about in 1978 and 1979), it would imply an enormous investment in developing, building, and operating a "super-shuttle" space-transportation system capable of economical operations to geostationary orbit, with payloads big enough to divide up a 100,-000-ton power plant into a reasonable number of flights. Estimates for such a craft vary all over the lot, but any of them makes the shuttle's original $7.2 billion investment look paltry. Preliminary designs suggest that the cost of transportation will be nearly *half* the total cost of each power plant placed into orbit.

But even that enormous investment might be acceptable even if the "brute force" supershuttle approach were used (and there are many fascinating ways to skin *that* cat), provided the return on the investment were commensurate. An early (1976) study by Klaus Heiss's firm, ECON, laid the ground rules: satellite solar power compared to what? Projecting the first commercial system as being possible in the late 1990s, preliminary cost estimates (including amortization of the enormous—typically $50 billion—initial investment) placed the cost of power delivered from a solar-power satellite to the utility grid at four to five cents per kilowatt-hour. This actually was quite competitive with projected fossil-fuel- or nuclear-generated electricity at that time (for comparison, in 1978 New York's Con Edison's *price* to residential users, which includes a few other elements besides costs, like taxes and distribution, was 11.3 cents per kilowatt-hour). So even if Heiss's cost estimates were way off, as was highly likely in so early a study, there was at least a respectable reason to keep on looking at the satellite power-system concept.

First impressions of such an incredible idea—a hundred thousand tons in orbit—tend to induce a true case of future shock in anyone. I remember when I first began to look at the solar-power-satellite concept in detail. It was in early 1974, when I took on the job of assembling the AIAA's solar-energy assessment. Up to that point I had

Should solar-power satellites prove economically feasible and environmentally sound (they are already technically feasible), large space-manufacturing facilities might be useful to build them on a "production-line" basis. The present shuttle could be used as a personnel carrier, but the tonnage of materials needed would require a large freighter shuttle, perhaps like the one shown at the left, called a "heavy-lift launch vehicle." Illustration courtesy of Boeing Aerospace Company.

simply pooh-poohed the whole ridiculous idea, like everyone else. But Peter Glaser, in his careful, accurate, slightly accented but perfectly grammatical style, was able to give me eloquent and thorough answers to all my technical questions. I went home, checked his numbers and his input data against the extensive AIAA files, recalculated his performance and cost estimates, and reexamined the assumptions he'd had to make to reach them. True, there were a lot of gaping holes (like the need for a hundred-to-one cost reduction in solar-cell costs), but there was at least a finite hope of filling them.*

After much soul-searching and a good deal of self-education in fields I knew little about, like microwave system engineering, I concluded that the SPS concept was at least worthy of further evaluation. This conclusion appeared in the AIAA assessment, along with such practical ideas as solar heating and cooling, and biomass energy, and it subsequently became a common subject for discussion at AIAA and other technical meetings.

The obvious question, of course, is why go to space to get solar energy? Isn't there plenty right here on the ground? The answer isn't quite so obvious, but it's very arguable. One must first assemble the arguments, pro and con. Here are the "favorables":

First of all, the year-averaged "insolation" (the solar engineers' term for usable sunlight) in the geostationary orbit is six times higher than it is in July in Arizona, eleven times higher than in the U.S. Midwest year-round, and twenty times higher than Boston year-round. Also, it's virtually constant, so unlike ground-based solar-power systems, the SPS can be used for what the utility engineers call "base load"—it's there all the time, 24 hours per day, 365 days per year, except for those short midnight periods around the equinoxes.

Next, all electric-power generating systems, even solar, reject waste heat into their environment; the higher their efficiency, the less they waste heat. The most efficient oil-fired power plants dump about 60 percent of the energy available from their oil into their smokestacks and into the water that cools their condensers—so-called "thermal pollution." Ground-based solar power plants are much less efficient, so they dump even more waste heat into the earth's biosphere for every kilowatt-hour of electricity they generate. But space-based

---

* The prospects for that hundred-to-one reduction in solar-cell costs keep getting better and better. The Department of Energy's most recent published forecast for 1986 was only twice the cost Glaser assumed in his conceptual designs.

power plants discharge all that waste heat out into limitless space; only the electricity actually used (plus the small loss due to conversion at the receiving antenna) eventually shows up in the earth's biosphere.

Then there's the use of still more valuable land. Ground-based solar-electric power plants need acres and acres of it: first, because of the relatively low overall plant efficiency of solar systems (typically from 5 percent to perhaps 25 percent, compared with 40 percent for the best oil-fired power plants), and second, because of the extra collector area needed to compensate for nightfall, clouds, and atmospheric interference. And land devoted to solar collectors can't be used for anything else.

The SPS earth-based receiving antennas, on the other hand, are not only smaller than the corresponding ground-based solar power plant's collector fields (for the same year-round average useful power level), but their construction is such that the land on which they're built can be utilized almost totally for agriculture or livestock grazing land. The "rectenna," as it's been nicknamed, is open grillwork, typically ten to fifteen feet above ground. Eighty percent of the sunlight striking the rectenna reaches the ground; 100 percent of the rainfall. All the rectenna's grillwork stops is the microwave beam from the satellite.

Finally, satellite power plants (which are not susceptible to earthquakes or corrosive rainfall, hurricanes or tornadoes, hail or snow or sleet, or even falling down!) are far, far away from their nearest neighbors. Everyone on earth likes the convenience of electric power, but each person wants the power plant that's needed to generate it to be located near someone *else*'s home town. Satellite power stations are at least 22,300 miles from *anyone*'s home town!

There are several arguments stacked *against* the SPS too. The major engineering problems I've already identified are important but probably solvable if those plants can be shown to be profitable, given our past history of successes in space endeavors. There are jurisdictional problems, too, such as who, if anyone, "owns" the geostationary orbit, and how presumably cheap satellite electric power should be marketed to the developing nations. But these problems are also subject to ready solutions as soon as satellite solar power becomes economical, again based on past experiences perhaps best exemplified by Intelsat.

The two most serious concerns, though, are to determine unequivocally that the environmental impact of the microwave-power-trans-mission process is no greater than that of alternative means for generating electric power, and to establish whether or not the eco-nomics of satellite solar power make them truly viable, without spend-ing billions of dollars just to find out. Some say that gamble would be worthwhile, given the $40 billion or $50 billion the United States lays out each year to buy imported oil, but it would unquestionably turn out to be the biggest gamble in history—and I'd hate to be the one responsible for that decision if the answer turned out to be no!

Although all evidence garnered to date points to the likelihood that the microwave-power-transmission beam will be far more benign in its effects on the environment than those of almost any other large-scale power-generation method, the very term "microwaves" carries an emotional connotation that, according to Congressman Mike Mc-Cormack, chairman of the House subcommittee responsible for ad-vanced energy concepts, may turn out to be even worse than the negative (but largely emotional) response to nuclear power. Part of the problem is clearly a lack of public understanding. We tend to think of microwaves as "frying" people—a not-unusual consequence, perhaps, of the proliferation of microwave ovens, which could indeed do just that. But we cheerfully watch television—transmitted cross-country or via satellite by microwaves—and fly happily in airplanes guided by radar, another form of microwave transmission. We might get very upset at being caught in a police radar speed trap, but we certainly don't worry about the effects of the radar beam on our bodies!

As in most cases of misunderstanding, the problem is one of "how much is bad?" A battery-powered flashlight has very different effects on the human body than an electric chair, although they both employ the heat generated by an electric current. Similarly, a microwave oven *will* fry objects placed inside it, whereas microwave-beam power levels used in communications cannot even be discerned by the body; they need sensitive and carefully designed antennas to sense their presence.

The microwave beam from an SPS would operate at a power level much closer to that of communications activities than that of ovens. Current concepts call for a peak power in the center of the micro-wave beam when it reaches the earth's surface of about 230 watts per square meter—less than one quarter the intensity of normal sunlight on a clear midsummer day in North America. A person sitting right on the center of the rectenna might feel pleasantly warm, but he certainly wouldn't fry! And at the boundaries of the rectenna, which may be four miles or more from the center, the intensities are far, far lower; in fact, simply by increasing the "exclusion area" (inside the fence which would surround the rectenna), it is possible to reduce the exposure of an "innocent bystander" to almost any desired level. Under the rectenna the exposure is equally low—the dipoles capture practically all the incident radiation. Cows grazing there would never even be aware of it. And birds, or people in airplanes flying through the beam, might notice a slightly warm feeling, but they'd be in the beam so short a time that there seems little possibility of any discomfort, much less any damage to their bodies.

Another misconception is that the satellite power station might be sabotaged, or even worse, seized by terrorists and the beam turned from its rectenna to the center of a city and focused so as to scorch the inhabitants. Unfortunately for sensationalists, that just isn't physically possible. The big satellite transmitting antenna isn't a simple focusing "dish"; it is an aggregate of literally thousands of individual transmitters, phased electronically to produce the effect of a focus. The phasing control is a "pilot beam," located in the center of the rectenna. Turn off the pilot beam, or turn the transmitting antenna away from it, and the phase control disappears. The thousands of transmitting elements wander helplessly, pointing in all directions. Since the entire earth is a tiny target from 22,300 miles away, much less the eight-mile pinpoint of the rectenna, the satellite's power is dissipated harmlessly through the infinity of space. It cannot be "focused" again until the pilot beam is reactivated and the transmitters rephased.

So the sensible heat generated by SPS microwaves in living creatures is certainly not an environmental problem, or at the very worst is one that can be dealt with. There are, however, other potential effects that may or may not be important, but which are much harder to identify and measure. One of the most critical could be any substantial heating of the upper atmosphere as a result of the interaction of the microwave beam with the electrically charged molecules and electrons that are present in the ionosphere. Tests conducted to explore this possibility, using the big radiotelescope dish at Arecibo "in reverse" as a microwave transmitter, have so far failed to detect any such problem in the microwave frequency range contemplated for SPS transmission, but these tests are nowhere near definitive as yet. Continued intensive experiments, probably including a scaled-down experiment from orbit, will be needed to establish the necessary confidence that runaway ionospheric heating cannot occur.

Another potential effect of microwaves could conceivably show up only after very long-term exposure to very low levels: that is, power levels far below those that produce sensible heating of body tissue. There is some evidence of such effects of microwave power densities below the U.S. maximum legal limit (a hundred watts per square meter), but the effects are obscure and hard to quantify, and many experts don't believe they exist at all. On the basis of this evidence, however, the U.S.S.R. set *its* legal maximum for microwave exposure a thousand times lower than that of the United States: a *tenth* of a watt per square meter.

It is clearly necessary to establish whether or not these insidious effects of long-term exposure to very low-level microwaves are significant. Microwaves are totally unlike much higher energy nuclear radiation or even X-rays, both of which can strip electrons from the atoms in body tissue and thereby cause observable (and measurable) damage. Microwaves can only cause atoms and electrons to vibrate a little faster than normal (that's what heats the tissue and makes a microwave oven work, at high microwave powers), and whether or not such movement can cause any harmful effects other than heating still needs to be established. But even if such effects *are* eventually found to be real, potential SPS practicality is only lessened, not eliminated: the net result will be that the rectenna's exclusion area will be increased, which simply adds to the cost and land requirements of the system. How much? That depends totally on how low the microwave exposure has to be. That's where some research is needed—and is already under way.

A third potential environmental effect could be in excessive contamination of the atmosphere by the burned rocket propellants needed to launch those millions of tons of power plant into orbit. The shuttle's solid-propellant rockets, for example, use a chemical containing chlorine, which, in quantities a hundred or more times greater than those projected for the shuttle itself, could cause environmentally significant changes in the upper atmosphere. Now, none of the "super-shuttle" design concepts for possible future SPS launches consider using chlorine or, in fact, any comparable chemicals. Most use only hydrogen and oxygen propellants, which when burned form environmentally benign water vapor, but even that much water vapor dumped into the stratosphere might constitute a problem. There's also the possibility that the white-hot rocket exhaust will react with the atmosphere to form some nitrogen oxides—nowhere near the amounts now dumped into our air by automobile exhausts, for example, but still worthy of careful consideration.

But all in all, if one had to hazard a guess *right now*, it is likely that there will be few, if any, surprises popping out of the SPS environmental closet. Our concern with environmental impact in today's world is much different than it was a few decades back, and in all areas of industrial activity careful foresight and evaluation have been found to go a long way. The environmental studies related to SPS *do* need to be completed, of course, but chances are that they won't turn up any problems we don't already know about and can deal with.

So costs will almost certainly be the hinge on which the SPS will swing. As in any major new undertaking, there are two kinds of costs —nonrecurring (investment) and recurring (operations)—in addition, of course, to the cost of the research, which is always necessary to validate the technology upon which the undertaking is based. But in the case of the SPS, there is one major element of the initial nonrecurring cost investment that makes it somewhat unique: the cost of finding out whether or not the whole idea is practical. This is generally accomplished by means of a "demonstration"—a somewhat smaller version of the final system, but as similar to it as possible in every other respect. In the case of a ground-based synthetic fuel plant, for example, the cost of a demonstration project might be as much as a few hundred million dollars. But the cost of the first demonstration SPS could run anywhere from $2 or $3 billion to perhaps $20 or $30 *billion*, depending on how "demonstration" is defined—and that's just to find out whether or not it's worth going ahead with the construction of full-scale satellite systems.

By far the biggest slice of the SPS demonstration cost is for transportation. Transportation is needed not only for the hardware, but also for the people or robot "teleoperators," if it turns out to be possible to use them, who have to build and assemble the power plants, along with their "construction shack" and maintenance supplies (the power plant would be far too large to be carried from earth into space intact; it would have to be built in orbit). Then, too, the demonstration plant probably *must* be in the geostationary orbit rather than in low earth orbit to really establish its operational characteristics, thus increasing the cost of transportation about five times over the basic shuttle-launched cost for every pound of payload.

So in all the preliminary systems studies that NASA has supported, the two key elements have been, first, to conceptualize the most efficient launchers and orbital-transfer rockets, and second, to reduce the total payload mass that has to be carried into orbit.

Never before have the imaginations of space engineers had such a magnificent arena in which to show their mettle! Here was a potential save-the-world project, bigger by hundreds than anything ever done before, but requiring no new science or technological breakthroughs. All the pieces of the puzzle were there, lying on the table; all that had to be done was to put them together.

First, of course, there was the "brute force" approach. The space shuttle (with the interim upper stage) is far too small to carry even a single demonstration power plant and its construction crew to geostationary orbit; it would take literally thousands of flights. Upgrading the shuttle by several straightforward changes could increase payloads by about 50 percent. Replacing the shuttle orbiter with a simple unmanned freighter (no reentry or landing capability) could more than double its payload capacity and also eliminate payload volume constraints, since there would no longer be the orbiter's bay to have to squeeze the payload into. Additional refinements, such as replacing the freighter's solid-propellant rockets with high-performance liquid-propellant ones, could gain another 50 percent, tripling the payload mass of the current shuttle. A proper high-performance tug, instead of the interim upper stage, would pick up another factor of two.

But the best that could be obtained by using such shuttle-derived launches would be to reduce the total number of flights by a factor of perhaps five or six. Too many flights would still be needed for a proper geostationary SPS demonstration. So the next step in the "brute force" approach would be to return to the old NASA behemoth of 1969-71: the fully reusable flyback booster. And then the skeletons *really* begin tumbling out of the closet! Lo and behold, here comes the old Air Force Aerospaceplane, a derivative of the hoary Dyna-Soar, now dusted off and labeled a "single-stage-to-orbit" launcher. Even Krafft Ehricke's monster Nexus was back in new clothes: the Boeing "heavy-lift launch vehicle," a big two-stage ballistic-reentry freighter, which would weigh almost fifteen million pounds and could carry a half-million pounds to low earth orbit— nearly ten times what the shuttle can do. That one even uses Bob Truax's water-recovery idea for its first stage!

But even though these big rockets would clearly pay off in "production"—that is, if the SPS demonstration were successful—their enormous investment cost would preclude their development for just the demonstration project. It soon became evident that real engineering ingenuity was needed.

The first obvious approach in reducing up-front transportation investments until SPS practicality could be established was to use the existing shuttle to its absolute limit. Engineers at General Dynamics' Convair division (then headed by former Air Force Assistant Secretary Grant Hansen) speculatively eyed that big, blimp-sized "throwaway" shuttle propellant tank, and got to work. "Suppose we *don't* throw those tanks away, but instead carry them into low orbit," they mused. (The extra propellant mass needed to do that, incidentally, would be negligibly small.) "Then we could use them as orbital storage depots."

Their reasoning went like this: The bulk of the mass needed to get a payload from low orbit to geostationary orbit is the space tug itself and its propellant—the 65,000-pound low-orbit shuttle payload shrinks to 5,000 pounds if the interim upper stage is needed to get it up to the geostationary orbit. Now, most projected shuttle payloads are *volume* limited rather than weight limited; fitting them into the shuttle bay is their limit rather than the 65,000-pound shuttle payload weight limitation. So Convair suggested that every shuttle flight be filled with water to make up the difference between the payload mass and the shuttle's limit of 65,000 pounds. The water could then be stored in one of the big orbiting tanks. A small solar-powered electrolyzer would be carried up in a single dedicated shuttle flight, and then used to electrolyze the water into its constituents—hydrogen and oxygen (a well-known and quite simple process; all it takes is lots of electric power). The hydrogen and oxygen would be stored in another propellant tank, to which a high-performance rocket engine would be attached (perhaps one of the shuttle's main engines). Presto! A fully reusable, high-performance space tug, able to lug hundreds of *tons* of SPS hardware from low orbit to geostationary orbit.

The SPS construction materials are brought from earth to low orbit by the shuttle in 50,000- or 60,000-pound batches and stashed there until the makeshift tug has accumulated its full propellant load. The tug saves enough of its propellant to return empty to low orbit for refilling after each trip to geostationary orbit.

This scheme seems at first to give something for nothing, but it really doesn't. To paraphrase, "There is no such thing as a free launch." The shuttle is simply used to its maximum capacity, making it possible (maybe) to buy the SPS demonstration at a much lower cost.

I interject the "maybe" because like all promising new ideas this one needs careful engineering efforts before we can be sure it makes good economic sense. Although no new technology is involved, the electrolyzer and its solar-power supply need to be designed, developed, and tested: the tank/engine "tug" needs to be worked out to make sure the stresses are allowable; the logistic scheme needs to be "system-analyzed" to make sure everything is where it's supposed to be at the right time; and so on. So much engineering and testing is still needed before the "orbital propellant processing" concept can be put into operation.

An idea for using the "throwaway" shuttle propellant tank even more effectively than in Convair's scheme was suggested by Princeton's Gerard O'Neill. One of the essential elements in his space colonization scenario (which I'll discuss later) is a method of transferring raw materials from the surface of the moon to his space colonies. The approach he came up with was a modification of an idea originally suggested by Arthur Clarke: a "mass driver," essentially a linear electric motor. This device, which has been developed extensively for high-speed train propulsion here on earth, simply stretches an ordinary electric motor out into a straight line: the current-carrying armature is forced along the "field coil" (a straight track) instead of being forced to rotate as in an ordinary electric motor. It works even better in the vacuum of space than it does on the earth. So, to get his lunar raw material off the moon, O'Neill suggested that each armature coil be wrapped around a "bucket" into which a few pounds of lunar rock could be placed. The bucket would then be accelerated by a solar-powered (or nuclear-powered) linear electric motor to a speed high enough to escape the moon's gravity. The bucket is then braked, again using the linear-electric-motor principle, and the rocks fly off into space, eventually to be caught and used by the colony. To maintain the very large electric currents needed for high bucket acceleration, "superconducting" coils are used—again, a well-known technology made easier by the low ambient temperature in space (metals become superconductors only at extremely low temperatures).

Despite its science-fiction aspect, the mass driver is wholly feasible; in fact, a simple model was built and operated by M.I.T. students and demonstrated at the 1975 Princeton/AIAA conference. Whether or not it is *practical* has yet to be determined. In any case, when the problem of reducing the up-front cost of an SPS demonstration came along, O'Neill adapted his mass-driver idea to a new propulsion concept. Since every chunk of mass thrown out by the mass driver produces a force in the opposite direction, like the recoil of a gun, why not use it as a rocket engine? But instead of lunar mass, use chopped-up pieces of the big throwaway shuttle propellant tank. The benefit of using the mass driver was obvious: instead of the special propellants needed by rockets, any old junk would do. No special properties were required; all the mass-driver's propellant needed was mass—a property of *all* matter.

O'Neill's calculations showed that with a solar-powered mass-driver "rocket" (carried into low orbit by a few dedicated shuttle flights and then used as a tug for geostationary-orbit-transfer flights), the whole SPS demonstration project could be accomplished with the shuttle, without an inordinately large number of flights, simply by using every ounce of those big 70,000-pound throwaway tanks. But again, this wonderful scheme depends for its realization on even more intensive engineering development than the Convair approach—and the rosy picture might not turn out to be so rosy after all.

Many other imaginative ideas were advanced to bypass that high-cost SPS demonstration barrier. Some used the shuttle tank; others suggested different kinds of demonstrations. Various logistic approaches were considered, such as assembling the whole SPS demonstrator in low orbit and flying it up to geostationary orbit using its own self-generated power to drive electric ("ion") rockets to provide the required thrust. But as in most new undertakings, when the dust kicked up by everyone trying to get into the act began to settle a little, a rational approach to the evaluation of solar-power satellites began to evolve.

Sure, the in-orbit propellant-processing scheme and the mass driver and its ilk might work out, but it would take years to find out, and, as usual, there just wasn't enough budget to pay for the intensive development needed on all these promising schemes. Meanwhile, though, there were lots of ground-based researches and experiments that could be done, not only on "shuttle-amplifier" transportation approaches, but also on microwave devices, on fabrication methods for large space structures, on environmental effects of the microwave beam, on photovoltaic and solar-thermal power systems, on optimizing engineering parameters (including the proper satellite power level), and on the thousands of engineering details associated with *any* large system. The cost of such ground-based research would be fairly low; at most, $20 million or $30 million per year for a few years. If the ground-based research efforts didn't turn up any showstoppers, it would then make sense to proceed to some shuttle-based tests in low earth orbit, perhaps in the early 1980s. Such tests could utilize NASA's twenty-five-kilowatt solar-power module and its descendants to evaluate power transmission and electrical system details, and to check out prototypes of ultimate system components in the space environment, where they would eventually have to work. Construction, assembly, shape control, and maneuvering methods for large structures could be developed and tested in zero gravity, and interaction of in-space-generated microwaves with the upper atmosphere studied further. Again, if all went well, it would make sense to proceed to the next step: a small-scale prototype solar-power satellite at perhaps the one-megawatt level to check out and confirm the technology-development progress made up to that point. Such a device might even be useful in low earth orbit, although it wouldn't be able to deal with some of the questions that could only be answered by a geostationary-orbit experiment. At that point, but *only* then, would it be necessary to make the multi-billion-dollar decision: Should we or should we not build a demonstration SPS—at perhaps the 100- to 1,000-megawatt scale—in geostationary orbit?

Threaded through this phased approach to the project would be the properly parsimonious tactic of piggybacking research and development elements onto other programs. Advanced satellite-communications projects such as Edelson's orbital antenna farm will require extensive in-space development of large-structure technology and power-system switching and integration. Follow-ons to Spacelab experiments will need bigger power supplies, and possibly even transmission of power between a "power depot" satellite and a number of free-flying space-experiment pallets. Evaluation of man's productivity in performing tasks in space is needed for all shuttle and Spacelab activities. These and other non-SPS-related space projects have much technology in common with the SPS. When such "synergisms" are all carefully planned and scheduled for maximum beneficial interaction, the total cost increment chargeable solely to SPS research needed to make the big "go or no-go" SPS demonstration decision appears small enough to be well worth spending, in view of the enormous promise of the SPS concept if it turns out to be practical.

This seems rather obvious today, but getting all concerned to go along with so logical an approach was one of the toughest jobs accomplished since Sputnik went into orbit.

After Glaser's first publication in 1968, it was understandably difficult to get anyone interested in so mind-boggling a scheme. The Mars flight had just been dealt its death blow, the idea of a manned

The space-shuttle orbiter can be used as the work base for construction of large structures in space. Long, incredibly low-mass beams are fabricated out of aluminum foil by an automatic beam-builder machine (B-2).

Automatic machinery helps shuttle astronauts assemble a "workbench" for large-scale in-space experiments. The large dark panel at the top right is a solar-cell array, which provides essential electric power.

space station had all but disappeared, and even the shuttle was in a life-and-death struggle with OMB. Gasoline was flowing copiously from the pumps and the nation's wires hummed briskly with electricity. Who, then, was this crazy man who wanted to put a few square *miles* of solar cells into geostationary orbit?

Glaser got his company, Arthur D. Little, to put up some of its own money for preliminary studies, and he brought along three others: Raytheon, which was interested in all that microwave hardware; Grumman, which thought there might someday be a market building those square miles of structures in space; and Spectrolab, whose interest as a manufacturer of solar cells was obvious. Glaser was also able to get a few small study contracts from NASA to help assemble some of the engineering data and analyses. Buried in NASA's Advanced Programs budgets, these miniscule amounts of money were scarcely noticed in the OMB and congressional budget reviews. The

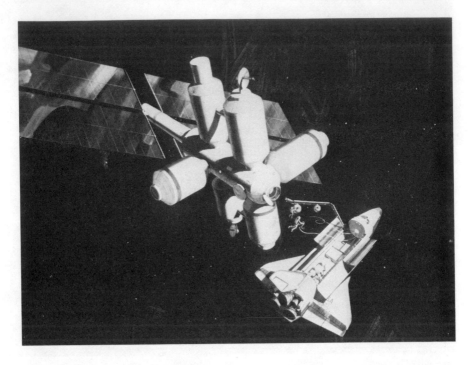

A "modular" space station to be ferried into orbit by several shuttle missions.

House Subcommittee on Space Science and Applications held hearings on the SPS in May 1973; the result was the creation in September 1974 of a NASA office at the Johnson Space Center to consolidate SPS study efforts. The hearings had little further effect; by 1974 NASA had spent a total of slightly over a million dollars.

Up to that point, of course, the AIAA had little to do with such pie-in-the-sky ideas as solar-power satellites and space colonization. Its concerns were in such relatively prosaic matters as shuttle development, reenergizing communications satellite research, making sure that the space-science program didn't go down the drain, and pushing hard for more research in aeronautics and in the basic space technologies of propulsion and power generation.

But in the spring of 1973 I was asked by the Institute of Electrical and Electronics Engineers (IEEE) to organize and chair a major symposium titled "Prospecting for Energy"; its purpose was to look into the future. Among the people I invited, along with speakers on

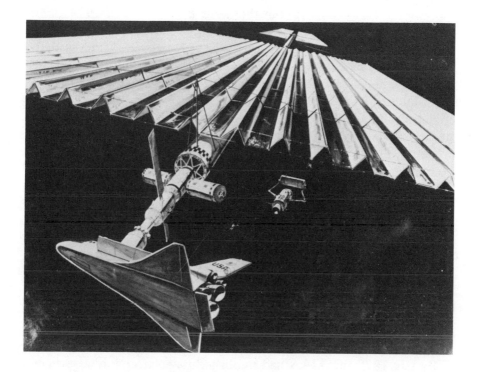

The shuttle-supplied space station is used as a "construction shack" from which to assemble enormous solar-power satellites.

nuclear fusion, hydrogen, and ground-based solar energy, was Peter Glaser. So when the time came for the AIAA to assemble its assessment of solar energy, I was at least prepared to listen to Glaser and to his associates from Raytheon, Grumman, and Spectrolab.

Now, although the SPS was clearly worth studying, a careful and relatively conservative approach to advancing and verifying its technology was warranted. But at this point—after the May 1973 hearings, the formation of a NASA space-power task group in 1974, and most important, the enactment in October 1974 of the Solar Energy Research, Development, and Demonstration Act and the Energy Reorganization Act—the solar-power satellite had suddenly sprung into visibility. And in the cutthroat process of hammering down federal budgets, visibility could spell disaster.

The SPS concept very quickly became a hot potato in the administration. Nobody knew what to do with it. Its technology was obviously in NASA's bailiwick, but the Solar Energy Act of 1974 clearly placed the responsibility for all solar-energy research and development for terrestrial use in the hands of the new Energy Research and Development Administration (ERDA).

So in mid-1975, when OMB was beginning to assemble the FY 1977 budget, responsibility for the SPS was assigned to ERDA. This effectively foreclosed upon NASA, so there was no funding for SPS studies in NASA's 1977 budget proposal to Congress.

But ERDA, meanwhile, said that *its* FY 1977 budget had already been assembled, and that there was no room to "shoehorn" a few million SPS dollars into their $2.4 billion research-and-development budget for that year. Actually, ERDA was under fire for its lack of stress on near-term solar-energy research, and wasn't about to re-program funds into so bizarre an area as solar-power satellites, which would have brought the solar-home enthusiasts down on the administration's neck.

It looked as if the SPS had "fallen in the crack"—there would be no funding at all in 1976-77—not even the paltry few hundred thousand that NASA had been burying in its annual Advanced Programs budgets in prior years.

By late 1975 the AIAA had published its solar energy assessment, had run several major articles on solar-power satellites in its monthly magazine, and had cosponsored Gerard O'Neill's Princeton Conference on Space Manufacturing Facilities. The AIAA's position, supportive of a vigorous SPS technology effort to "define the problem" but *not* a demonstration SPS, was beginning to crystallize. But it was clear that without intervention, the SPS would be lost in the ERDA-NASA buck-shuffling. And the only source for effective intervention at this stage in the budget process was the Congress.

Congress had been casually interested in the SPS up to this point, but not sufficiently to dig deeply into something that involved so miniscule a portion of the federal budget. The whole SPS debate hinged on a few million dollars—scarcely a matter for intense concern by committees whose purview embraced the $3.5 billion NASA budget or the $6 billion ERDA budget. But the AIAA, whose interests had much longer range than those of elected representatives or appointees of the elected President, was concerned that a subject that *might* have significant impact on so important an area as the world's energy future was being swept under the administrative rug. I met with the staff of the Senate Aeronautical and Space Sciences Committee and outlined the reasons for holding full hearings (by the Subcommittee on Aerospace Technology and National Needs) on solar-power satellites. The staff was cautious about holding such hearings and hesitant to make such a recommendation to the subcommittee chairman, Senator Wendell Ford, but after talking to us, one of them later told a reporter, "They [the AIAA] made me take a second look."

The Senate's hearings were held on January 19 and 21, 1976 (the House Subcommittee on Space Science and Applications held similar hearings a few weeks later), and Senator Ford's grilling of John Teem, the ERDA assistant administrator for solar, geothermal, and advanced programs, produced some most illuminating byplay. Teem admitted that "due to a communications glitch" in his agency, he had just heard that the SPS project had been assigned to his office "last week," and his FY 1977 budget had already been sent to Congress! As Senator Ford so unerringly forecast,

> I am concerned that if you have gotten something you don't want, what are you going to do with it? . . . With something being thrust on you that you didn't want. . . . Your people won't have much enthusiasm for the potential here. . . . What I want to know is who is going to carry the ball from now on and who has the responsibility for deciding whether we develop a satellite solar-power system? . . . It might be put on the back burner, and . . . it would be a long time before you got around to making a judgment.

Although Teem did indicate his intention "to give solar-power satellites full consideration," despite the "glitch," such good intentions went for naught when he resigned a few weeks later because of the unwillingness of his top brass in ERDA to allow him the staff he needed to manage his burgeoning solar-energy development program. His place was taken by Robert L. Hirsch, former director of ERDA's nuclear-fusion research effort. Since the SPS was often cited as being competitive with the equally esoteric, but heavily funded—$460 million in FY 1979—fusion program both in its commercial-operations time frame (early twenty-first century) and in its projected economic potential, it seemed apparent that the SPS would get short shrift from ERDA.

The congressional hearings on the FY 1977 budget did have some impact, though. The House Authorization Committee, expressing its dismay at the failure of *both* NASA and ERDA to request any funds for SPS, added $5 million to NASA's budget request. The Senate Authorization Committee decided it was more important to request a clarification of the administration's energy reorganization policy, without requesting funds. The two Appropriations committees followed the same pattern, and the Conference Committee (whose job is to resolve differences between the Senate and the House) adopted a compromise of $2.5 million for NASA, to which ERDA added another $0.6 million. A similar pattern was followed for FY 1978, with $4.5 million eventually getting allocated to SPS research.

Of the $7.6 million authorized for the two fiscal years, NASA used its $4.2 million to develop preliminary Phase A concept analyses, both in-house and by outside contractors (mainly Boeing and Rockwell International). But ERDA's $3.4 million seemed to disappear; all that showed up was a program plan for future efforts, developed by a joint ERDA/NASA task force.

By now congressional interest in the SPS had accelerated to a high level. Solar energy was making headlines, and the SPS in particular drew considerable enthusiasm from back-home constituencies. ERDA's lackadaisical approach began to raise all sorts of hackles on Capitol Hill. So when the FY 1979 budget request reached Congress early in 1978, the stage was set for another knock-down, drag-out fight between Congress and the administration.

The SPS had already figured heavily in Tiger Teague's January hearings on the future of space. Its paltry funding, along with obvious lack of interest on the part of the new Department of Energy (DOE) (which had risen phoenixlike from ERDA's ashes on October 1, 1977), had the members of Teague's powerful Science and Technology Committee calling for a clear definition of the administration's long-term space and energy priorities (see discussion in Chapter Six). But the real action began to show up on February 8, 1978, when both Department of Energy and NASA officials showed up to testify on the *overall* national DOE/NASA energy effort before Don Fuqua's Subcommittee on Space Science and Applications.

It was quite a show.

DOE was asking for $4.6 million for SPS in their FY 1979 budget, the bulk of which was to be spent not by NASA, but by DOE itself on such matters as environmental factors, socio-economic aspects, and alternative energy source comparisons—uncovering "all the reasons not to do it," as one House staffer put it. (Pres Layton's metaphor was even more graphic. He cited the DOE study as "starting with *three* strikes against it—the only hope is that the catcher will drop the ball!")

Appearing before Fuqua's committee was Dale Myers, newly appointed undersecretary of DOE and former associate administrator of manned space flight for NASA. As an "old friend" of the Space Committee, I'm sure he expected little or no flak; just the routine oversight review of the $120 million "pass-through" of DOE funds to NASA for their various energy-technology efforts. The portent was obvious as soon as we saw that an unprecedented nine congressmen (almost the entire subcommittee) had shown up for what was normally a relatively minor activity. I was there that day to testify for the AIAA in *support* of a significant increase in SPS technology funds. For once I was glad to be on the right side!

The congressmen went after Myers hammer and tongs. His agency had proposed a $10 billion budget on energy—perhaps the world's hottest topic these days—but he was quizzed for almost the full two hours of his appearance on that puny $4.6 million SPS program! Chairman Fuqua first tried to identify what happened to the $3.4 million ERDA/DOE had purportedly spent in 1977 and 1978. It turned out that only *one person* was assigned by DOE to the SPS effort, although Myers hastened to add that there was considerable staff support as well. Congressman Ronnie G. Flippo from Alabama jested, "Aha! So *he's* the three point four million-dollar man!" After asking Myers how many employees DOE had in total (18,500), Fuqua, referring to that one man, said, "That's just about the level of effort we *figured* it was getting! . . . SPS has been a stepchild of ERDA and DOE. This program has great support from Congress. I've never seen any place in the government where one man can get anything done. I hope your reorganization will give it more effort."

Later questioning showed it to be even worse—that "3.4-million-dollar man" was only assigned *part* time to SPS; he didn't move to become full-time project director until May 1.

On another tack, Flippo asked Myers if the funding level was sufficient; weren't the sixty man-years already spent on SPS "paper studies" enough? Shouldn't DOE now move more actively into technology verification and other *experimental* work? Upon Myers' response that "we need a lot more analysis," Flippo blasted, "You don't have all the environmental answers on [nuclear] fusion, right? Yet you spend hundreds of millions on fusion and nothing on SPS! . . . Your comments express my fears . . . DOE has already decided, and your [tiny] budget reflects it!"

Congressman Albert Gore, Jr., of Tennessee then took up the cudgel. He stressed the Carter administration's typical approach in emphasizing the short term, letting the long term "sit it out" for a while. Long-term confidence even increases short-term flexibility, he said, and "it seems you ignore this in your short-term efforts." Gore insisted that OPEC (Organization of Petroleum Exporting Countries) reacts to alternative energy prospects, even long-term ones like SPS, in setting its oil prices, a point Myers had earlier denied. (Just the day before, incidentally, DOE Deputy Secretary John O'Leary had told an AIAA meeting in Washington that a solid projection of future low costs for solar cells *would* put a cap on oil prices; further, Klaus Heiss's ECON had clearly documented the sizable impact energy research had on *current* oil prices, even very long-range research having payoffs as far off as a century in the future.)

Congressman Louis Frey (Florida) was next to work Myers over. First he led Myers gently by the nose, asking how long the shuttle was studied before making a commitment to proceed; answer: three to four years. He established that another "advanced" energy scheme, ocean thermal-electric conversion, took five years before escalating into subscale demonstration projects. "We've been compounding this error over the past ten years," Frey suddenly thundered. "We haven't utilized the potential of NASA. Sixty man-years after ten years! In ten more we'll have a hundred and twenty—working on the biggest problem in the world! We're *past* the study point; we should be building. . . . I try to keep the budget under control, but this is *one* area we should be spending in!"

Bob Gammage of Texas added his fuel: "You've detected the spirit of this committee today. [The SPS] *will* be expensive; we know that. We also know it *can* be done, and *will* be done. That's what distresses Congress; it's regarded as a stepchild by the administration, whereas it should be a major activity. We should be developing these long-term resources as rapidly as possible. . . . [This effort] has been 'bootlegged' at NASA for a long time because Congress was short-sighted. We're not now, though!"

Myers doggedly stuck to his (that is, the administration's) point:

don't proceed until you know what you're doing. The congressmen took no issue with the principle itself, but they wanted to move a lot faster than the present snail's pace toward accumulating the necessary knowledge that would tell how and when to proceed.

The AIAA's testimony, which followed right on the heels of Myers' grilling, was much more to the subcommittee's liking. The institute's technical committees had adopted a sound approach to the mechanics of developing the data needed to make an SPS decision, and had decided it would cost about $30 million per year "on the ground" for a few years, before proceeding on to more expensive in-space experiments. The institute reiterated its conclusions that a demonstration was not yet appropriate (it would, in fact, be detrimental if conducted too early) and that even settling on a preliminary "base-line" design by early 1980, as DOE wanted to do, was premature. There were too many options still to be considered in depth (like the up-front economies described earlier), and money was needed to consider them.

It turned out that Flippo had already introduced (on January 30) a separate Solar Power Satellite bill, calling for a specific effort by DOE at a level of $25 million per year. At the Joint Energy and Space Subcommittee hearings on that bill in April 1978, I reiterated the AIAA's position, and took the opportunity, during over an hour's questioning by the congressmen, to provide them with some insight into the key technical, environmental, and economic details of the SPS concept. The message appeared to get through loud and clear. As Don Fuqua (chairman of the Space Subcommittee) commented,

> The level of effort being devoted to these [DOE] paper studies is insufficient to obtain definitive answers to the questions which arise related to technical feasibility, environmental concerns, economic feasibility, and others. With the continuing energy crisis all potential energy sources should be thoroughly evaluated to determine their value to our Nation. Even though the concept appears to offer an attractive inexhaustible energy alternative, the idea has been treated much like a stepchild by Department of Energy officials. This legislation [Mr. Flippo's bill—HR 12505] does not attempt to immediately commit the Nation to an expensive development program; however, it will enable us to move forward with a technology program that will adequately address the unresolved issues.

The Flippo bill surprised friend and foe alike (New York's Congressman Richard Ottinger opposed the SPS, in true Proxmire style, by warning that its microwaves would "zap" everyone for miles around —a physically impossible consequence) by breezing through the House, 267 to 96. But without a companion bill in the Senate, it could go nowhere. On April 7, 1978, I had testified on behalf of the AIAA before the Senate Subcommittee on Research and Development of the Committee on Energy and Natural Resources, which oversees the Department of Energy's budget. After a long string of witnesses touting the nuclear-fission breeder reactor, the SPS, a truly bizarre concept to these nonspace-oriented senators, must have seemed like a breath of fresh air. The two senators present, Spark Matsunaga of Hawaii (who chaired the hearing in Senator Church's absence) and John Melcher of Montana, were fascinated. Some of their comments from the record follow:

Senator Matsunaga: Thank you very much, Dr. Grey. I am much impressed with your idea of space solar power . . . maybe yours is the solution to perfecting our environment and at the same time have sufficient energy to meet our needs here."

Senator Melcher: I think it's without doubt a program that must be pursued as rapidly as we can; I particularly do not feel that the Department of Energy has the last word on where we place our priorities.

Senator Matsunaga: We certainly appreciate your taking your time out and carrying us into the great future, the twenty-first century.

But the most important feature of that hearing was a series of searching questions, mainly from Senator Melcher, involving the level of current expenditures by the DOE and what the AIAA's recommendations were vis-à-vis those of Mr. Flippo's SPS bill (they were very close). The bottom line: that very afternoon Mr. Melcher introduced the essential companion Senate bill to Mr. Flippo's—S-2860. Hearings were held on August 14, despite the extremely crowded Senate calendar that year, and it seemed highly probable that if the bill ever got to the Senate floor it would pass with flying colors, just as it had in the House.

But real life is often very different than that in storybooks. The Senate bill got bottled up in the Energy Committee because of jurisdictional concerns—a frequent occurrence in the political arena. Senator Stevenson, who was responsible for space, wanted NASA to play a significant role in a project having such major space implications, and he got his powerful committee chairman, Howard Cannon, to inter-

A "constellation" of thirty solar-power satellites as they might look from the state of Washington in June. These thirty satellites could provide more than the entire current U.S. electric-power demand. Illustration courtesy of the Boeing Aerospace Company.

cede. Senator Henry Jackson, on the other hand, as chairman of the Energy Committee, wanted to keep his jurisdiction over all energy options for terrestrial use. The result was a badly emasculated bill with no NASA participation—a situation that could never have been reconciled with the strong House position in a House/Senate conference. Senator Harrison Schmitt got so incensed at the resulting inaction that he went ahead and submitted his *own* bill, much like Congressman Flippo's, although he recognized quite well that a bill introduced by a junior Republican would stand little chance against one endorsed by a committee. Nevertheless, his point was well taken: NASA must have a substantial role in any SPS research and technology effort, for the sake of synergism with other advanced space programs, if for no other reason. However, neither Schmitt's nor the emasculated Melcher bill got through the Senate that year. But there *was* at least one good result of all the pushing and shoving. The Department of Energy increased its FY 1980 budget request for SPS research from the $3 million originally planned to over $8 million, and the House and Senate agreed to give NASA $2 million more in FY 1979, specifically for SPS research. It wasn't enough, but it was at least a positive signal.

During all this, the AIAA was not, of course, the only organization supporting SPS research and development, although it was certainly the most prestigious and by far the most conservative. The AIAA position paper on solar-power satellites, when it was finally released for publication in late 1978, was most properly a model of caution in recommending, with all the necessary caveats, the technology advancements and verification efforts needed. Meanwhile, Peter Glaser had formed an industry group, the Sunsat Energy Council, with the avowed purpose of promoting an early SPS demonstration. Its legal counsel was the former chairman of the Senate Aeronautical and Space Sciences Committee, Frank Moss. Although it of course supported the Flippo SPS bill strongly, Sunsat's proposal was about twice as ambitious: to spend $200 million over the next five years on SPS development.

Another group of organizations was promoting an even more active approach to a much more far-reaching concept. The L-5 Society of Tucson, Arizona, the Space Studies Institute of Princeton, New Jersey, and the Working Group on Power from Space of the Universities Space Research Association, headquartered in Houston, Texas, all espoused active consideration (and commensurate funding) of a serious effort to explore the use of *nonterrestrial* materials for manufacturing solar-power satellites. And therein lies another episode of swashbuckling adventure in the story of *Enterprise*.

The space colonization concept that Gerard O'Neill began popularizing in the mid-1970s had really taken hold of a generation who in the post-Vietnam war period were seeking a new cause. The marvelous idea of extending mankind's limits almost indefinitely, as promised by O'Neill's multiple-space-colony concept, offered just such a vehicle. They jumped on board in droves, and began drumming up interest in O'Neill's ideas by talking to school and college groups, by besieging their congressmen and senators with letters and phone calls, and by calling attention with whatever means their fertile and totally captivated minds could dream up. During the 1975 Princeton Conference on Space Manufacturing Facilities, a group of them got together and formed the L-5 Society, named after a point in the moon's orbit equidistant from the earth and the moon. At that point the centrifugal force on an object due to its orbital speed would be exactly balanced by gravitational forces from the earth and moon, so that the object would remain there forever without any need for propulsion. This point was deduced by the mathematician Joseph Louis Lagrange, who named it as one of five "libration" points in the earth-moon system—hence L-5. An orbit around L-5 was one of the early locations identified by O'Neill for his colonies. The L-5 Society's clearly stated long-range goal was "to disband the society in a mass meeting at L-5." Their motivation was almost religious in its fervor, and their messiah was Gerard O'Neill.

The subject of space colonies has received considerable public attention, not only in newspapers, periodicals, and television documentaries and panel shows, but also in several hard-cover books, the most notable of which was O'Neill's own *High Frontier*. Although of great general interest, the subject concerns us here mainly because of its impact on space enterprise; I direct those readers who wish further information on space colonies to O'Neill's and other books.*

Despite the enormous accolades O'Neill received from the enthusiastic youth sector (as well as members of the "lunatic fringe," such as Timothy Leary), he ran into a brick wall when he attempted to get recognition and financing from the space establishment. A few far-seeing NASA planners recognized in O'Neill's ideas a revival of their long-lost hopes for extensive manned operations in space, and realized the value of the public support he had almost single-handedly garnered. Captain Robert Freitag, who had fired up Burt Edelson's enthusiasm at that first meeting on Navy satellite communications systems, and Jesco von Puttkamer of NASA's Advanced Programs office were able to divert a few thousand dollars to O'Neill's studies, and the director of NASA's Ames Research Center, Hans Mark (who later became deputy secretary of the Air Force in the Carter administration), provided funds for several summer studies of O'Neill's con-

---

* Gerard K. O'Neill, *The High Frontier: Human Colonies in Space* (New York: William Morrow & Co., 1977), also a Bantam Books paperback, 1978; Thomas A. Heppenheimer, *Colonies in Space* (New York: Stackpole Books, 1977); Frederic Golden, *Colonies in Space* (New York: Harcourt Brace Jovanovich, 1977).

cepts in cooperation with Stanford University. A few congressmen, too, persuaded by influential constituents like toy heiress Barbara Marx Hubbard (an early O'Neill convert) and Dean Stephen Cheston of Georgetown University, made supportive statements. Senator Barry Goldwater even agreed to join the board of directors of the Arizona-based L-5 Society.

But aside from these few oases in the wilderness, space colonization was generally considered by those who held the purse strings as just a little bit farther down the pike than extrasensory perception. O'Neill desperately needed to get the space establishment on his side if he was ever going to get his ideas seriously considered or, even more important, adequately funded. Early in 1975 two events occurred that saved the concept of mass movements of people into space: O'Neill got the support of the AIAA and he came up with the idea of tying his space colonies to solar-power satellites.

The AIAA's involvement with O'Neill's concepts came about, as do many significant events, mainly because the timing was just right. As seen earlier, the AIAA was the product of a 1963 amalgamation of two societies: the staid, conservative Institute of the Aerospace Sciences and the enthusiastic, flamboyant American Rocket Society. After its first decade, the AIAA was subjected to much criticism because it was becoming too conservative, with too much of an industry viewpoint. Critics asked what had happened to the excitement generated by those crazy amateurs who fired their even crazier rockets behind sandbags in the New Jersey meadows in 1931? Where was the wild enthusiasm that resulted after each successful rocket-launched space mission in the early 1960s? In 1974 the institute was on the lookout for activities that might help to resurrect the kind of pioneer spirit it seemed to have lost. I spotted Walter Sullivan's May 13, 1974, story in *The New York Times*, describing O'Neill's first one-day Princeton conference on space colonies, and in my capacity then as administrator of technical activities of the AIAA I shot off a memo (on May 16) to all the institute's technical committees, suggesting that their next meeting agendas consider space colonies as an area for AIAA activity.

It took some doing, but by that fall I had secured the approval of the AIAA's board of directors for the AIAA to lend O'Neill its support by cosponsoring the May 1975 Princeton conference. In fact, AIAA board member Rene Miller, the head of M.I.T.'s prestigious

Department of Aeronautics and Astronautics, became so fascinated by the subject that he invited O'Neill to spend the academic year 1976-77 at M.I.T. as visiting Jerome C. Hunsaker professor. At M.I.T., incidentally, O'Neill was brought into contact with electromagnetic expert Henry Kolm of M.I.T.'s Francis Bitter Magnet Laboratory, who provided O'Neill with the expertise needed to make the "mass driver," a key element in O'Neill's concepts, a potentially practical and useful device.

The May 1975 Princeton conference formally launched the space colonization idea as a matter deserving serious consideration rather than as Sunday-supplement material designed to catch the public's fancy. With the AIAA behind it, the program boasted such "establishment" names as Hu Davis (NASA Johnson Space Center), Bob Salkeld (later chairman of AIAA's Space Systems Technical Committee), Arthur Kantrowitz (president of AVCO's Everett Research Laboratory), Lou McCreight (General Electric), Ludwig Glaeser (Museum of Modern Art), Gus Rauschenbach (COMSAT), Bob Freitag and Jesco von Puttkamer (NASA), Al Hibbs (Jet Propulsion Lab), and John Billingham (NASA's Ames Research Center), as well as some old friends: Del Tischler, Philomena Grodzka, Gordon Woodcock (Boeing) and Peter Glaser. I presented one of the four summary lectures on the final day; the others were by O'Neill, Hibbs, and Billingham. (The AIAA later published the text of the proceedings as a hard-cover book, *Space Manufacturing Facilities (Space Colonies),* which also included the text of the 1974 conference as a "historical" appendix.)

The AIAA's support of his efforts gave O'Neill the institutional backing he had to have. But a hardheaded economic basis for so costly an undertaking as space colonization was also necessary. That basis (or at least its potential) was conveniently provided by the solar-power satellite program, which was just beginning to achieve visibility in late 1974. If the SPS turned out to be a worthwhile endeavor and construction of "production" versions were to proceed, what better use for all those people in O'Neill's space colonies than to build the power plants? Here was a built-in economic rationale for their existence: with the potential payback that some economists were predicting, based on delivered electricity at prices around five cents per kilowatt-hour, the space colonies could become self-supporting over time spans as short as a decade.

The heart of O'Neill's economic argument was a new and extremely interesting wrinkle. Among the biggest problems faced by SPS devotees was the high costs of developing the big space transportation system needed to launch the materials for those 100,000-ton power plants to geostationary orbits, and also the environmental impact of the launching rockets—hundreds per year, each ten times bigger than the shuttle. So, O'Neill reasoned, why not take materials from the surface of the moon, launch them to a "space manufacturing facility" (see the reason for the title of the 1975 Princeton conference?), and use them to build solar power plants? The power plants could then be ferried easily from the space factory to their geostationary-orbit position, and begin delivering gigawatts of electric power to an energy-hungry earth.

O'Neill had the physics of planetary flight working for him: because of lower gravity, it takes only about a twentieth as much energy to throw a pound of payload off the moon as it does off the earth. Also the absence of an atmosphere on the moon permits the use of an electromagnetic "thrower"—the mass driver—which needs only electric power for its operation (available from either nuclear or solar energy), instead of chemical rockets with their potentially polluting exhaust gases. Moreover, the moon rocks gathered by the six Apollo lunar-landing missions had been found to contain a high percentage of such important solar-power-satellite component materials as aluminum, titanium, iron, silicon (for all those solar cells), and lots and lots of oxygen.

So instead of continuing to push space colonization as the solution to "limits-to-growth" problems on earth, O'Neill switched gears and touted his space colonies as "construction shacks" whose inhabitants would build solar-power satellites out of nonterrestrial materials. The 1975 Princeton conference was the first public presentation of this scheme. O'Neill later wrote a series of articles for the AIAA's magazine, *Astronautics and Aeronautics*, elaborating upon the details of this approach, and it was also published in the prestigious magazine *Science* in December 1975.

Meanwhile, O'Neill hadn't stopped his publicity campaign. He was a frequent guest on television talk shows, almost rivaling Carl Sagan in popularity. With the help of Washington-wise supporters like Barbara Marx Hubbard and Steve Cheston, he was also able to get Tiger Teague, chairman of the powerful House Committee on Science and

Technology, to submit Concurrent Resolution HR-451, calling for "every feasible means [to] be mobilized to explore and assess the resources of the 'high frontier' of outer space" and asking the Office of Technology Assessment to study "the feasibility, potential consequences, advantages, and disadvantages of developing as a national goal for the year 2000 the first manned structures in space for the conversion of solar energy and other extraterrestrial resources to the peaceful and practical use of human beings everywhere." O'Neill was also successful in getting New Jersey Senator Harrison Williams to sponsor a bill that would provide the National Science Foundation with one million dollars to be spent in two years on solar-power-satellite research, particularly the nonterrestrial-materials option.

I had gotten to know Gerry O'Neill and his wife Tasha (short for

In the event that solar-power satellites turn out to be so good that tens or hundreds of them are needed, it would make sense to utilize materials already in space, instead of having to drag everything up against the earth's heavy gravity. This is a lunar mining station, which uses a linear electric motor called a "mass driver" to throw lunar material to a space-based power-satellite factory.

Natasha) quite well after the 1975 Princeton conference. During his tenure as Hunsaker professor at M.I.T., he often had to commute between Cambridge and Princeton, which he did in his pretty little four-place red-and-white Piper Comanche single-engine plane (both he and Tasha are skilled private pilots). Since we both operated on incredibly tight schedules, we sandwiched in our meetings by having him fly to East Hampton (New York) airport as a "way station" on his Cambridge-to-Princeton shuttle. Florence and I would pick Tasha and him up in East Hampton, and we'd all spend many a pleasant evening in my Bridgehampton home, feasting on the superb Long Island fish and fresh vegetables, and working out the details of AIAA/ Princeton collaboration on developments in space.

Unfortunately, though, O'Neill was totally captivated by the enormous publicity he was capable of generating, and he was therefore easily hoodwinked by self-serving types who provided him access to even more publicity. I often warned him about the people with whom he was surrounding himself; he did himself and his cause much damage by the consequent semi-lunatic-fringe aura that began to pervade his serious and important research activities. Fortunately, the solid AIAA image did much to counteract that aura, and the nonterrestrial-materials option still represents a significant potential approach to the wide-scale commercial deployment of solar-power satellites, should the phased research program and eventual demonstration prove them to be economically practical.

I wasn't the only one concerned about O'Neill's understandable thirst for publicity. I'm not knocking publicity—public acceptance is a key element in any national effort, as I've reiterated so many times in congressional testimony and elsewhere—but when the flavor of that publicity implies sensationalism or irresponsibility, its value in supporting any undertaking with real potential benefit becomes prejudiced. O'Neill's most voluble critic in this regard was also one of his first converts—an abrasive young near-genius named Tom Heppenheimer.

Born in 1946 of German immigrant parents who came to the United States in 1936 to escape the Nazis, Heppenheimer spent most of his early years in the intellectual desert of Panama's Canal Zone, where his father was a toolmaker. Despite the lack of stimulation (he says that "all the way through grammar school, high school, and college, all I wanted was to be left alone to pursue my own ideas"), he won a National Science Foundation fellowship to study for his Ph.D. at the University of Michigan's aerospace engineering department, where he was delighted to encounter the first real challenge to his innate intelligence.

While at Michigan he began what was to become his favorite activity: poking his vinegary intellect into national aerospace policy. He and another firebrand student, David Fradin, formed the Federation of American Students for the Supersonic Transport (FASST) to battle the misinformation that the anti-SST coalition and their Washington champion, Bill Proxmire, were broadcasting. When the SST battle was lost, FASST changed its name (but not its acronym) to the Forum for the Advancement of Students in Science and Technology, and at present it is probably the biggest and most important student organization lobbying in the interest of technology as the potential saviour of mankind.

His bright new Michigan Ph.D. didn't help Heppenheimer much in his career, though. After brief and abortive periods working for Systems Applications, Inc., and Rockwell International, he went to Cal Tech for a post-doctoral research faculty stint. That's when he really got turned on to planetary science—and encountered O'Neill and his ideas. He was totally captivated. At his own expense he attended the 1975 Princeton conference; he became one of the founding members of the L-5 Society; and he was an outstanding participant in the first (1975) NASA/Stanford summer study of space colonization.

But Heppenheimer, brilliant as he was, had a disquieting arrogance about him that precluded any possibility of working easily with people. His personal life was a mess. After a year or so of "O'Neill watching," he turned from a worshiper to a critic (of O'Neill himself, not of space colonization, which continues to be Heppenheimer's primary motivation in life). Almost paranoid in his enmity, he derogates O'Neill as "an uneducated opportunist who surrounds himself with sycophants who tell him how great he is instead of with real scientists (like Heppenheimer!) who will challenge but abrade him." Heppenheimer insists O'Neill "stole" the idea of the mass driver from him (O'Neill himself has clearly stated on a number of public occasions, as well as in his publications, that he got the idea from a *Scientific American* article by M.I.T.'s Henry Kolm), and that O'Neill also stole Heppenheimer's concept of the achromatic trajectory, a unique approach to launching lunar raw materials from the moon's surface so they reach a given point in space (the space factory) with almost perfect accuracy. Again, Heppenheimer's comprehensive analysis of this concept, which I had acclaimed as "elegant" in my summary presentation at the May 1977 Princeton conference, is clearly and gladly acknowledged by O'Neill, who considers Heppenheimer a truly brilliant scientist, but a total loss in working with anybody but Heppenheimer.

An obvious explanation of Heppenheimer's turnaround from adulation to vitriolic animosity was O'Neill's refusal to bring him to Princeton when a research staff opportunity opened up there via a NASA grant in 1976. "He was afraid of the competitive challenge I, as a *real* science practitioner, would offer," Heppenheimer told me. "Instead, he hired [Brian] O'Leary. O'Leary is a dreamer; he won't challenge or compete with O'Neill; he just tells him how good he is!"

Accordingly, Heppenheimer has chosen to compete with O'Neill on his home ground—publicizing space colonies. His book *Colonies in Space* is indeed very well written and a serious competitor to O'Neill's *High Frontier.* Unable to find a technical job he can live with, Heppenheimer sells real estate in California and collects royalties on his books, so that he can devote most of his time to scientific analyses of the astrodynamics involved in space colonies and solar-power satellites. Whatever his relationship with O'Neill, Heppenheimer will undoubtedly continue to pop up, like other gadflies before him in the space enterprise, because of his unquestioned technical ability and personal (albeit abrasive) flamboyance.

Totally different from Heppenheimer in virtually all respects is Brian O'Leary, O'Neill's research sidekick at Princeton. One of the first scientist-astronauts selected by NASA back in the 1960s, his disenchantment with what he thought was the squelching of any real scientific opportunity during the Apollo program had turned him into a severe critic of the shuttle, and he was extensively used as such by Walter Mondale during the senator's 1972 anti-shuttle campaign.

Soft-spoken, almost boyishly attractive with his curly reddish hair, open face, and always-ready smile, O'Leary first encountered O'Neill's ideas in 1974, when the Princeton physics professor lectured at the small New Hampshire college where O'Leary was a faculty member. The opportunities offered by space colonies in his fields of astrophysics and planetary research were virtually limitless. He became an O'Neill convert almost immediately, and when the staff job opportunity opened up at Princeton, he jumped at it.

O'Leary's ideas transcend even O'Neill's in some areas. His research on asteroid trajectories revealed that numbers of sizable asteroids regularly come quite close to the earth's orbit, with more and more such "earth-approaching" asteroids being discovered each year. Now, asteroids have been found (by remote spectrographic analysis) to contain enormous quantities of valuable materials. Some may be almost pure nickel-steel, and there is considerable evidence that others, like already-discovered meteorites called "carbonaceous chondrites," contain both carbon and hydrogen—the two critically needed elements that have not yet been found in useful quantities on the moon. O'Leary therefore picked up an old idea suggested back in the early 1960s by AVCO's renowned Arthur Kantrowitz—mining the asteroids for raw materials—and ran with it. Besides expanding the search for earth-approaching asteroids, to increase the probability of finding a rich "strike," he proposed adapting O'Neill's mass-driver propulsion concept to perform a truly stupendous feat: bringing home (to the space-based factory) a whole asteroid—millions upon millions of tons of valuable minerals! The solar- (or nuclear-) powered mass driver would simply mine the asteroid for the mass it needed to develop its thrust; the remainder of a single, relatively small (one-mile) asteroid could supply enough materials for hundreds of solar-power satellites. Should such a concept prove out, it could reduce the ultimate cost of power delivered from an SPS by factors of two or more below that of any competitive ground-based power source—again, provided the millions of engineering "details" could be worked out satisfactorily.

The space shuttle, of course, was an essential element in O'Leary's scheme—to carry the mass driver and its power supply into orbit, among other things. So O'Leary found himself, after all his negativism during the anti-shuttle crusade of the early 1970s, not just grudgingly going along with it, but an out-and-out devotee of shuttle development.* Without it, his asteroid-retrieval dream would remain just that—an unachievable dream.

* He was quite willing to admit the shortsightedness of his earlier views on the shuttle. In fact, when Glen Wilson challenged him at a Washington party in 1976 to write a letter to Senate Space Committee Chairman Frank Moss recanting his previous negative position, he readily and gladly did so. It's printed on p. 1102 of the committee's hearing record for the FY 1977 NASA authorization.

Although many of the people O'Neill's ideas drew out of the woodwork were just hangers-on—the usual assortment of acolytes and "weirdos" who attach themselves to any out-of-the-ordinary movement—some were truly fascinating characters. At the first Princeton conference, I remember Florence's and my utter delight, after our years of association with conservative engineer-types like Pres Layton, Del Tischler, and Burt Edelson, to encounter "Earth Mother" Carolyn Meinel Henson, a tall, articulate blonde (daughter of solar-energy pioneers Marjorie and Aden Meinel) who discoursed learnedly on the relative advantages of rabbits versus sheep and chickens as protein sources in a space colony! Or sociologist Magoroh Maruyama, whose individual words on "Diversity, Survival Value, and Enrichment: Design Principles for Extraterrestrial Communities" were all in completely understandable English, but made no sense to us at all. Or Marjorie Stuart, a self-appointed designer of efficient space

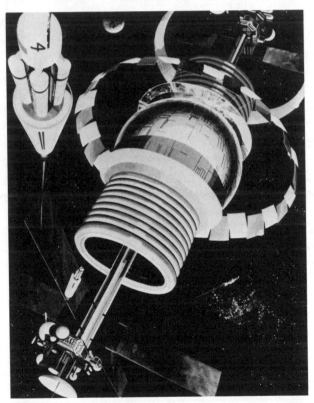

Eventually it might be economically worthwhile to base the power-satellite construction work force permanently in space. This is one of many designs for such space habitats.

colonies, who used her business acumen as a builder of stage magicians' accoutrements to skillfully pack all the space colony's necessities into the smallest possible space (she designed Doug Henning's famous "disappearing elephant" gadgetry, among others).

But the most fascinating thing about these people was that they were deadly serious about the whole matter of space colonization. In fact, a few years of tangling with the Washington bureaucracy and its characteristic of brushing off any new ideas that might rock the boat a little only stiffened their resolve and, indeed, sharpened their tools—hacking away at virtually immovable objects. The L-5 Society (almost single-handedly run by Tucson, Arizona's, Carolyn Meinel Henson and her husband Keith) changed in a few years from a "bunch of weird, young space nuts" to a viable, energetic, lobby-wise, tightly knit organization of well-informed space-program supporters (shades of the old American Rocket Society), boasting thousands of members around the world, including many staid, old AIAA members like me! Their monthly "slick" magazine is well crafted and beautifully written. They know exactly where they're headed—into space, in *their* generation—and what's more, they know how to go about getting there. The tools are all in hand, the economics have a good chance of being practical (although sizable), and, most important, the pioneering spirit that carried our forebears across uncharted oceans and untracked wildernesses has risen again, embodied in dedicated, capable, but unfettered young minds like those of the Hensons and Tom Heppenheimer.

The future is theirs. I think they'll know what to do with it.

THE FUTURE

"As the cathedrals were the symbols of a faith and a system of values, so may be the launching pads of Cape Canaveral, the deep-space antennas of Arecibo and Goldstone, the computerized control rooms of Houston and Pasadena. This is, for better or worse, a technological society, and the monuments of its exploration of space are some of the highest expressions of its faith in what is worth striving for and what may be attainable."

—*John Noble Wilford*
The New York Times
July 4, 1976

THERE EXISTS TODAY A SMALL BAND OF DEDICATED SCIENTISTS WHOSE faith in their quest has withstood ridicule, budgetary starvation, and decades barren of promising results or even vague indications of potential success. Their grail is the elusive concept of probability; their altar is the inconceivable enormity of the cosmos. They seek to detect intelligent life elsewhere in the universe.

The strength of their faith might seem born of fanaticism rather than of reason, until one ponders for a moment the consequences of success in their search. The discovery of an intelligent race of beings would affect our own human race not only in the technological sense of John Wilford's bicentennial message; it would very likely stir the very roots of the sociological framework on which our modern life is based. Who can guess what might ensue? New technologies needed to feed the earth's mushrooming populations or to provide ever-increasing sources of energy; a different basis for the world's religions; new legacies of arts and letters; a change in our views of human and international conflicts; new approaches to education, the development of undiscovered branches of science; and on and on.

The implications are truly staggering, but they may forebode danger as well as benefit. Will we be aborigines to be victimized by a race of superbeings? Or savages who learn truth at the knees of infinitely wise mentors? Or near-equals who struggle for a competitive edge in whatever arena is appropriate for interstellar conflict, whether military, commercial, or philosophical?

As so often happens, the practicing scientists have left these knotty consequences of their activities—in this case, extraterrestrial contact —to the statesmen and politicians by simply avoiding the philosophical question: the program that once was called CETI (*Communication* with Extraterrestrial Intelligence) has recently become SETI (*Search* for Extraterrestrial Intelligence). That is, "We'll find 'em; somebody *else* will decide what to do about 'em!"

Serious consideration of SETI could scarcely exist until people were able to accept Copernicus' revolutionary postulate that the earth revolves around the sun. But once it was realized that the earth was not the center of the universe, the idea that there might be creatures on other worlds became quite reasonable. Bernard du Fontenelle's *Plurality of Worlds* (1728) and Alexander Copland's *The Existence of Other Worlds: Peopled with Living and Intelligent Beings* (1834) explored the philosophical aspects of this new concept. The flames were fanned by astronomer Schiaparelli's observation of "canali" on Mars in 1877 and 1881-82. When Percival Lowell later chose to interpret Schiaparelli's Italian "canali" as "canals" rather than "channels," the myth of the intelligent Martians was born. Marconi, in fact, reported in the early 1920s that he had detected Martian radio signals! And H. G. Wells' *War of the Worlds* was only the first in a long series of novels that popularized extraterrestrial life right here in our own solar system. Later Venus and even Jupiter's and Saturn's moons joined Mars as the fictional domiciles of all sorts of intelligent creatures, for example, Kurt Vonnegut's *Sirens of Titan*.

But reality eventually caught up with imagination. Mariner 9's photos of Mars in 1971 showed it to be much like the moon in its desolation, and the spectacularly successful landings of Viking's self-contained biological laboratories in 1976 detected no sign of even microbial life. The Soviets' Venera spacecraft in 1969, 1972, and 1975 revealed Venus as totally hostile to life, with its blazing 900° F

This robot laboratory made the first full-fledged search for life on another planet. Viking's long arm scraped up soil from two different places on Mars in 1976, but found no living things.

The four mushroom shapes on this Pioneer spacecraft explored Venus' atmosphere in detail in December 1978. No life was expected; earlier Soviet spacecraft had found only a horrendously hot (900° Fahrenheit), high-pressure, mostly carbon dioxide atmosphere under Venus' perpetual cloud cover. Photograph courtesy of Hughes Aircraft Company.

temperatures and enormous ninety-atmosphere pressures. Mercury's sun-blasted orb was an obviously inhospitable cradle for life, as verified by Mariner 10 spacecraft photos in 1973 and 1974. The likelihood that the gas giants Jupiter and Saturn can sustain living creatures is generally agreed as being slight, and even if life were found on their frozen moons, it is not likely to be intelligent life. And Uranus, Neptune, and Pluto are so far away from the sun that their icy cold terrain forms an unlikely habitat. So although there's still a chance that we may someday discover rudimentary life forms in our solar system, it's almost certain that any extraterrestrial *intelligence* we may eventually encounter will come from the planets of a star other than our own sun. The next nearest possible source, then, is over four light-years away: an inconceivable distance even in the space age.

Astronomical distances are difficult to grasp. They are measured in light-years—the distance light travels, at 186,000 miles per *second*, in a full year. Since a year contains a sizable number of seconds—60 seconds per minute times 60 minutes per hour times 24 hours per day times 365 days per year—a single light-year is beyond our earth-bound comprehension: almost 6 million million miles. And that's not all; the galaxy in which our sun is but one small obscure star among billions is 60,000 light-years across—a distance not even worth translating into miles. At the highest speeds our most sophisticated

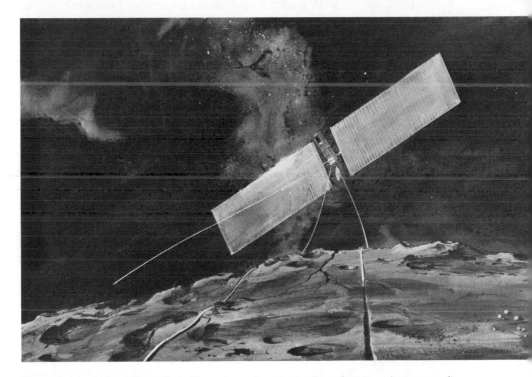

There *is* a small chance that life—although almost certainly not intelligent life—might still be found in our own solar system, despite our lack of success on Mars and Venus. Here a "cosmic anteater," a robot search spacecraft powered by ion rockets, rendezvouses with a small asteroid and fires "sticky strings" to collect samples for retrieval and testing in its robot laboratory.

spacecraft have yet traveled, perhaps 40,000 miles per hour, it would take about 80,000 *years* just to reach the nearest star, four light-years away.

These sobering interstellar distances tend to discourage thoughts of "space Beagles" to explore the starry islands of space for fascinating races of aborigines, superbeings, or perhaps creatures like us. The only remaining recourse to SETI enthusiasts, therefore, is interstellar communication, which can be conducted at the relatively practical speed of all electromagnetic radiation: 186,000 miles per second.

A host of questions immediately come to mind. How many of those stars out there have planets? Are earthlike planets a common occurrence in the universe, or are they very, very rare? Is an earthlike planet necessary for intelligent life, or could chemistries other than our carbon-hydrogen-oxygen system develop the complex molecules needed to conduct such elaborate processes as cerebral thinking? And, of course, the ultimate question—if intelligence *is* common among the untold billions of stars in the universe, mustn't there be thousands, maybe millions, of other races out there who developed intelligence sooner than we did? *Why haven't we heard from them?*

The answers are readily ticked off. There are over 250 *billion* stars in our own Milky Way galaxy—and the universe contains tens of billions of such galaxies. So although we can't be certain, the probabilities point overwhelmingly to the existence of a myriad, perhaps billions, of earthlike planets that could have chemistries quite similar to ours and that have been warmed by a sun much like ours for sufficient time to have developed life as we know it. There are those— UFO (unidentified flying object) enthusiasts and "cult" authors like Erich von Daniken, for example—who argue that we have already been contacted. But even if we choose to discount UFO stories (and most of us do), the physics of interstellar distances provide a quite reasonable answer to that key question of why we haven't been contacted yet: it's still too soon. The first perceptible evidence of intelligence on this planet was generated in 1895, when Marconi sent out his first wireless signals. Allowing time for a round trip, the only extraterrestrials who might be able to advise us that they know we're here are located in a sphere around our sun no more than forty light-years in radius—a sphere that contains only a few hundred stars.

SETI pioneer Philip Morrison stated SETI's mission most succinctly during a space flight report conference I organized for the American

Rocket Society in the New York Coliseum back in 1961: "We just listen and we will hear. But," he cautions, "I do not know how long we will have to wait . . . this is an experiment for the centuries."

Morrison's excitement is irresistibly contagious. He was a Manhattan Project physicist during World War II, and later a physics professor at Cornell (I took his course in atomic physics there in 1947). In the 1950s he became intrigued by the prospects for possible contact with intelligent alien races. As he said it to a House of Representatives subcommittee in September 1978,

> My interest began during a chamber-music performance in the Cornell student center when I first came to think about the promise of gamma-ray astronomy. . . . I am afraid I paid less than due attention to the quartet. By the end of 1958, I had published the first summary of what one might learn from gamma-ray astronomy. . . . A few months after its publication, one spring day in 1959, my ingenious friend Giuseppe Cocconi came into my office, which then looked northward out over a small lake to the green hills of Ithaca. Giuseppe had an unlikely question. "Would not gamma rays," he asked, "be the very medium of choice for communication between the stars?" They would work, that was plain, and my answer was enthusiastic yet cautious. Shouldn't we look at all the spectrum for its possibilities, and genuinely seek out the best means for such a link? . . . Certainly neither of us knew the rudiments of radio astronomy. . . .
>
> We wrote and rewrote together the five-page letter *Searching for Interstellar Communications* which from the first we had hoped to publish in the rather speculative pages of *Nature*. . . . During the months that we were working out the letter, it would be agreeable to think that I read [Joseph Needham's] translation from old Teng Mu, "How unreasonable it would be to suppose that, besides the heavens and earths we can see, there are no other heavens and no other earths?" [from the *Lute of Po Ya*, thirteenth century A.D.]. . . . We knew of course that our proposal was both unorthodox and improbable, but . . . its argument compels serious attention. "The probability of success is difficult to estimate; but if we never search, the chance of success is zero." I sent the letter to London via Professor Patrick Blackett, the influential and imaginative physicist then in Imperial College, who I knew personally. . . . He acted promptly and successfully, and the note soon appeared.

It was the first scientific paper ever published on the subject. When I was assembling the prestigious panelists for my 1961 space flight report, Morrison was by far the dominant figure in this new and exciting field. Although a practical, hard-shelled engineer, I was mesmerized by the waves of enthusiasm that seemed to well from this stooped, gnomelike evangelist of science as he hammered home the implications of his analyses and his arguments for a vigorous SETI program:

> Radio transmission began not more than seventy-five years ago. . . . If we take the view, as I do, that we are by no means unique, then our galactic friends have already found many previous civilizations. This [ours] is just one more, and possibly a Ph.D. in some department of anthropology will be granted for finding this one. . . . At the moment we cannot exclude the hypothesis that very considerable efforts *are* being made to contact us from numerous stars—as many as tens of millions—in our galaxy. We would not have heard them.

And later on he put his finger on what might turn out to be the most important result SETI could have: "Were we to locate but a single extraterrestrial signal, we would know immediately one great truth: that it is possible for a civilization to maintain an advanced technological state and *not* destroy itself."

At least one person was listening to Morrison: Frank Drake of the National Radio Astronomy Observatory. "At this very minute," he wrote, "with almost absolute certainty, radio waves sent forth by other intelligent civilizations are falling on the earth. A telescope . . . pointed in the right place and tuned to the right frequency could discover these waves."

In 1960 Drake began the first search for signals from other worlds —a project he dubbed Ozma, after the Princess of Oz, "a place far away, difficult to reach, and populated by exotic beings." He chose the natural emission frequency of hydrogen, the most plentiful element in the universe, to carry his signal, which he focused to a narrow bandwidth. He aimed his beam at two stars, Tau Ceti and Epsilon Eridani, both about eleven light-years from earth.

The very first day of his search, April 8, 1960, the incredible happened. The control room at Green Bank, West Virginia, buzzed with excitement: a strong, obviously artificial signal came in loud and clear from Epsilon Eridani! But it was only the first of a long string of disappointments whose origin is now one of the SETI researchers' primary concerns: interference by signals from earth-based or satellite-based communications systems. The little green men from Epsilon Eridani turned out to be a secret U.S. military experiment.

SETI activity grew rapidly after Ozma. A month after my 1961 space flight report in New York, Morrison and Drake, under National Science Foundation auspices, assembled an august group of scientists at Green Bank to discuss the possibility of extraterrestrial intelligence. Scientists included chemistry Nobel Prize winner Melvin Calvin, Bernard Oliver of Hewlett-Packard, and a young Cornell biologist-astronomer named Carl Sagan. John Lilly, a specialist in communicating with the dolphin, one of our earth-based species believed to possess considerable intelligence, suggested a name for this group: The Order of the Dolphin. The meeting's main outcome was a statistical prediction for the number of intelligent races one might find elsewhere in the universe who would be capable of communicating with us: somewhere between forty races and fifty million races. True, this is a range of possibilities so broad as to be almost meaningless, but it is extremely significant nevertheless, simply because the lower limit was *not* zero (a later study by the RAND Corporation, in 1964, came up with the number of planets potentially inhabitable by man: 600 million).

The history and prospects of SETI have been documented and analyzed in many reports, papers, and books, not the least among the latter being *The New York Times'* science reporter Walter Sullivan's *We Are Not Alone* (1964), and Shklovskii and Sagan's *Intelligent Life in the Universe* (1966). But perhaps the most succinct and complete compilation of the dreams, the frustrations, and the facts of the SETI effort is a little-known publication of the House Committee on Science and Technology, prepared by Marcia S. Smith of the Congressional Research Service's (CRS) Science Policy Research Division in the Library of Congress. Its title, *The Possibility of Intelligent Life Elsewhere in the Universe.*

Marcia Smith, a dedicated and active supporter of women's rights in the often chauvinistic halls of Congress, has become a fixture (and a most welcome one) at every congressional committee hearing related to space. She and her colleagues at the Congressional Research Service have documented the whys, whats, and wherefores of solar-power satellites and international space programs, and have performed complete historical analyses of the entire United States space program since its inception. Marcia—small, slim, and beautiful, with a crown of luxurious brown hair worn long and straight—graduated from Syracuse University with a degree in political science, and came to Washington to seek her fortune at the heart of the U.S. political system. Unfortunately, all she could get were secretarial jobs, first at George Washington University for a few months, and then with the AIAA's newly established Washington office. But Johan Benson, the director of that office, quickly recognized that her capabilities were far in excess of his office's demands. A former CRS analyst himself, he passed the word to his old compatriots. CRS hired her a few weeks later.

Marcia and two of her colleagues, Barbara Luxenberg and Lani Hummel Raleigh, work directly for senior CRS analyst Charles Sheldon; they have been targeted by one wag at the library as "Charlie's Angels." Among them, they provide the bulk of space-policy research activity requested by the various congressional committees. I had the rewarding experience of working with "Charlie's Angels" on several occasions and, of course, Marcia has been a good friend ever since she started her stint with the AIAA. The job she did on the SETI documentation was characteristic of her work— complete and technically accurate, yet marvelously sensitive to the excitement and the implications of so fascinating a subject. Most important, her extensive experience in reviewing and analyzing international space programs (a major undertaking by Charlie and his angels) brought out the obvious implications of SETI to the cause of international cooperation.

These implications were also clearly recognized outside the United States. The Soviets held a national meeting on the subject in 1964, and hosted the first international SETI conference in Yerevan in 1972. Both the United States and the U.S.S.R. instituted formal SETI research programs in 1974, although the Russians still used the original designation CETI. It was recognized that Ozma and its successors, because of their low power, could detect only a signal of great strength such as a beacon or other intensely focused signal. When Hewlett-Packard's Bernard Oliver and NASA's John Billingham cochaired a summer study at Stanford University whose purpose was to come up with a practical, workable method for detecting extraterrestrial intelligent life, their solution was Project Cyclops, a system of 1,500 hundred-meter (football-field-sized) antennas covering twenty-five square miles (over twice the size of New York's Manhattan Island) and costing (in 1971) $20 billion. The Russians, in 1974, came up with an almost equally ambitious proposal to search from 1975 to 1990 the entire shortwave radio spectrum, from 1000 to 100,000 megahertz (million cycles per second), using not only large, kilometer-sized earth antennas, but also larger satellite antennas in orbit around the earth. Unlike the United States, which considers Cyclops a radio astronomer's dream project and has denied any budgetary support, the Soviets appear to be proceeding with their 1974 CETI plan.

By 1978 NASA had spent only some $800,000 in support of all those prior years of SETI activities, invisibly buried in various NASA departmental budget allocations. But in the FY 1979 budget they sought 600,000 clearly identified budget-line-item dollars to accelerate their efforts, plus another $1,400,000 in tracking and data acquisition budgets. In the not-too-original but highly appropriate words of one congressional staffer, "That's when the shit hit the fan." Predictably, Senator Proxmire promptly awarded NASA his "Golden Fleece of the Month" and, more important, campaigned mightily in both his Appropriations Subcommittee and in the public press for cancellation of SETI. "In my view," he said, "this project should be postponed for a few million light-years [sic]." Although the senator's concepts of time and distance weren't so good, his demagoguery was at its best: "Like so many other big spending projects, this is a low-priority program which at this time constitutes a luxury which the country can ill afford. . . . At a time when the country is faced with a sixty-one-billion-dollar deficit, the attempt to detect radio waves from solar systems should be postponed until right after the federal budget is balanced and income and social security taxes are reduced to zero." A fine-sounding statement, but in a $500 billion federal budget it seemed a little heavy-handed for a $2 million annual expenditure over the next seven years, especially for a program that for a relatively miniscule investment just *might* turn out to be the most important single action ever taken by mankind.

Nonetheless, Proxmire won that round. The SETI effort for FY 1979 was cut to zero, and NASA would have to "return to the well" for any future appropriations.

Meanwhile, there was another problem facing SETI researchers

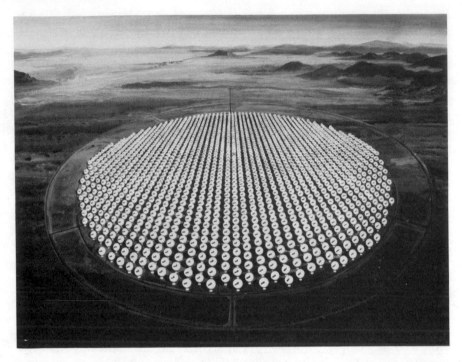

This ten-mile field of antennas was suggested in 1971 as one approach to a systematic search for intelligent signals from the stars. It was called Project Cyclops.

that, surprising as it may seem, was even more critical than lack of funds. Governments and legislators move on, and future ears might turn out to be more receptive. But each year, SETI's worst operational problem was becoming more and more serious: the electromagnetic spectrum was being gobbled up by ever-increasing commercial and military communications demands. This problem for radio astronomers is exactly like the equivalent problem faced by optical astronomers who complain that there are few places left on earth where city lights or air pollution do not interfere with good "seeing." But optical astronomers have an option: to move into space with their telescopes, because useful optical telescopes can be relatively small. The current space telescope design, for example, is quite capable of being launched by the space shuttle, and offers many times the "seeing" capability of much larger earth-based telescopes. Radio telescopes, on the other hand, especially those needed to detect distant SETI transmissions, need to be much larger (Arecibo's dish is a fifth of a mile in diameter) and cannot readily be put into space (or on the far side of the moon, an ideal location), except at enormous cost. SETI enthusiasts are therefore fighting desperately to preserve at least one segment of the frequency spectrum, a segment that has been dubbed "the water hole." This is the band bounded by the natural emission lines of hydrogen and the hydroxyl radical, which not only happen to be the chemical constituents of water but also are the most prevalent "natural" frequencies in the radio universe. I quote an almost poetic passage from an early NASA report: "Nature has provided us with a rather narrow band in this best part of the spectrum that seems especially marked for interstellar contact. . . . Standing like Om and Um on either side of a gate, these two emissions of the dissociation products of water beckon all water-based life to search for its kind at the age-old meetingplace of all species: the water hole."

The best possible place for a Cyclops-like radiotelescope array to search the heavens for intelligent signals would be on the far side of the moon, where the entire moon shields the telescopes from stray manmade signals emanating from earth.

But the water hole might *not* happen to be the best frequency for search. Simply because it *is* so crowded with natural emissions, some scientists think other less-occupied regions of the spectrum might be better. But which ones? To search all stars at all frequencies is certainly possible—it was the approach taken by the Cyclops project—but it is very, very expensive, and would truly be an "experiment for the centuries."

But the signs kept pointing to the probability that SETI research, if it were to proceed, might have to go that expensive and lengthy course. By 1979 searches of over six hundred nearby stars at 1,420 megahertz—the hydrogen emission line first explored by Ozma in 1960—had turned up nothing. Spot checks at other frequencies were similarly barren. Yet, despite this lack of success, SETI researchers were not at all discouraged. They had begun, in fact, to wonder about what to do if SETI *were* successful. Elaborate languages based on binary (computer language) systems were developed. "Teaching/learning" methods for extraterrestrials were conceived. A much-publicized plaque, bearing what our space scientists fondly hoped was an intelligible message telling "who we are," was placed on board the Pioneer 10 and 11 spacecraft launched in 1972 and 1973 to study Jupiter and Saturn before departing from our solar system for the interstellar void. Of course, the chance that these spacecraft with their plaques will ever be seen by "anyone," much less picked up and deciphered, is vanishingly small. As plaque-designer Carl Sagan wrote in *The Cosmic Connection*, "Placing a message aboard Pioneer 10

A 210-foot tracking radiotelescope, one of the largest in the world. Such telescopes can be used to search for signals from intelligent races out among the stars.

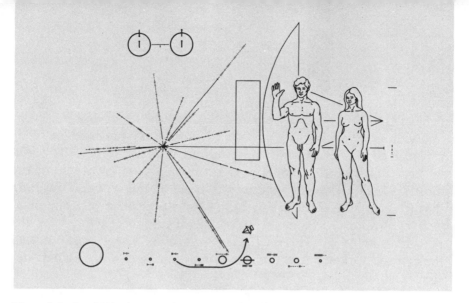

The originals of this famous plaque are now hurtling out of our solar system aboard Pioneer spacecraft 10 and 11. They tell who and where we are to any intelligent extraterrestrials who might happen to spot the Pioneers—a literally "one-in-billions" possibility.

is very much like a shipwrecked sailor casting a bottled message into the ocean—but the ocean of space is much vaster."

A much more elaborate "extraterrestrial communiqué" was placed aboard two Voyager spacecraft launched in 1977 to Jupiter and Saturn and then, again, into interstellar space. This new message was a two-hour copper recording carrying electronic photos, messages of greeting from world leaders, and miscellaneous sounds of earth and its inhabitants. Again, though, the chances that "anyone" will ever receive these messages is incalculably remote.

Then there were those who looked beyond "first contact" to the possible consequences. Despite the enormous barrier of astronomical distances, a few hardy pioneers tried to conceive methods that might be used to travel to the planets circling that remote star where intelligence would someday be detected. Chemical rockets are out: at the speeds achieved by Pioneer and Voyager, even with the extra "gravitational slingshot" speed they picked up by being whipped past Jupiter's enormous mass, it would take 80,000 years just to reach the nearest star (at which they aren't aimed anyway). The power of nuclear fission *could* be used, but would be practical only in the form of nuclear "pulse" propulsion, which many people deem unacceptable. In this concept the spaceship is kicked along on its course by thousands of tiny nuclear bombs dropped behind the spaceship and exploded one after the other, each imparting part of its "blast" to push the ship on its course. Strange as it may sound, this scheme, called

Project Orion, was actively pursued in the early 1960s and was eventually dropped not because of lack of practicality but because of its political and environmental ramifications. Orion's eulogy, delivered by Princeton physicist/philosopher Freeman Dyson,* was one of the most eloquent commentaries ever published on the perennial juggling that goes on between technological and sociological values. The manager of Project Orion, incidentally, was Theodore Taylor, later the hero of John McPhee's *The Curve of Binding Energy* and an avid foe of nuclear-power development using plutonium, the original "design fuel" for Orion.

The Orion concept was later resurrected in a more acceptable form, using "clean," laser-activated nuclear-*fusion* reactions (which use isotopes of ordinary hydrogen for fuel) to generate the pulses of thrust, thereby avoiding the whole nuclear-fission bugaboo. I had earlier suggested (in one of my consultant's reports to Aerojet in 1957) an even more advanced continuous fusion rocket, using the "magnetic mirror" concept (first disclosed publicly in 1956) to contain the billion-degree temperature of the fusion reaction. Bob Bussard, the father of the nuclear rocket, had taken the fusion propulsion scheme another step further: in 1960 he visualized an "interstellar ramjet," which would cruise through the galaxy scooping up the hydrogen atoms scattered thinly throughout "empty" space to use as its fuel.

Many other "lunatic-fringe" ideas were put forth to power interstellar spaceships, ideas like enormous solar-sail "slingshots" whipping spacecraft from star to star by using the pressure of sunlight itself, or the "matter-antimatter" annihilation reactions observed in nuclear physics experiments, but which lack any known source for practical quantities of antimatter. Even these bizarre schemes, though, involve hundreds and possibly thousands of years for interstellar hops. Humans can essay such trips in only two ways: by arresting normal life processes for centuries without damaging the human organism (a real possibility now being explored in considerable detail by cryogenic experiments on human tissues and live animals), or by using self-sufficient spaceships manned by crews whose descendants of many generations would finally arrive at the intended destination.

Despite these gloomy prospects for flinging ourselves (and/or our

---

* Freeman J. Dyson, "Death of a Project," *Science,* Vol. 149 (1968), pp. 141-44.

descendants) across the vastnesses of interstellar space, optimists like Bob Bussard continue to "keep the door open." A superb engineer in his own right, he coauthored the first textbook on nuclear rocket propulsion, published in 1956, and then went on to take his Ph.D. in plasma physics in the Princeton fusion research program, which is where I met him for the first time. I was already using his book as a principal text in my nuclear power plants course at Princeton, and, of course, he was the logical candidate to discuss advanced propulsion at my 1961 space flight report program.

Even then, his imagination knew no bounds. After he'd returned from Princeton to Los Alamos, we spent many long evenings on my frequent visits there dreaming up new but practical approaches to nuclear rocketry, fission *or* fusion pulse propulsion, electric rockets powered by multi-megawatt nuclear power plants, and such.

Bussard finally left the (then) Atomic Energy Commission to form his own company, although he later returned for a short period in the early 1970s to head up the AEC's engineering program office in nuclear fusion. I lost track of him for several years, when all of a sudden, in 1976, a handwritten letter showed up at the AIAA, decrying the loss of drive and sense of wonder that had been a hallmark of the old American Rocket Society. On the spur of the moment, AIAA executive secretary Jim Harford invited the writer of the letter (Bussard, of course) to make his case at the next AIAA board of directors' meeting.

That was an occasion worth recounting. Bussard tall, darkly handsome with a hawklike, hunched stance and brooding black eyebrows—stood and faced the long table of aerospace executives, professors, and heads of federal agencies and departments. Although a former technical vice-president of the AIAA, he had been out of contact so long that he knew few of the board members, and few of them knew him except by reputation. He started slowly, groping for the right words, but not for long. Bussard warmed to his subject quickly, and let his audience have it—right between their nearsighted eyes:

> When I got interested in the American Rocket Society back in 1938 or so, it was kind of a collection of crazies. Everybody was looking at the big problem: can we ever go to the moon? . . . The world was young and new and exciting; the war hadn't come and gone, and all those new things to do were just sitting out there.

Then, a few months ago, I looked at the AIAA's 1977 Annual Meeting Program with its theme "Aerospace in the Third Century." A provocative title—a long way to look ahead. But as I looked through the detailed program, I saw mostly ideas like intercity air transport, freight hauling with vertical-takeoff aircraft, better air-traffic control, and other things that matter to us this year and next year—the things that matter to the survival of corporations and federal bureaucracies. That worried me. I wondered, where did all that childlike enthusiasm and innocence go?

I had just written a proposal to do research and development on a problem in advanced nuclear physics. I looked at my proposal and thought about the "third century," and something struck me. Here I am, a physicist and engineer of sorts who had just written a proposal. If I had taken that 1976 proposal back to, say 1913, only sixty-three years ago, and had given it to the brightest physicist—the most skilled and brilliant man on the planet Earth in physics—he would have been able to read most of the words, but he wouldn't have understood the first thing about the proposal, the concept, the ideas, the physics, what it was about, or why. If I had given it to Lord Rutherford, he wouldn't have known what to do with it.

And that shows that something's wrong with the way we're looking forward into the third century. What's happened to the American Rocket Society and its successor, the AIAA? Where's that crazy, visionary view of the future?

I'd like to talk about a couple of things that *may* have some impact on the future. But remember, like Lord Rutherford, I can't know what the technology sixty-three years hence will be. Given the same kind of human imagination and creativity that characterized the last sixty-three or hundred years, in the next hundred the things they'll be talking about are things I wouldn't even understand!

With that caveat (which he then promptly, and characteristically, proceeded to ignore), Bussard fired up his boilers and scattered ideas like buckshot on the big board table, all based on existing physics and, in some cases, current research programs. He started with the concept of transmitting energy over long distances by lasers, high-power particle beams as rocket engines, and high-energy-density power plants for space, and then went on to concepts for interplanetary flight.

"I think it's worth remembering that the American Rocket Society was founded because people thought it would be exciting for man to leave his planet. In fact, it was originally the American *Interplanetary* Society, until someone back in the thirties got cold feet and changed its name!"

Bussard sketched out his scenario—advanced interplanetary shuttles by the end of the century; fusion power here on earth by 2010, followed by fusion-powered rocket engines of the kind we dreamed about in the late fifties and sixties. By the middle of the twenty-first century we'd have learned enough to build fusion rockets capable of powering unmanned interstellar probes. Then one more quite predictable technological advance—super-high magnetic fields—could make the hydrogen-scooping interstellar ramjet a reality, and then, why not? "Let's take a *real* third-century look," Bussard said pointedly as he peered out from under his black brows at the transfixed board. "Let's celebrate the Tricentennial by aiming for a manned 'ramjet' mission to the stars in 2076. We could even launch it on July Fourth!"

That one raised conservative eyebrows all along the table, but Bussard continued to press home his point. "This whole schedule is *not* unreasonable," he reminded them, "if we look at it in the same context as my Lord Rutherford analogy."

He didn't end there. Diffusion of mankind throughout the entire galaxy—*not* the evolutionary process that most sociologists and SETI enthusiasts generally conceive of, but the far more probable star-to-star diffusion of the human race—could occur in subsequent centuries, with the almost absolute certainty of contacting one or more extraterrestrial race somewhere along the way. "All I really want to leave with you," Bussard concluded, "is the thought that we open our minds and think beyond next year's budget with its two thousand— or maybe twenty thousand—cruise missiles, and go back and enjoy the idea that it's O.K. to think freely. You represent a group with an unbroken history of having the greatest creativity of any that's existed in this country. Don't abdicate that position!"

The applause (not normally heard at AIAA board meetings) was long and thunderous. To its credit, despite the fact that Bussard's mind-stretching ideas were in direct opposition to the rigid conservatism enforced by ever-increasing budget-consciousness on all sides, the board later authorized the formation of a new AIAA Task Force on Future Flight Systems to consider technologies beyond the year 2000, with Bob Bussard as its first chairman.

Bussard's talk started us thinking about America's "third century." What might be the chain of events that the AIAA board of 2076 might look back on? I tried to put myself in their shoes and review the "history" of that third century . . .

The creation of Bussard's new task force symbolized a basic change in the attitude of the nation's people toward space activities. Perhaps it was the enhanced public awareness generated by popular articles and books on space colonization, or big multi-million-dollar "slick" science-fiction visual spectaculars such as *Star Wars, Close Encounters of the Third Kind,* and *Battlestar Galactica.* It could have been that the public finally realized the value of "via satellite," "our satellite photo today shows . . . ," and the incredible images from Landsat. Maybe it was simply that no U.S. astronaut had been in space for five years while the Soviets (and their Czechoslovakian, Polish, and East German comrades) popped in and out of their Salyut space station every few weeks in the late 1970s.

But it was probably the first few launches of space shuttles from Cape Canaveral, starting in early 1980, that did it. When *Enterprise's* sister ships left their pads in the full glare of global television coverage (via satellite, of course), the comparison of their ungainly, obviously utilitarian hulks with the slim, graceful Saturn rockets of Apollo brought home clearly to everyone that the space age was real, that it would impact the life of every person on earth, and, most of all, that it was *here.*

The people of the United States went space-crazy. They badgered their congressmen to raise the NASA budget—after a decade of hammering it down as a waste of tax money. Proxmire actually was defeated in his first post-shuttle reelection bid by a young Wisconsin space-buff engineering professor. But our real entry into space-age maturity began when the space telescope launched by the shuttle in 1983 turned its bright 2.4-meter eye, undimmed by air pollution, haze, or the diffraction of atmospheric gases, toward Barnard's star. Astronomers who examined those first unenhanced photometer scans couldn't believe their eyes. Adjustments were made, the focus was improved ever so slightly, and the computer-enhancement techniques so successful on early Landsat images were pushed to their utmost. Finally, there could be no further doubt: Barnard's star, only six light-years away and the second nearest star to our sun, was blessed with four clearly visible planets.

Astronomer Peter van de Kamp had announced back in 1964 that he had discovered a "companion" to Barnard's star, but his discovery was subsequently discredited due to what other astronomers thought was a "possible systematic error" in his data. So when the spectrophotometer hastily fitted to the space telescope by the next shuttle crew revealed that Barnard Two's spectrum indicated an oxygen absorption band—suggesting not only the pressure of oxygen but *gaseous* oxygen at that—it was almost unanimously decided that the first known extrasolar planet be named after its discoverer. Van de Kamp's planet became the Sunday-supplement subject for over a year, and prospects for life—maybe even *intelligent* life—were debated on TV talk shows *ad nauseam*.

The impact of the space telescope's revelation on the U.S. (and

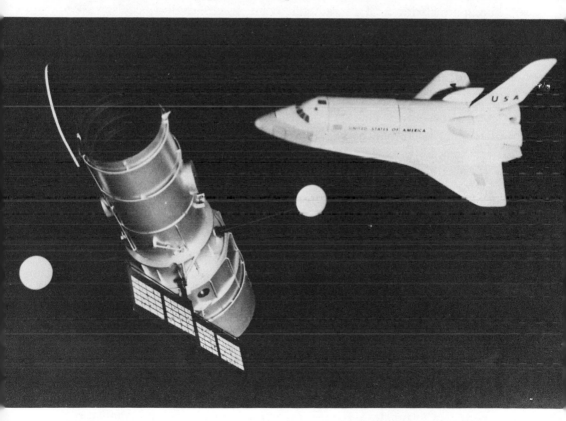

The 2.4-meter (100-inch) space telescope to be launched by the shuttle in 1983. Because it will be unobscured by the earth's atmosphere, it might be able to detect planets circling nearby stars—a rather likely prospect.

the world's) space program rivaled that of the original Sputnik. SETI scientists were practically buried in money to build not only the first increment of Cyclops, but to put it in orbit, minimizing the interference caused by the proliferation of communications signals that had resulted from the laissez-faire policy decision by the 1979 World Administrative Radio Conference, which had opened to commercial use virtually the entire shortwave radio spectrum. And because the U.S.S.R. had been working on a space-based radiotelescope for years, the orbital Cyclops project became the first major cooperative international effort since the establishment of the Antarctic research station.

The "fallout" was also spectacular—a hundred-meter spot-beam communications antenna was a cinch to build and maintain in orbit compared with a SETI radiotelescope antenna. Burt Edelson's orbital antenna farms multiplied like rabbits in the geostationary orbit, taking over all communications, navigational, meteorological, and remote earth-sensing functions—at costs one-tenth those of the pre-shuttle era. Buying shuttle payload space became harder than getting fifty-yard-line seats at the Super Bowl, and congressional clamor for a second-generation shuttle brought the old NASA fully reusable dream to operational reality by 1990. On-board electric power was the bottleneck for a while, but it was resolved by the simultaneous development of a family of compact molybdenum fast-spectrum nuclear-fission power plants and ultra-thin photovoltaic "membranes" with efficiencies twice those of the silicon cells used in NASA's first solar-electric propulsion stage.

So by 1990 all the pieces of the jigsaw puzzle were in place. Large structures had been built and used in space; megawatts of electric power were available; a big fully reusable shuttle was flying into orbit on an almost daily schedule; and mankind was geared up to looking outward instead of inward. The next step was obvious, but it was precipitated, perhaps a few years ahead of its time, by two unrelated and disastrously unfortunate circumstances.

The world energy crisis of the late 1970s hadn't gone away, but it had been staved off repeatedly by increased oil production and accelerated use of nuclear power. The United States and the U.S.S.R. were also fortunate in having large coal reserves, but the mainstay of Europe, Japan, South America, and Africa became plutonium breeder reactors, most of which were patterned after the relatively simple

In 1977 Robert W. Bussard, a nuclear-fusion physicist and early nuclear-rocket pioneer, postulated a manned colonization expedition to the stars by the end of the United States' third century. Photograph courtesy of *Astronautics and Aeronautics*.

French Phenix and Superphenix designs that had operated so success-fully in the 1970s.

Solar energy was in wide use for hot-water supply and for heating and air-conditioning homes and offices, but ground-based plants for solar electricity were not yet economical, despite herculean demon-stration efforts by the U.S. Department of Energy. (The new solar-cell membranes, incidentally, were useful only in the benign environment of space; they wouldn't last an hour in the wind, rain, and gravity of earth.) And world energy consumption, particularly of electricity,

A single-stage-to-orbit space shuttle of the future carries its payload into the depths of space. It could be bringing relief maintenance workers to a solar-power satellite, or vacationers to a space habitat, or perhaps colonists to the starship preparing for Bussard's inter-stellar expedition.

continued to accelerate. The Third World wanted its share of the comfort pie it had envied the industrial nations in the 1970s and 1980s, and wasn't to be denied.

But in 1991, a molten-sodium coolant reservoir ruptured in the first Superphenix breeder, which had gone "on line" at Creys-Malville, France, in 1983. The accident wasn't even related to the reactor core, which was shut down safely just as the emergency core cooling engineers had predicted for decades. But years of safe, reliable operation had made the operating utility company too complacent. The system malfunctioned due to inadequate maintenance, and the hot sodium reacted instantly with external cooling-water jets, spraying slightly radioactive sodium over a few acres of France.

Nobody was hurt, but it could have been much worse. All Phenix-type reactors, worldwide, were shut down posthaste for long-overdue maintenance of never-used safety systems. Power rationing went into effect immediately, since the universal shutdown cut the availability of electricity by an average of 40 percent in many nations.

Unfortunately, the Soviets, who had crossed the line from oil exporters to oil importers in 1985, had chosen that same week to ensure their future oil supply by a military take-over of Saudi Arabia. The heavy machinery of a Soviet military operation had too much inertia to be affected by the French breeder accident. Despite the predictable world clamor and strenuous efforts by United States diplomats, the "liberation" of Saudi oil riches proceeded smoothly and completely. A good fraction of the "free world's" oil supply dried up—suddenly.

The United States was affected far less than the rest of the world, because of its heavy reliance on coal and the absence of French-designed Superphenix breeders. The Saudi oil cutoff and the consequent disruption in other Mideast oil shipments were serious but manageable problems: the Strategic Petroleum Reserve built up over the preceding decade filled the gap nicely, at least for a year or two.

But the stage had been abruptly set for the inevitable. Given the rapid advances in space technology and public acceptance, and the now-escalated energy crisis, the proper path was obvious. No "show-stoppers" had been found after ten years of low-level research and technology efforts, and again Congress forced a reluctant administration into action. A one-year project to place a demonstration 500-megawatt solar-power satellite into geostationary orbit was authorized, and funds were allocated for a prototype mining base on the moon to explore the practicality of using nonterrestrial raw materials.

Despite sharp cutbacks in U.S. industrial capability due to oil rationing, and the enormous drain on U.S. capital needed to keep the energy-starved friendly nations from foundering, both projects were finished ahead of schedule. What's more, they both worked— the decades of planning, research, and technology development *really* paid off. Every utility and energy company in the United States jumped in with both feet; virtually the entire $500 billion needed to capitalize a decade's worth of electric-power-generating plants went into solar-power satellites.

By the turn of the century, 25 percent of U.S. energy was being delivered from space, at far lower cost than now incredibly expensive oil and nuclear-generated electricity. The U.S. utilities and energy conglomerates were making money hand over fist, selling cheap electricity at bargain rates to the energy-starved nations of the world. Most of the profits were poured back into the development of non-terrestrial materials sources, as the costs and environmental impact associated with hourly launches of big single-stage-to-orbit space shuttles were beginning to get worrisome.

By 2010 the first all-lunar-material space power plant was in geostationary orbit, built by shifts of workers ferried from earth to the orbiting "construction shack." Three years later the first self-sufficient space factory/colony, incorporated as the International Space Power Plant Manufacturing and Maintenance Corporation, delivered a full-sized 10,000-megawatt power plant to waiting Southern California Edison Company operators in a geostationary orbit over the Pacific. They were paid for the job at a healthy 20 percent profit, plus 2 percent of the gross for forty years, in exchange for maintenance and repair services. At the bargain rate of five cents per kilowatt-hour delivered to the Los Angeles grid with 95 percent availability, that 2 percent racked up nearly $100 million per year for the infant corporation (plus the initial $1 billion profit from the sale of the plant to Southern California Edison)—and that was only their first. The space enterprise was solidly ensconced in its orbital niche, and growing by leaps and bounds.

On earth, meanwhile, the development of nuclear fusion had been proceeding at a steady but relatively slow pace compared with the "space boom." The long-awaited "zero-net-power" feasibility demonstration, proving that a deuterium-tritium* fusion reaction could at least sustain itself, had been accomplished on schedule in the Princeton Plasma Physics Laboratory's Tokamak test reactor in 1982. Commercial demonstration took a little longer—solving the materials problems imposed by unshielded seventeen-million-electron-volt neutrons proved to be as difficult as many engineers had predicted—but the first 5,000-megawatt fusion power plant began delivering electricity to New Jersey's Public Service Electric and Gas Company's customers just before the turn of the century. It wasn't long before a magnetic-mirror deuterium-fueled fusion rocket was fired up at the resurrected Nuclear Rocket Development Center in Jackass Flats, Nevada. Then, in 2012, the first fusion-powered spacecraft, boosted into orbit by one of Translunar Spacelines' sleek single-stage-to-orbit shuttle freighters, delivered three astronauts to Mars and returned them quickly and safely to the lunar mining station, where they transferred to the regular weekly earth-moon shuttle for their triumphant New York ticker-tape parade.

Their fusion-powered spacecraft, parked in lunar orbit, was refueled with deuterium and sent, unmanned, to Saturn's moon Titan, where astronomers back in 1944 had discovered a dense methane-hydrogen atmosphere over what was believed to be a water-ice surface layer. The possibility of volcanic activity and the consequent presence of potentially life-sustaining pools of warm water had prompted physicist Donald Hunter to write in *Scientific American*'s September 1975 issue, "[Titan's] close exploration cannot fail to be highly rewarding."

And rewarding it was. The Titan lander, whose on-board remote sensors were programmed to detect water while still in orbit and guide the Viking-type robot laboratory accordingly, soft-landed in six inches of liquid water. Its siphon delivered a sample into the analysis chamber, and a signal was flashed to earth. An hour and twenty minutes later, when the electrifying news reached the Jet Propulsion Laboratory's Goldstone receiving antenna, the planetary scientists hugged each other and leaped around the lab like idiots. Microbial life existed—elsewhere than on earth! That discovery might not *seem* so important, but it was actually the key piece of information needed to

---

* Isotopes of hydrogen, used since 1952 to fuel hydrogen bombs.

A highly likely prospect for at least microbial life exists on Saturn's largest moon Titan, which was found in 1944 to possess a heavy atmosphere. Here a Viking-like robot spacecraft is parachuted down to sample Titan's surface and test it for life.

settle for once and for all the nagging fear that life on earth might be a freak, a one-of-a-kind accident. As Philip Morrison had put it so elegantly in the 1961 space flight report: "Once *might* be an accident, but *twice* is pretty good statistics that it isn't!"

Once the motive was there, the capability was easily developed. Project Daedelus, an interstellar exploration of Barnard's star conceived in great detail by the British Interplanetary Society and published back in 1978, provided the blueprint. Only ten years after the electrifying discovery on Titan, the first unmanned interstellar test probe, using multi-megagauss magnetic fields to fuse the interstellar hydrogen atoms and protons swept into its enormous, scooplike ramjet intake, was on its way to Barnard's star at nearly a tenth the speed of light, transmitting high-fidelity electronic images back to the new lunar farside SETI radiotelescope as it sped through the void. The earth's energy crisis and the "clouded crystal-ball syndrome" (optimistic in projecting the near-term; pessimistic in forecasting the far-term) had joined forces to beat Bob Bussard's mind-boggling 1977 scenario by over thirty years! And sure enough, by 2050 the first manned starship was being assembled at Plant No. 9 of the International Space Power Plant Manufacturing and Maintenance Corporation, using tough nickel steel mined from the corporation's latest acquisition from the asteroid belt.

The original interstellar probe and its companions, still en route, had probed Van de Kamp's planet and the other three planets of Barnard's star throughout the entire radio spectrum, but with no sign of intelligent response. Their instrumentation had, however, long since verified that Van de Kamp *was* an earth-type planet with a thirty-hour day, an oxygen-nitrogen atmosphere, and what appeared to be considerable water coverage. So although SETI's goal was still to be achieved, there seemed little question that humans could survive on Van de Kamp.

By 2050, the earth had, in fact, become quite crowded, although the plentiful solar energy from space had raised the worldwide standard of living beyond even that enjoyed only by the highly developed nations in the 1970s. The space colonies had drawn off a few million people, but the promise of wide-scale industry (other than power plant construction and operation) had never truly developed, so there was only a limited prospect for employment. And although the deep-space colonies *were* a haven for retirees because of their benign environments (much as Florida was for northern senior citizens in the 1960s and 1970s), there was a whole generation of young would-be pioneers with no place to go.

It was no surprise, therefore, that the United Nations Committee for Interstellar Development was swamped with enthusiastic responses to its worldwide "Notice of Opportunity to Colonize Van de Kamp's Planet." Just selecting the thousand pioneers to ensure the presence of all the necessary technical and sociological skills *and* the optimum hereditary physical characteristics took nearly five years. The trip itself would not be too arduous—the interstellar fusion ramjet, now well proved by its unmanned interstellar forerunners, could accelerate to cruising velocity (half the speed of light) in a year. So the total trip, including deceleration at Van de Kamp, would take less than fourteen years.

That fourteen years became popularly known as "Bussard's myopia." Instead of *launching* the world's first manned flight to the stars on July 4, 2076, as he had so cheerfully suggested in 1977, the U.S. Tricentennial was to be celebrated by the first human *landing* on an extrastellar planet. Neil Armstrong's "one giant step for mankind," as many of us had intuitively sensed all along, turned out to be only the first tentative baby step after all.

The space enterprise had finally grown up. Negotiating the rocky road of brand-new technological problems, serious political roadblocks, and the vagaries of public consciousness had been touch-and-go at times, but the almost evangelistic doggedness of NASA and the many individuals who pursued the space-enterprise dream had paid off. As they had predicted just a few decades after Sputnik, space had given the peoples of the earth the answers to some of their most pressing social problems and had simultaneously provided the pioneering opportunity that seems to be an essential element in human progress.

When contact is eventually made with another galactic civilization, it's reassuring to think that we will be able to greet them as equals.

THE CHRONOLOGY OF ENTERPRISE

I. *THE CONCEPTION* (Before Sputnik 1)

360 B.C.   Gellius' steam "pigeon"
1st century B.C.   Hero's "aelopile" (steam turbine)
2nd century A.D.   Lucian's *True History; Icaro-Menippus*
13th century A.D.   Chinese gunpowder rocket
1634.   Johannes Kepler's *Somnium*
1638.   Francis Godwin's *The Man in the Moon*
1648.   Cyrano de Bergerac's *Voyage to the Moon*
1652.   Cyrano de Bergerac's *History of the States and Empires of the Sun*
1728.   Voltaire's *Micromegas*
1728.   Bernard du Fontenelle's *Plurality of Worlds*
1834.   Alexander Copland's *The Existence of Other Worlds: Peopled with Living and Intelligent Beings*
1835.   Edgar Allan Poe's *Hans Pfall: A Tale*
September 17, 1857.   Konstantin Tsiolkovsky is born in Russia
1865.   Jules Verne's *From the Earth to the Moon; Around the Moon*
1869.   Edward Everett Hale's *Brick Moon*
1877-82.   Schiaparelli observes Mars
1883.   Tsiolkovsky grasps the rocket principle
August 25, 1898.   Tsiolkovsky completes the formulation of his rocket-propulsion theory
1900.   H. G. Wells' *First Men in the Moon*
1903.   Tsiolkovsky's *The Exploration of Space with Reactive Devices*
December 17, 1903.   The Wright brothers make the world's first powered-airplane flight at Kitty Hawk, North Carolina

December 1919. Robert H. Goddard's *A Method of Reaching Extreme Altitudes,* published by the Smithsonian Institution.

1923. Hermann Oberth's *The Rocket Into Interplanetary Space*

March 16, 1926. Goddard launches the world's first liquid-propellant rocket

March 21, 1930. The American Interplanetary Society is founded (later, the American Rocket Society; then by merger the American Institute of Aeronautics and Astronautics, AIAA)

July 1930. Goddard moves to Roswell, New Mexico

October 15, 1932. The Institute of Aeronautical Sciences is founded (later the Institute of Aerospace Sciences; then by merger the American Institute of Aeronautics and Astronautics)

October 30, 1938. Orson Welles' *War of the Worlds* radio show

July 1942. Goddard moves his lab to Annapolis, Maryland

1944. Methane-hydrogen atmosphere is discovered on Saturn's moon Titan

1945. Arthur C. Clarke publishes the synchronous-orbit communications satellite concept

1945. Robert W. Bussard conceives the nuclear rocket engine

April 16, 1946. First United States launch of a German V-2 rocket

February 13, 1947. *Sacramento Bee* publishes first description of a shuttle rocket to the moon

May 3, 1949. First Navy Viking sounding rocket launched

May 11, 1950. First photo of earth from space (by a Viking rocket)

1950. Arthur C. Clarke publishes "Electromagnetic Launching as a Major Contribution to Space Flight" (the progenitor of the space colonies' mass driver)

September 1951. First International Astronautical Congress

1952. Minimum Orbital Unmanned Satellite of Earth (MOUSE) is proposed

September 1952. H. Julian Allen completes blunt reentry body theory

August 20, 1953. First big American-built long-range missile (Redstone) is launched

April 15, 1954. U.S.S.R. sets up the Permanent Interdepartmental Commission for Interplanetary Communications

July 29, 1954. United States announces intention of launching an artificial satellite during the IGY

July 30, 1954.   Soviets announce their artificial satellite program

September 20, 1956.   Jupiter-C missile flies 3,400 miles

May 1957.   Soviet sounding rocket reaches 132 miles altitude carrying nearly 5,000 pounds, including two dogs who were safely parachuted back to earth

July 1, 1957.   The International Geophysical Year (IGY) starts (it ends December 31, 1958)

II. *THE CHILDHOOD* (Sputnik 1 to Apollo 11)

October 4, 1957.   The world's first artificial satellite, Sputnik 1, is launched by the U.S.S.R.

November 3, 1957.   Sputnik 2 is launched successfully by the Soviets

December 6, 1957.   The first American "all-up" satellite, Vanguard 1, fails on the launch pad

January 31, 1958.   The United States launches its first successful artificial satellite, Explorer 1

March 17, 1958.   The U.S. Navy launches the first successful Vanguard satellite

May 15, 1958.   Sputnik 3 is launched successfully by the Soviets

July 29, 1958.   The National Aeronautics and Space Act is signed, creating the National Aeronautics and Space Administration (NASA)

October 1, 1958.   National Aeronautics and Space Administration (NASA) opens its doors

December 17, 1958.   Project Mercury, the first U.S. manned-space-flight program, is announced by NASA administrator T. Keith Glennan

December 18, 1958.   The first U.S. communications satellite, SCORE, is launched

December 31, 1958.   IGY ends

January 19, 1959.   The Rocketdyne 1.5-million-pound-thrust F-1 rocket engine is contracted by NASA

August, 1959.   NASA launches its first successful satellite

September 14, 1959.   U.S.S.R.'s Lunik 2 lands on the moon

October 6, 1959.   U.S.S.R.'s Lunik 3 transmits photographs of the lunar farside, giving the world its first view of the "back of the moon"

October 21, 1959. Huntsville's Saturn rocket program is transferred to NASA

1959. Philip Morrison and G. Cocconi publish "Searching for Interstellar Communications," the first paper on the search for extraterrestrial intelligence (SETI)

April 1, 1960. First U.S. weather satellite, Tiros 1, is launched

April 8, 1960. Frank Drake conducts the first search for extraterrestrial intelligence

August 12, 1960. Echo 1, U.S. communications satellite, is launched

April 12, 1961. The U.S.S.R. places the first human in orbit (Yuri A. Gagarin) and returns him safely to earth

May 5, 1961. Alan B. Shepard, Jr., makes a successful suborbital flight and becomes the first American in space

May 25, 1961. President Kennedy announces the U.S. goal of placing a man on the moon and returning him safely by the end of the decade

August 6-7, 1961. U.S.S.R.'s Gherman S. Titov becomes the second human in orbit

October 1961. The American Rocket Society presents its "Space Flight Report to the Nation" in New York's Coliseum

November 1961. SETI meeting called "Order of the Dolphin" is convened

December 1961. United Nations treaty governing space activities is signed

February 20, 1962. John H. Glenn, Jr., is the first American to orbit the earth

July 1962. Telstar, launched on July 10, transmits live intercontinental TV broadcast of summer Olympics

July 1962. NASA selects Lunar Orbit Rendezvous (LOR) for the Apollo missions to the moon

January 1, 1963. The American Rocket Society and the Institute of Aerospace Sciences merge to form the American Institute of Aeronautics and Astronautics (AIAA)

January 1963. Robert C. Truax proposes Sea Dragon launcher

February 1963. Communications Satellite Corporation is formed

1964. Walter Sullivan's *We Are Not Alone*

January 1964. Krafft Ehricke proposes Nexus; other large-rocket concepts published

January 1965. First nuclear reactor (U.S. SNAP 10A) goes critical in space (it is shut down safely in March 1966)

April 6, 1965. Early-Bird communications satellite (Intelsat 1) is launched

April 20, 1966. Orbital Astronautical Observatory fails after two days in orbit

1966. Iosifs Shklovskii and Carl Sagan's *Intelligent Life in the Universe*

January 27, 1967. Three American astronauts, Virgil I. Grissom, Edward H. White, and Roger B. Chaffee, die in Apollo fire during ground training

November 22, 1968. Peter Glaser's "Power from the Sun: Its Future" (first paper on solar-power satellites) is published in *Science*

January 1969. "Phase A" studies of the space shuttle start

May 1969. The Lagrange libration point, L-5, is identified as a potential space habitat

July, 1969. The U.S. Air Force Manned Orbiting Laboratory (MOL) is canceled

July 16, 1969. The United States launches *Apollo 11*, the first mission to land humans on the moon: Neil A. Armstrong, Edwin E. Aldrin, Jr., and Michael Collins

July 21, 1969. Neil Armstrong and "Buzz" Aldrin are the first humans to land on the moon, and Armstrong becomes the first to set foot on a heavenly body other than the earth

---

III. *THE ADOLESCENCE* (Apollo 11 to the Space Shuttle)

August 1969. The Space Task Report is issued, recommending major new space initiatives

October 1969. NASA administrator Thomas Paine begins touring Europe and Japan seeking support for the space shuttle

March 7, 1970. President Nixon presents his space message, implying a limited space program in the future

May 1970. Shuttle economic study contract is issued to Mathematica, Inc.

April 1971. Senate votes down a federal supersonic transport (SST) prototype development

May 1971. Mathematica's first economic shuttle study is completed

June 1971. Contract for the main shuttle rocket engine is issued to Rocketdyne

September 1971. "Cyclops" SETI proposal is formulated.

October 28, 1971. Oskar Morgenstern and Klaus Heiss's letter suggesting a Thrust-Assisted-Orbiter System (TAOS), the basis for the 1979 space shuttle, goes to NASA

January 5, 1972. President Nixon authorizes development of the space shuttle

March 1972. NASA decides to use solid-propellant rocket boosters for the shuttle rather than liquids

July 23, 1972. The first Earth Resources Technology Satellite (ERTS-1, now called Landsat 1) is launched

July 1972. Shuttle prime contract is awarded to North American Rockwell, Inc. (now Rockwell International)

September 5-11, 1972. First international SETI conference is held in the U.S.S.R.

January 5, 1973. NASA cancels all nuclear-reactor propulsion and power efforts

January 21, 1973. AIAA issues its assessment, *New Space Transportation Systems*

May 25, 1973. First Skylab crew is launched: Charles Conrad, Jr., Joseph P. Kerwin, and Paul J. Weiz

August 1973. European Space Agency contracts with NASA to build Spacelab for use with the shuttle

August 31, 1973. First Phenix breeder reactor goes critical in France

December 25, 1973. Solar-power satellite patent is issued to Peter Glaser

May 10, 1974. First Princeton Conference on Space Colonization

October 1974. Solar Energy Research Development and Demonstration Act is signed into law

November 1974. Gerard K. O'Neill publishes space colonization article in *Physics Today*

January 22, 1975. Landsat 2 is launched

April 23, 1975. AIAA issues its assessment, *Solar Energy for Earth*

May 7-9, 1975. Second Princeton/AIAA Conference on Space Manufacturing Facilities

May 8, 1975. L-5 Society is formed in Princeton, New Jersey

July 15, 1975. U.S./U.S.S.R. Apollo-Soyuz mission is launched

July 20, 1976. First Viking spacecraft lands on Mars to search for extraterrestrial life

September 17, 1976. Space-shuttle orbiter *Enterprise* is rolled out

October 12, 1976. First Getaway Special shuttle payload is signed up by R. Gilbert Moore

January 10-14, 1977. AIAA annual meeting, "Aerospace in the Third Century"

May 9-12, 1977. Third Princeton/AIAA Conference on Space Manufacturing Facilities

October 1, 1977. U.S. Department of Energy is formed

October 25, 1977. Completion of shuttle orbiter atmospheric flight tests

December 14, 1977. Senator Adlai Stevenson III requests review of shuttle main-engine program

January 24, 1978. Soviet nuclear-powered Cosmos 954 reenters atmosphere over Canada

March 5, 1978. Landsat 3 is launched

1978. British Interplanetary Society publishes *Project Daedelus: The Final Report in the BIS Starship Study*

April 7, 1978. Senator John Melcher submits Solar Power Satellite bill (S-2860)

June 22, 1978. Solar Power Satellite bill (HR 12505) passed by the U.S. House of Representatives

June 26, 1978. Seasat 1 is launched

September 21, 1978. Senator Harrison Schmitt submits National Space and Aeronautics Act of 1978

September 27, 1978. Senator Adlai Stevenson III submits Bill No. S-3530, Space Policy Act of 1978

September 30, 1978. Senator Harrison Schmitt submits NASA Solar Power Satellite Program Act of 1978

October 1, 1978. President Carter announces a revised date for the first space-shuttle orbital flight: Sept. 28, 1979

October 11, 1978. President Jimmy Carter issues space policy statement

October 12, 1978. Senator Adlai Stevenson submits Bill No. S-3589, Earth Data and Information Service Act of 1978

October 12, 1978. Congressman Don Fuqua submits bill establishing the Space Industrialization Corporation

November 29, 1978. AIAA issues its position paper on solar-power satellites
March 1979. First official target date for shuttle launch
May 14-17, 1979. Fourth Princeton/AIAA Conference on Space Manufacturing Facilities
June 1979. Second official target date for shuttle launch
September 24, 1979. World Administrative Radio Conference (WARC) begins
September 28, 1979. Third official target date for shuttle launch
November 9, 1979. Fourth official target date for shuttle launch

---

IV. *THE MATURITY* (A Scenario for the Future)

December 1979. WARC opens up broadcast frequency spectrum
May 1980. First orbital shuttle flight test is successful
1982. Tokamak Fusion Test Reactor at Princeton University demonstrates "zero net power," confirming technical feasibility of fusion power
1983. Space telescope confirms existence of four planets circling Barnard's star
1983. First Superphenix breeder reactor goes critical at Creys-Malville, France
1985. U.S.S.R. begins to import oil
1988. Photovoltaic membrane developed
1990. The first fully reusable shuttle is launched
1991. U.S.S.R. "liberates" Saudia Arabia
1992. Demonstration 500-megawatt solar-power satellite begins to deliver power to earth
1998. The first commercial fusion power plant goes on line in New Jersey
2000. Solar satellites provide 25 percent of total U.S. energy needs
2007. First fusion rocket using all-deuterium fuel is tested successfully in Nevada
2010. First solar-power satellite power plant constructed of lunar materials goes on line
2012. First fusion-powered spacecraft carries people to Mars and back

2013. First solar-power satellite built by a self-sustaining space settlement goes on line

2013. Microbial life discovered on Titan by soft-landing fusion-powered automated spacecraft

2017. Proton (hydrogen) fusion is accomplished, using multi-megagauss magnetic fields

2023. First unmanned fusion-ramjet-powered interstellar test probe is launched to Barnard's star

2045. Probes enroute to Barnard's star confirm that Van de Kamp's planet is habitable by humans

2062. First manned interstellar spaceship is launched to Barnard's star with a thousand hand-picked colonists on board

July 4, 2076. First landing on an extrastellar planet by people from earth

ACRONYMS

ABM	antiballistic missile
ABMA	Army Ballistic Missile Agency
AEC	Atomic Energy Commission
AIAA	American Institute of Aeronautics and Astronautics
ALSEP	Apollo Lunar Science Experiment Package
ARS	American Rocket Society
BuAer	Bureau of Aeronautics (U.S. Navy)
CETI	Communication with Extraterrestrial Intelligence
CETS	European Conference on Satellite Telecommunications (French)
COMSAT	Communications Satellite Corporation
COSPAR	Committee on Space Research (of the International Council of Scientific Unions)
CRS	Congressional Research Service
DOD	Department of Defense
DOE	Department of Energy
ELDO	European Launcher Development Organization
ERDA	Energy Research and Development Administration
ERTS	Earth Resources Technology Satellite (later Landsat)
ESA	European Space Agency
ESC	European Space Conference
ESRO	European Space Research Organization

FASST	Federation of American Students for the Supersonic Transport (later changed to Forum for the Advancement of Students in Science and Technology)
FY	fiscal year
GAO	General Accounting Office
IAF	International Astronautical Federation
ICBM	intercontinental ballistic missile
IEEE	Institute of Electrical and Electronics Engineers
IGY	International Geophysical Year
IOC	initial operational capability
IUS	interim upper stage (later inertial upper stage)
JATO	jet-assisted takeoff
JPL	Jet Propulsion Laboratory
LACIE	large-area crop inventory experiment
LOR	lunar-orbit rendezvous
MIRV	multiple independently targeted reentry vehicle
MOUSE	minimum orbital unmanned satellite of earth
MRBD	Mercury Redstone Booster Development
NACA	National Advisory Committee for Aeronautics
NASA	National Aeronautics and Space Administration
NASC	National Aeronautics and Space Council
NATO	North Atlantic Treaty Organization
NERVA	Nuclear Engine for Rocket Vehicle Applications
NOAA	National Oceanic and Atmospheric Administration
OART	Office of Advanced Research and Technology
OMB	Office of Management and Budget
OMS	Orbital Maneuvering System
OMSF	Office of Manned Space Flight
OPEC	Organization of Petroleum Exporting Countries
SCORE	Signal Communications by Orbiting Relay Equipment

RCS	Reaction Control System
RTAC	(NASA's) Research and Technology Advisory Council
RTG	radioisotope thermoelectric generator
SALT	Strategic Arms Limitation Treaty
SBS	Satellite Business Systems
SEPS	solar-electric propulsion stage
SETI	Search for Extraterrestrial Intelligence
SNAP 10A	Space Nuclear Auxiliary Power System No. 1OA
SPAR	Space Processing Applications Rockets
SPS	solar-power satellite
SRB	solid rocket booster
SST	supersonic transport
SSUS-A	spinning solid upper stage—Atlas
SSUS-D	spinning solid upper stage—Delta
TAOS	Thrust-Assisted Orbiter System
UFO	unidentified flying object

ACKNOWLEDGMENTS

Much of the material on which *Enterprise* is based came from interviews with Burt Edelson, Philomena Grodzka, Klaus Heiss, Tom Heppenheimer, Pres Layton, Myron Malkin, Marcia Smith, Del Tischler, and Glen Wilson (in alphabetical order). Other important resources included the American Institute of Aeronautics and Astronautics' monthly magazine, *Astronautics & Aeronautics*; a 1975 Master's thesis by Gary F. Geraets developed under the direction of Professor John M. Logsdon of George Washington University's School of Public and International Affairs; hearings records and Committee Prints of both the Senate and the House of Representatives; and various NASA publications and photographs.

I am particularly indebted to Morrow's Senior Editor Howard Cady for his sage advice and guidance. My gratitude to Associate Publisher Sherry W. Arden, who initiated this *Enterprise*, knows no bounds. And Elna Lund, who converted reams of chicken scratches into legible typescript on an incredibly tight schedule, deserves (and gets!) my eternal thanks.

JERRY GREY

INDEX

ABM. *See* Antiballistic missile
ABMA. *See* Army Ballistic Missile Agency
Abrams, George J., 158–159
Advent project, 139, 140
AEC. *See* Atomic Energy Commission
Aerojet Engineering Corporation, 27, 30, 31, 46, 78, 107, 118, 120, 185
Aerospace Corporation, 71, 76, 163, 168–169
Aerospaceplane, 103, 209
Agnew, Spiro, 15, 18ff.
AIAA. *See* American Institute of Aeronautics and Astronautics
Air Force, 101, 108
  and anti-satellites, 140
  lunar probe, 47
  and missile development, 38
  and space shuttle, 66–68, 74, 103
  and space tug, 99, 161
Aldrin, Edwin "Buzz," Jr., 18, 56ff.
Allen, H. Julian, 103–105
ALSEP. *See* Apollo Lunar Science Experiment Package
American Astronautical Society, 154
American Institute of Aeronautics and Astronautics (AIAA), 85–86, 157, 178, 192, 222, 246, 253
  assessment of space shuttle, 86–88, 98, 101, 155, 163
  and future of space research, 253–254
  and solar-power satellites, 196, 202–203, 218, 224, 226
  and space colonies, 228–229
  Task Force on Future Flight Systems, 255
  Technical Committee on Space Processing, 152
American Interplanetary Society, 255
American Rocket Society (ARS), 27, 35, 39, 85, 118, 228, 237, 242–243, 253, 254–255
American Telephone & Telegraph Co. (AT&T), 135, 138–139
Anderson, Clinton, 68–69, 75, 100
Antiballistic missile (ABM), 76
Anti-satellite, ship-launched, 140
Apollo Lunar Science Experiment Packages (ALSEP), 181, 277
Apollo program, 15–16, 17ff., 18ff., 19–20, 50–53, 54, 56ff., 66, 80–85, 106, 110, 111, 139, 151, 181, 196

Apollo–Soyuz flight, 151, 152ff.
Applications Technology Satellite (ATS), 6, 167ff., 168ff.
Ariane, 124, 163
Armstrong, Neil, 11, 18, 19, 56ff.
Army Ballistic Missile Agency (ABMA), 38, 47
Arthur D. Little Company, 196, 215
Artificial satellites
  background of, 39–40
  Clarke and, 135–137
  economic payoff of, 134
  first U.S. successful, 49
  for meteorology and weather forecasting, 141–143
  for "Personal Communication Systems," 172–173
  plan for, 21–22
  and remote sensing, 143–149
  repair of, 97
  role of, 53
  shuttle retrieval of, 156ff.
  Soviet, 48–49, 116
  See also Landsat; Satellite communications; Seasat; Sputnik; Vanguard program
Ashley, Holt, 102ff.
Astronautics. *See* Space research
Atlantis, 20
Atlas ICBM, 38, 40, 134
Atomic Energy Commission (AEC), 38, 184, 277
ATS. *See* Applications Technology Satellite
AT&T. *See* American Telephone & Telegraph Co.

Barnard's star, 256–258, 263–264
Bayh, Birch, 65
Bekey, Ivan, 163, 168–169, 171ff., 172–174, 182, 189, 192
Bellman, Don, 45–46
Benson, Johan, 246
Billingham, John, 229, 246–247
Blackett, Patrick, 243
British Interplanetary Society, 35, 263
Brown, Jerry, 180
"Brute force" supershuttle approach, 201, 209
BuAer. *See* Bureau of Aeronautics
Bureau of Aeronautics (BuAer), 27